Common Core State Standards and the Speech–Language Pathologist

Standards–Based Intervention for Special Populations

Common Core State Standards and the Speech–Language Pathologist

Standards-Based Intervention for Special Populations

Lissa A. Power-deFur, PhD, CCC-SLP, ASHA-F

PLURAL
PUBLISHING
INC.

5521 Ruffin Road
San Diego, CA 92123

e-mail: info@pluralpublishing.com
Website: http://www.pluralpublishing.com

Typeset in 10½/13 Palatino by Flanagan's Publishing Services, Inc.
Printed in the United States of America by McNaughton & Gunn, Inc.

Library of Congress Cataloging-in-Publication Data

Power-deFur, Lissa A., author.
  Common Core State Standards and the speech-language pathologist : standards-based intervention for special populations / Lissa A. Power-deFur.
      p. ; cm.
  Includes bibliographical references and index.
  ISBN 978-1-59756-618-6 (alk. paper) — ISBN 1-59756-618-7 (alk. paper)
  1. Speech therapy for children—Standards—United States. 2. Children with disabilities (Education)—Standards—United States. 3. Common Core State Standards (Education)
I. Title.
  [DNLM: 1. Child. 2. Disabled Persons. 3. Education, Special—standards.
4. Communication Barriers. 5. Curriculum—standards. LC 4015]
  LB3454.P69 2016
  616.85'50071—dc23
                                        2015017691

Contents

Foreword

Imagine a high school student sitting in his history class and not being able to hear the teacher discuss famous American heroes. Think of the eighth grader who struggles to organize her thoughts when writing an essay about her dreams for the future. How sad to observe a first grader excited to learn to read but unable to see the words printed on the pages of her books. Consider the boy in sixth grade who wants to be a marine biologist but cannot recall the names of specific types of fish. To speak, to listen, to understand, to write and read, to recall facts, and to plan and create a myriad of cognitive and communication acts are the sparks and essence of interaction and learning.

Communication is the foundation of all learning. Children with speech, language, and hearing disabilities are at a huge disadvantage as they progress through school. They often perform poorly on assessments, have difficulty recalling information, and struggle to find the words or speak intelligibly enough to answer their teachers' questions. Unfortunately they fall further and further behind as they encounter increasingly complex subject matter and academic challenges.

The recent focus in education on the Common Core State Standards has heightened our awareness of the communication skills needed to achieve success in school. However, speech-language pathologists, educators, and special educators struggle to understand their roles and responsibilities in relation to aligning treatment services with the standards. They continue to search for efficient and effective ways to ensure that their instruction and intervention help students gain the foundational and advanced communication skills they need to negotiate the difficult school pathway.

Throughout Lissa Power-deFur's career, she has strived to foster better understanding of these critical aspects of school service delivery. Her willingness to share her vast knowledge and expertise is noteworthy through her many publications, presentations, and volunteer efforts. She has skillfully clarified complex processes such as determining eligibility for services, aligning intervention services with curricular standards, and forming collaborative teams. This book is a prime example of her commitment to elevating the quality of services for students with disabilities. She lays a solid foundation for understanding the historical and beneficial aspects of the common core state standards. She does an excellent job of helping the reader understand specific elements of the language and literacy standards and the communication skills required for mastery. Lissa's practical five-step analysis process helps crystalize our thinking about the language and speech skills needed to successfully access the curriculum. The organizational framework of the book is a major strength. Lissa invited several leaders to join her in compiling this practical book. Their chapters follow a consistent format. First, the characteristics of a specific communication disorder are presented. Then the chapter facilitates understanding of the typical challenges each disability population is likely to experience in accessing the curriculum due to the skills required for success. Next, recommendations are made for applying the model to that population, providing a realistic context for implementation. Finally, case studies allow readers to relate the discussion to their therapy programs and classrooms.

Lissa has provided a resource that will be very useful to practitioners, educators, and aspiring professionals.

—Jean Blosser, CCC-SLP, EdD,
ASHA Fellow
President, Creative Strategies
for Special Education

Introduction

If a group of speech-language pathologists and their colleagues were meeting to discuss implementation of the Common Core State Standards (CCSS) within their school district, one might hear the following:

- "With all the children on my caseload, how can I possibly incorporate the standards into my therapy?"
- "Aren't the goals we write on the children's IEPs (Individualized Education Programs) the standards that children should aspire to?"
- "Why do we need to consider the CCSS since we have goals on the IEP, and the IEP is a legally binding document?"
- "My students have so many needs, how can I possibly address those and the CCSS also?"
- "These standards were developed by policy makers who have probably never worked with children like I do on a daily basis. They just aren't practical."
- "This is just another education fad that will go away."

With the advent of the Common Core State Standards (CCSS), professionals working with children with disabilities are finding they need to incorporate the CCSS into their interventions. As the magnitude of the CCSS can be overwhelming, and the students receiving speech-language services have so many skills to learn, it may be easy for a speech-language pathologist (SLP) to feel it is a fruitless endeavor to attempt to address the CCSS.

This book is designed to support SLPs who work with school-aged children as they strive to enable their students to meet the linguistic expectations of the CCSS. The genesis of this book can be traced to my work in public education at the Virginia Department of Education (VDOE). Working in special education with a focus on children with speech-language impairment and children who were deaf and hard of hearing, I became convinced that all special education and related services personnel, including SLPs, needed to focus their intervention to enable the children to progress in the general curriculum. As general education standards were articulated through the creation of Virginia's Standards of Learning (SOLs), a framework for the general curriculum was established. A careful review of this framework made clear that all students with disabilities, including those with communication disabilities, must meet the linguistic expectations of the general curriculum to successfully exit the K–12 system ready for work or postsecondary education. Over the ensuing years, I have devoted time to working with professionals and graduate students in understanding the educational relevance of our work as speech-language pathologists (and members of education teams) in understanding the linguistic complexity of the standards, and in framing intervention to support mastery of the standards. With establishment of the CCSS in 2010, I began to have opportunities to apply these same concepts to the CCSS, opportunities that have culminated in writing this book.

The purpose of this book is to enable speech-language pathologists and their education partners to develop skills in analyzing the linguistic and communication expectations of the CCSS and use that information to develop interventions tailored to the unique needs of individual children. The book begins with an illumination of the CCSS. Chapter 1 provides the framework for the work of the National Governor's Association and the Council of Chief State School Officers in establishing the CCSS. By understanding the context for the CCSS, readers will have a better understanding of how the CCSS fits into the public education systems where they work.

This unfolding of the CCSS continues with Chapter 2, as it analyzes the language and communication expectations of the CCSS. Chapter 2 discusses the multiple aspects of language that are reflected in the standards—from those pragmatic skills required to adjust communication to the purpose and audience to the morpho-syntactic skills needed for generating complex oral and written communication and analyze new vocabulary. Chapter 3 provides a five-step approach to analyzing the standards with a goal of creating interventions designed to support students' development of language and communication skills in the context of the expectations of the CCSS. This model presumes the SLP's involvement in teams that analyze the standards, specifically the analysis of the linguistic and communication expectations of the standards. Further, the SLP has an important role in analyzing the linguistic expectations of the general curriculum, both classroom instruction and instructional materials. The model promotes the SLP's collaboration with a variety of education partners in analyzing students' specific needs and planning both direct and classroom-based interventions.

The next seven chapters are devoted to the discussion of the CCSS with specific populations. Each is designed to provide a background regarding the specific population, with a focus on the linguistic and communication needs of that population. The chapters provide illustrative examples of CCSS that will be challenging for these students. Each chapter includes multiple case studies that promote a collaborative approach to analyzing students' needs and designing and implementing intervention. Chapter 4 launches this approach with a discussion of children with speech-language impairment, addressing children with speech sound, language, fluency, and voice disorders. These students may be receiving services as "speech only" students (those who are eligible for special education with a speech-language impairment and no other disability) or as students who have one or more additional disabilities. The next six chapters discuss children with other disabilities or challenges facing them as they are mastering the general education curriculum.

Peggy Agee addresses children with autism, building on three theories that offer explanation regarding difficulties students with autism have in mastering the curriculum. These difficulties stem from students' difficulty in understanding the minds of others (Theory of Mind); conceptualizing the whole by assembling perceptual parts (Weak Central Coherence); and planning, organizing, and executing behavior in order to achieve a specific goal (Executive Dysfunction). The case studies in this chapter provide valuable insight into successful approaches with this population.

Brenda Seal provides a thorough discussion of the needs of children who are deaf and hard of hearing, addressing both students who communicate using American Sign Language (ASL) and those who communicate with listening and speaking. Brenda's thorough analysis of the implications of the CCSS and her case studies that reflect the continuum of students who are deaf or hard of hearing provide the reader with a rich understanding of the nuances they should consider when working with this population.

Julie Durando lends her expertise with students who are blind and students who have both deafness and blindness. Both low incidence populations, with whom many SLPs have limited experience, are discussed in depth in the chapter, providing the reader with rich background information to enhance the reader's ability to meet the needs of these students. Julie's case studies bring to life the unique challenges of these populations.

Sharon deFur and Lori Korinek, long-recognized experts in the field of specific learning disabilities (SLD), highlight the challenges students with SLD will face with the CCSS and standards-based education. Their thorough analysis of the nature of SLD and rich case studies provide the reader with a solid foundation for understanding the educational needs of this population.

Perry Flynn addresses secondary-level students, with a focus on students with intellectual disabilities. He provides information and examples to remind the reader that the work of the SLP is not completed when students exit middle school, and that the SLP has an important collaborative role in facilitating students' successful exit from the public education system into postsecondary employment and services.

In the final chapter in the book, Judy Rudebusch and Elda Rojas remind readers of the importance of remembering the unique communication challenges that are experienced by English language learners (ELLs). Rudebusch and Rojas provide a valuable summary of ELL services and the nature and needs of students who are ELLs. The case studies in this chapter capture the unique role SLPs will play on the teams serving this population of students.

These seven chapters provide the reader with a solid foundation for applying the analysis model presented in Chapter 3. Through the various authors' use of the framework for analyzing the standards and developing interventions accordingly, this book provides readers with a large collection of information and strategies to add to their toolboxes. Armed with this additional information, it is my hope that the reader will feel more confident in approaching the CCSS as a tool for supporting students in the general curriculum, rather than as an additional obligation.

Returning to the questions one might overhear, which opened this chapter, the SLPs who use this book should be skilled with an approach to incorporate the CCSS into their planning for all the students with disabilities they serve. The research-based foundation of the CCSS provides direction regarding the expectations of the general curriculum that SLPs should consider as they develop IEP goals that address students' unique needs in accessing the curriculum. Although politics will always be involved in public education and may alter states' approaches to the CCSS, the philosophy that students should meet high standards has been a focus of public education for over three decades and will not likely disappear. The analysis approach presented in this book, and the chapters that apply this analysis to various groups of students, will support SLPs' work in any education setting that relies on achievement standards.

Acknowledgments

I would like to express my deepest appreciation to the amazing collaborators on this project. A collection of the finest professionals assisted me in writing chapters that captured their areas of expertise and passion: Peggy C. Agee, Sharon H. deFur, Lori Korinek, Julie Durando, Perry Flynn, Judy Rudebusch, Elda Rojas, and Brenda C. Seal. These consummate professionals (and friends) shared hours of time to develop chapters related to specific populations of children with disabilities. I would additionally like to thank Jean Blosser for her willingness to write the Foreword. There are a number of others who provided tremendous assistance during the development and refinement of the book. Johanna Montague's eye for editing was tremendously valuable in the refinement of these chapters. A number of graduate assistants at Longwood University, Farmville, Virginia, provided research support that I especially appreciate: Carli Rogers, Sarah Snowa, and Katie McGinn. The support and encouragement of my husband, Patrick, and my colleagues at Longwood have been invaluable. Of course, I have to thank Ray Kent for thinking of me as an author on this important topic. Last, I would like to thank the children with whom I have worked and the speech-language pathologists (SLPs) and educators with whom I have spoken in Virginia and throughout the country. You have inspired my commitment to the importance of analyzing the linguistic complexity of general education standards, especially the CCSS. It is only through gaining a full understanding of this complexity and then pairing this analysis with an understanding of students' strengths and needs that meaningful intervention can be developed to support students' acquisition of these important academic expectations. I would love to hear your stories and experiences as you apply the concepts presented herein to your students.

Contributors

Peggy C. Agee, SLPD, CCC-SLP
Associate Professor
Communication Sciences and Disorders
Longwood University
Farmville, Virginia
Chapter 5

Sharon H. deFur, EdD
Professor of Special Education
School of Education
College of William and Mary
Williamsburg, Virginia
Chapter 8

Julie Durando, EdD
Director
Virginia Project for Children and Young
    Adults with Deaf-Blindness
Partnership for People with Disabilities
Virginia Commonwealth University
Richmond, Virginia
Chapter 7

Perry Flynn, MEd, CCC-SLP
Consultant in Speech-Language
    Pathology
North Carolina Department of Public
    Instruction
Associate Professor
Department of Communication Sciences
    and Disorders
University of North Carolina Greensboro
Greensboro, North Carolina
Chapter 9

Lori Korinek, PhD
Professor of Special Education
School of Education
College of William and Mary
Williamsburg, Virginia
Chapter 8

**Lissa A. Power-deFur, PhD, CCC-SLP,
ASHA-F**
Professor
Communication Sciences and Disorders
Director
Speech, Hearing and Learning Services
Longwood University
Farmville, Virginia
Chapters 1, 2, 3, and 4

Elda M. Rojas, MEd
Director
Newcomer and ESL Programs
Dallas Independent School District
Dallas, Texas
Chapter 10

Judy Rudebusch, EdD, CCC-SLP
Education Consultant
Learning Legacy, Inc.
Irving, Texas
Chapter 10

**Brenda C. Seal, PhD, CCC-SLP,
ASHA-F**
Professor
Department of Hearing, Speech and
    Language Sciences
Gallaudet University
Professor Emerita
Communication Sciences and Disorders
James Madison University
Washington, District of Columbia
Chapter 6

I dedicate this book to my parents, Harriet and Burton,
in thanksgiving for all I learned from them.

CHAPTER 1

The Common Core State Standards

Lissa A. Power-deFur

DEVELOPMENT OF COMMON CORE STATE STANDARDS

The Common Core State Standards (CCSS) are an initiative of the National Governors Association (NGA) and the Council of Chief State School Officers (CCSSO) in collaboration with the Bill and Melinda Gates Foundation. Their vision was to create a challenging education for all students which would enable them to complete high school prepared for either college or careers (Petrilli & McCluskey, 2014; Phillips & Wong, 2010; Thurlow, 2012). The Gates Foundation advocated for clearly articulated, high standards that would give students both academic and content knowledge as well as cognitive skills, including problem solving, collaboration, and academic risk taking (Phillips & Wong, 2010). The focus of these high standards was not to increase the amount of content, but rather to increase students' ability to transfer learning from one context to another. The CCSS were designed to "measure up to international standards," enabling greater success for America's high school graduates in the global marketplace (National Parent Teacher Association, 2010; Phillips & Wong, 2010).

Education Standards Movement

The CCSS reflect the nation's interest in raising the academic standards for all students, an interest commonly known as the education standards movement. This movement began in the late 1980s, when federal and state governments and business leaders first led initiatives designed to ensure that all graduates of U.S. high schools attained certain skills and could compete with the highest-performing countries (Marzano & Haystead, 2008). It was (and in some cases continues to be) the viewpoint of many educators, politicians, businesses, and parents that the academic progress of America's students was not keeping pace with our counterparts across the globe. Many educational associations identified the lack of consistent standards and the variance in standards from state to state and district to district as causal. The Association for Supervison and Curriculum Development (ASCD) noted that many schools provided learning experiences that were not challenging; therefore, they were not motivating, educating, or preparing students, and their students needed remedial education for careers and further education. Other schools failed to hold high expectations for all students or placed such a heavy emphasis on academic rigor that they produced emotional stress in their students (ASCD, n.d.). ASCD asserted that the CCSS moved us toward ensuring a whole-child approach to education, one that engages and challenges every child in every school and community (ASCD, n.d.).

In 1989, President George H. W. Bush and the nation's governors held an education summit at which they established education goals. These included student competencies across all education areas. During this period, state departments of education began the process of developing state-level standards in mathematics, language arts, and the sciences. Organizations representing the various teaching disciplines similarly developed model standards, which were often a resource to states during the development process (Kendall, 2011; Marzano & Haystead, 2008).

As the standards movement progressed, it changed education in a number of areas, such as instructional time, curriculum, student outcomes, student expectations, and assessment (Kendall, 2011; Marzano & Haystead, 2008). Prior to the standards movement, educators generally allocated instructional time based on availability; that is, whatever time was available became the needed time. The standards movement dictated specific instructional time, and it raised attention to the time needed for student mastery. Consequently, schools began to allocate specific blocks of time for core subjects, especially reading, that could not be interrupted.

Before the standards movement, the textbook frequently defined the curriculum and the expectations of students. In contrast, the movement presumed that educators specializing in the content area, rather than textbook publishers, knew best what students should know and be able to do. Additionally, prior to the standards movement, curriculum may have varied by classroom, as teachers may have taught their favorite topics repeatedly or skipped topics they had less comfort in teaching. The standards movement promoted a belief that all students should receive an education in key content areas with clear, measurable standards for content and skills applicable to all students. Subsequently, curriculum became shaped by state-level standards. Teachers focused instruction on the expected standards for that grade level, while textbooks and educational materials became aligned with the standards (Kendall, 2011; Marzano & Haystead, 2008).

Prior to the standards movement, student outcomes were described in terms of inputs. For example, "Carnegie units," the amount of time at school, was a common measure for school accreditation. With the standards-based education movement, state assessments of student achievement became the basis of measuring student outcomes. State assessments, previously characterized by infrequent comparisons with a national sample and/or minimum competency testing, changed to become foundational for accountability. Student assessment data became the basis for gauging schools' success, and schools became engaged in analysis of assessment data to improve student learning (Kendall, 2011; Marzano & Haystead, 2008).

The reenactment of the Elementary and Secondary Education Act in 2002, renamed No Child Left Behind (NCLB), capped a decade of work to establish standards in states and to hold educators accountable for student performance. NCLB linked school accreditation with student performance on state assessments. Student performance data are disaggregated into groups (i.e., racial-ethnic, limited English proficiency, socioeconomic, and disability status), thus drawing attention to the educational performance of these subgroups of students. NCLB included sanctions for low-performing schools, dramatically changing the focus of public education (Kendall, 2011; Marzano & Haystead, 2008).

The majority of states had adopted state-level standards by the early 21st century; however, many educators and policy makers cited concerns with having a state-by-state approach due to variability across the country (Kendall, 2011; Marzano & Haystead, 2008). The CCSS were developed to ensure that all students, no matter their location at any time during their school year, would similarly be prepared for success.

Our mobile society presents academic challenges to the many students who live in multiple states during their schooling. U.S. Census data regarding general mobility indicate that in 2009, 15.4% of the population lived in a different residence than it did in 2008. The majority of those moved within the same county (67.3%) and an additional 17.2% moved within the state. However, 12.6% moved state to state, and 2.9% moved abroad or returned stateside (U.S. Census, 2011). This mobility has the potential for creating gaps in these students' achievement. For example, if a student moves from State A to State B at the end of third grade, a particular math skill may be taught in the fourth grade in State A but was taught in the third grade in State B. As a result, the student would receive no instruction on that skill. Conversely, a standard covered in Grade 3 in State A may be taught for the first time in Grade 4 in State B, resulting in potentially unnecessary repetition. This disruption in the presentation of content is not limited to students moving from state to state, as high levels of variability in curriculum occur across school districts within the same state and, less frequently, among schools in the same district. With the adoption of the CCSS, student transience no longer carries the risk that key content will be missed or other content will be needlessly repeated.

Multiple state standards also generated concerns regarding the cost of preparing educational assessments tailored to specific states' standards. Similarly, there is an increased cost of preparing state-specific educational textbooks and other materials. In both situations, the economies of scale associated with adoption of common standards nationwide enable less expensive production of assessments and educational materials. Further, it is more likely that publishers will be creating materials that can be used across all CCSS participating states, rather than materials tailored to specific states.

Creation of the Common Core State Standards

The NGA and the CCSSO began their efforts in 2009 to develop the CCSS, creating, for the first time, common standards for all states in the areas of English/Language Arts and Mathematics. CCSSO and NGA engaged teachers, state education agency leadership, education administrators and content area experts, as well as a variety of business leaders. The following organizations are among those that collaborated: ACT, the College Board, the National Association of State Boards of Education, the National Parent Teacher Association, the State Higher Education Executive Officers, the American Association of School Administrators, the U.S. Chamber of Commerce, and the Business Roundtable (NGA & CCSSO, 2010c). The developers used a body of evidence in the development process, which included research, national data from the National Assessment of Educational Progress (NAEP), and surveys addressing the skills required of students entering college and workforce training (NGA & CCSSO, 2010c). Following a period of public comment, NGA and CCSSO made revisions incorporating the input from a variety of sources, including teachers and parents. With the establishment of the CCSS, standards for college- and career-ready high school graduates were articulated.

The developers of the CCSS focused on developing a core of essential content and skills for all students, enabling them to be literate citizens, skilled in critical thinking, problem solving, and analysis. The developers looked to the strengths of the existing state standards and designed the standards to be

- research and evidence based;
- clear, understandable, and consistent;
- aligned with college and career expectations to enable success of all students as they leave high school;
- based on rigorous content and application of knowledge through higher-order thinking skills; and
- informed by other top-performing countries in order to prepare all students for success in our global

economy and society (NGA & CCSSO, 2010c).

Through the development of standards that are influenced by the successes of other countries, rooted in the reality of what students need for college and/or career, and multifaceted in their objectives, NGA and CCSSO hoped to create standards that would be an effective resource in the classroom and improve the education of students nationwide.

The NGA and the CCSSO released the CCSS in June 2010. The standards enable educators and parents to identify what a student should know and be able to do at the end of each grade. In essence, the standards become a map for teachers to measure progress during the school year and to ensure they are prepared for the next grade level. With the standards, teachers across the country are able to focus on consistent goals and benchmarks to ensure their students are progressing. The standards provide consistency in expectations for students. Teachers now know the standards students should have met prior to entering their classrooms, regardless of where they were educated previously (National Parent Teacher Association, 2010; NGO & CCSSO, 2010c).

Ultimately, the intention is that all students will graduate from high school with the skills and knowledge to be successful in college or career. As John Kendall reported (2011), 35% of postsecondary institutions reported the need for an average of 1-year remediation for students upon college entry. Successful implementation of the standards means students are prepared for entry-level careers, freshman-level college courses, and workforce training programs. The CCSS assume that comparable skills are necessary to matriculate to college as to enter the workforce: college ready is also career ready.

State Adoption

The CCSS is a state-level, rather than federal initiative, led by two organizations that represent the political and education leadership at the state level. The standards intend to retain flexibility at the state, district, and individual school levels to make possible implementation of the best curriculum, materials, and instructional approaches that will enable students to meet the standards. Although the standards promote equity, ensuring that all students are prepared with clear goals and expectations, the standards do not dictate instructional strategies to state and local educators. The responsibility for designing and implementing lesson plans remains with building-level educators.

A goal of the standards was for participating states to work together to develop teaching materials and comprehensive assessment systems. This enables economies of scale as educators collaborate across state lines. This collaboration enables the development of textbooks, digital media, and other teaching materials that support the education of students in a majority of states. The standards also allowed for creation of common comprehensive assessment systems rather than state-by-state assessment systems. Two consortia, the Partnership for Assessment of Readiness for College and Careers (PARCC) and the Smarter Balanced Assessment Consortium (Smarter Balanced), are developing assessments aligned with the CCSS (PARCC, 2013; Smarter Balanced, n.d.) that were released in the 2014–2015 school year. PARCC

represents 19 states, and Smarter Balanced represents 17 states and one territory. Their goal is to enable comparable results across representative states in the consortia.

State adoption of the CCSS is voluntary; however, the federal government is clearly playing a role to encourage states' participation. In 2010, following establishment of the CCSS, the U.S. Department of Education (ED) linked state adoption of the standards to grant funding in the $4 billion "Race to the Top" program. In addition, the ED provided $350 million to develop national assessments aligned with the CCSS. In 2012, the ED provided waivers to key parts of NCLB for states that adopted the CCSS or had their own state standards certified as "college- and career-ready" by a state college system (Petrilli & McClusky, 2014). Despite these programs, the federal government is not overseeing the CCSS initiative. The NGA and the CCSSO remain committed to leadership on the CCSS initiatives and implementation.

Currently, 43 states, the District of Columbia, four territories, and the Department of Defense Education Agency (DoDEA) have adopted the CCSS. See the Common Core State Standards Initiative website (http://www.corestandards.org) for a current list of states and territories that have adopted the standards.

DESCRIPTION OF THE COMMON CORE STATE STANDARDS

The College and Career Readiness (CCR) standards serve as the anchors to the CCSS, defining cross-literacy expectations for all students to be ready for college or career. There are grade-specific standards (K–12) that define end-of-year expectations in a cumulative progression that brings students to college and career readiness by the end of high school. There are standards for each grade level through Grade 8, with two-year bands for the high school grades (9–12). The standards ensure that all students, regardless of income, geography, disability, and English language learning status have the opportunity to engage in equally challenging work (PTA, 2010).

The standards address literacy skills continuously from kindergarten through high school and across subject areas. Laura Justice (2013) comments that the English Language Arts standards are an improvement over state standards as they provide developmentally appropriate, rigorous expectations. Larry Ainsworth (2013) notes that the English Language Arts standards are clearer (better clarity and specificity), higher (increased rigor), and include "spiraled learning progressions" from grade to grade.

There are three main sections of the English Language Arts and Literacy Standards: comprehensive English Language Arts (ELA) at the K–5 level and, at the 6–12 level, an ELA section and a Literacy in the History/Social Studies, Science, and Technical Subjects section. Each section is divided into strands. The English Language Arts at both K–5 and 6–12 levels have four strands: Reading, Writing, Speaking and Listening, and Language. The 6–12 History/Social Studies, Science, and Technical Subjects section has two strands: Reading and Writing. Each strand begins with a set of College and Career Readiness (CCR) Anchor Standards that are common across all grades and content areas. Each CCR anchor standard has a grade-level standard that aligns the CCR

statement with grade-appropriate expectations (NGA & CCSSO, 2010c).

The Standards' organization at the K–5 level, including Reading, Writing, Speaking and Listening, and Language across the curriculum, reflects that, typically, one teacher is responsible for instruction in all areas. The standards have Language as a foundation and present an integrated model of literacy, with close connections between the four literacy standards (NGA & CCSSO, 2010c).

The standards are spiraled, connecting standards from one grade to the next. This "staircase of complexity" (Peery et al., 2011) enables educators to identify the standards that must be met prior to entry into the next grade. See Table 1–1 for an example in the area of Vocabulary Acquisition and Use from the Language Standard, highlighting the spiraling of information related to comprehension and use of root words and inflections.

The reading standard focuses on both students' reading skills and the material that they read. The standards reflect a staircase of increasingly complex texts and expect students to have extensive experience reading stories, dramas, poems, and myths from diverse cultures and different periods by graduation (NGO & CCSSO, 2010c). Historically, K–12 reading has favored narrative over expository texts, yet expository reading is the most common at the college and workforce level. As a result, the CCSS has a strong focus on expository text. This focus, however, does not diminish the role of fiction and literature.

In the area of writing, the standards posit that students need to "learn to use writing as a way of offering and supporting opinions, demonstrating understanding of the subjects they are studying, and conveying real and imagined experiences and events" to build a foundation for col-

Table 1–1. Example of Spiraling Nature of CCSS in Vocabulary

Grade	Inflections and Root Words
K	Use the most frequently occurring inflections and affixes (*-ed, -s, re-, un-, pre-, -ful, -less*) as a clue to meaning.
1	Use frequently occurring affixes as a clue to meaning. Identify frequently occurring root words and inflectional forms (e.g., *look, looks, looked, looking*).
2, 3	Determine meaning of new word formed when known prefix/affix is added (e.g., *happy/unhappy*). Use root word as clue to meaning.
4, 5	Use common, grade-appropriate Greek and Latin affixes and roots as clues to meaning (e.g., *telegraph, photograph, autograph*).

Note. Adapted from NGA & CCSSO (2010c).

lege and career readiness (NGA & CCSSO, 2010c). The Writing Standards also develop an area that, in general, has not been fully developed previously—that of argument. The new focus on argument highlights critical thinking and consideration of multiple viewpoints, a skill expected by both universities and employers. This type of writing is an addition to more traditional informative/explanatory texts and narratives. Research standards are included within the writing strand.

The Speaking and Listening Standards focus on enabling students to be productive members of rich conversations, by contributing, developing, and analyzing ideas during conversations. The standards focus on skills needed for a range of oral communication and interpersonal skills, including making formal presentations, listening carefully to ideas, working collaboratively, and adapting speech to context and task.

The Language Standards focus on the essential skills needed for standard spoken and written English, developing students' skills in the conventions of Standard English grammar, usage, and mechanics. The vocabulary standards address understanding words and phrases and their nuances with a focus on general academic and domain-specific words and phrases (NGA & CCSSO, 2010a). The Speaking and Listening and Language Standards are further explored in Chapter 2.

There are two sets of Mathematics Standards: Mathematics Practice and Mathematical Content. Mathematics Practice focuses on areas of K–12 expertise, whereas Mathematical Content focuses on conceptual categories (e.g., number and quantity, algebra, probability and statistics). The K–12 and high school Mathematic Content standards include a standard (what students should understand and be able to do), a cluster (a group of related standards), and a domain (ideas that connect standards and topics, often across grades). The mathematic standards reflect a learning progression, organizing knowledge and skills into a sequence that reflects knowledge of how students learn and the logical structure of mathematics (Kendall, 2011).

Supplemental Materials

The NGA and the CCSSO are maintaining their commitment to the Common Core through joint management of a website, which includes an array of supplemental materials that serve as resources for educators. The standards include sample texts that demonstrate the level of text complexity that is appropriate for each grade level. The standards present these as exemplars of texts that provide rich opportunities for use within the classroom. However, the standards do not dictate use of these texts and thus allow teachers to retain the flexibility to make their own decisions regarding appropriate texts.

The CCSS website includes a model for evaluating a text's level of complexity that incorporates quantitative tools, qualitative criteria, and the relationship between the individual reader, the task, and the text (found in CCSS Appendix A). CCSS's Appendix A also addresses oral language and vocabulary. CCSS's Appendix B includes a variety of exemplars from texts that demonstrate the types of reading (in terms of complexity and quality) that are appropriate at various grade levels. The third CCSS appendix, Appendix C, provides samples of student writing at each grade level that meet or exceed proficiency expectations in the areas of argument, informational/expository, and narrative (NGA & CCSSO, 2010c).

IMPLICATIONS FOR CHILDREN FROM SPECIAL POPULATIONS

The CCSS are designed to be inclusive of students with disabilities and English language learners (NGA & CCSSO, 2010a, 2010b). Both populations often lack the foundational knowledge and skills to achieve in the general curriculum and require special focus for their achievement. Contrary to the common approach used

during the development of state-level standards, the CCSS appear to have been developed with students with disabilities in mind (Thurlow, 2012). The standards recognize that CCR is appropriate for students with disabilities to be prepared for further education, employment, and independent living.

CCSS identifies that both students with disabilities and English language learners are heterogeneous in nature, yet students in both groups will be challenged in meeting the standards without support. According to the CCSS document, "Application to Students with Disabilities," instruction for students with disabilities must incorporate the necessary supports and accommodations needed to enable the students to succeed in meeting the concepts and skills identified in the standards (NGA & CCSSO, 2010b). These supports include an annual Individualized Education Program (IEP) with goals written to enable attainment of grade-level standards and that addresses the student's unique needs in accessing the general education curriculum through supports, accommodations, and modifications. The CCSS highlights the importance of adequate preparation of special educators (and related service personnel) to enable them to provide high-quality, evidence-based, individualized instruction. Further, the CCSS document speaks to the importance of using the principles of universal design for learning (UDL) (National Center on Universal Design for Learning, n.d.). These principles engage students through presentation of information in diverse formats and allowing for a variety of methods to demonstrate mastery. The CCSS document also highlights the importance of using assistive technology to ensure access to the general curriculum.

In its commentary on the standards in 2011, the Council for Exceptional Children (CEC) cited that the literacy, numeracy, and cross-disciplinary skills allow for the "widest possible range of students to participate fully from the outset" (CEC, 2011). The CEC further commended the reference to appropriate accommodations for students with disabilities (e.g., use of Braille and/or assistive technology such as speech-to-text technology, use of a scribe for writing, and inclusion of sign language within the Speaking and Listening standards). It is important that educators ensure that students with disabilities receive the necessary support from various forms of assistive technology that they need (Thurlow, 2012).

The application of the CCSS to students with disabilities is not without its challenges. The CEC asserts the necessity of preparing both special educators and general educators in the knowledge and skills needed to enable success of students with disabilities. Special educators need to have broad and specific knowledge of the grade-level standards that their students must achieve in order to develop appropriate instruction and of the accommodations necessary to enable both access to and mastery of the standards (CEC, 2011). An additional challenge is that educators have historically had low expectations for students with disabilities, an expectation that is likely to continue. By focusing on the standards during the annual IEP process, the standards can raise teams' expectations for their students' achievement (Thurlow, 2012).

Special educators have long been concerned about the application of standards to students with more significant cognitive disabilities. Beginning in spring 2011, a consortium of 12 states developed the Dynamic Learning Maps (DLM) Essential Elements. The developers designed these to link the content of the CCSS with the expectations for students with the most significant cognitive disabilities. Speech-language pathologists and their education collaborators will want to look to the DLM maps at http://dynamiclearningmaps.org for detailed information on meeting the CCSS for this population. Another consortium of states is leading the National Center and State Collaborative project that is building an alternate assessment based on alternate achievement standards (AA-AAS) for students with the most significant cognitive disabilities (National Center and State Collaborative, n.d.). The AA-AAS represent grade-level content with "less depth, breadth, and complexity" (National Center on Educational Outcomes, n.d.).

The document, "Application of Common Core State Standards to English Language Learners," highlights the need for instructional personnel to tap the skills English language learners bring to the classroom (NGA & CCSS, 2010a). Educators should recognize that second-language learners often have significant knowledge and skills in their first language, while understanding the challenges many of these students have based on their background (e.g., socioeconomic status, quality of prior schooling, and level of English language proficiency). The CCSS document highlights the importance of immersing students in literacy-rich school environments, providing students with foundational skills in English, and providing opportunities for classroom discourse and interaction to develop communication skills.

As the standards were designed to be both robust and relevant to the world students would enter upon graduation, they provide a clear framework of what students are expected to learn. The developers included students with disabilities and English language learners in the expectations for achievement. Since these students are general education students first and receive special education and/or English language learning services to support mastery of general education expectations second, the standards are foundational for all special populations. Although the standards indicate it is beyond their scope to delineate the support needed for these special populations, the standards highlight that "all students must have the opportunity to learn and meet the same high standards if they are to access the knowledge and skills necessary in their post-high school lives" (NGA & CCSSO, 2010c).

Common Core State Standards and Individualized Education Programs

The National Association of State Directors of Special Education, representing state education agency leadership in special education, urges special education teams to create standards-based IEPs that are aligned with state academic achievement standards (Holbrook, 2007). This approach focuses on using data on student performance to close the achievement gap between the student's performance and grade-level standards. By necessity, special education teams following this approach become more familiar with general education standards. One step in the seven-step process articulated by Holbrook (2007) includes development of measurable goals. Holbrook guides special education teams to develop measurable goals specific to the student's needs that can reasonably be expected to be achievable in one year.

As speech-language pathologists and IEP team members implement the standards-based IEP approach, linking the IEPs of their students with the standards, there is a temptation to use the standards as the students' IEP goals. Recalling that the standards reflect the expectations of general education, use of the standards for goals would fail to address the unique needs of individual students. Further, if the IEP goal is a duplicate of the goal for general education students, this could imply that the students do not need special education, as the special education goal is the same as the general education standard. As the purpose of the IEP is to identify the specially designed instruction (special education) that is needed to access the general curriculum, the IEP goals should focus on the special education needs to access the standards. IEP teams should write goals to enable the students to achieve those tasks that underlie achievement of the standards (ASHA, n.d.; Murza, Malani, & Hahs-Vaughn, 2014; Power-deFur & Flynn, 2012). For example, following two- and three-step directions may be required for a student to achieve grade-level standards. The IEP should reflect those skills needed to be able to follow these directions (e.g., understand the vocabulary and the compound and complex sentence structure of directions).

ROLE OF SPEECH–LANGUAGE PATHOLOGISTS

Speech-language pathologists have a unique role to play in applying their skills and knowledge about students and students' language and communication skills to facilitate the students' success with the standards. Speech-language pathologists play a distinct and well-established role in education due to their expertise in language and communication, including the metalinguistic skills needed to access the curriculum (Blosser et al., 2012; Ehren, 2014; Power-deFur, 2010; Rudebusch, 2012; Wallach, 2008). Given their focus on language, speaking and listening, and literacy, the standards mesh well with speech-language pathologists' skills in language, literacy, metalinguistics, and oral communication. Language and communication underlie the English Language Arts standards in all domains; these competencies are essential to successful academic, social, and career/employment outcomes.

Students with speech-language impairments need support to access the CCSS in the areas of language, speaking and listening, and literacy across the disciplines. The language of academics is more specialized than that of social communication in syntax, morphology, and pragmatics, with a high volume of content that is specific vocabulary and highly complex morpho-syntactic skills. Competency in the CCSS depends on the integrity and integration of the students' language skills. The following examples are illustrative:

- Phonology: Add or substitute individual phonemes in simple one-syllable words to make new words (CCSS.ELA-LITERACY.RF.K.2.E).
- Morphology: Use common, grade-appropriate Greek and Latin affixes and roots as clues to the meaning of a word (CCSS.ELA-LITERACY.L.4.4.B).
- Syntax: Form and use the perfect verb tense (CCSS.ELA-LITERACY.L.5.1.B).

- Semantics: Demonstrate understanding of figurative language, word relationships, and nuances in word meanings (CCSS.ELA-LITERACY.L.5.5).
- Pragmatics: Follow agreed-upon rules for discussions, such as gaining the floor in respectful ways, listening to others with care, and speaking one at a time about the topics and texts under discussion (CCSS.ELA-LITERACY.SL.3.1.B).

The above language skills play a vital role in the students' creation of new learning. The CCSS enables educators to set goals for students with disabilities and English language learners that elevate their academic language skills. The standards are rich with language and communication skills, which are further discussed in Chapter 2.

The CCSS provide an opportunity for speech-language pathologists to change the common perception of their role from that of speech therapy ancillary to the curriculum to speech-language services that are a vital part of the school teams' striving to ensure mastery by all students. Speech-language pathologists' breadth of knowledge of language and communication makes them vital partners with teachers and administrators.

Speech-language pathologists' specialized knowledge and skills in language form (morphology, syntax, and phonology), content (semantics, specifically vocabulary and word relationships), and use (social interaction and discourse skills) provide them with tremendous expertise in analysis of the language expectations of the CCSS. Further, the speech-language pathologist's skills in providing direct language and literacy intervention, designing intervention strategies, modifying curriculum and classrooms, and conducting observational analyses, screenings, and assessments give them the knowledge to design interventions that enable student success. Speech-language pathologists will identify language skills that may be at the root of students' difficulty in achievement and assist students to develop, access, or use skills and strategies needed for achievement.

Speech-language pathologists will find that they implement this role in both scaffolding for students who need instructional intensity and our "language lens" (Ehren, 2014) and engaging with teachers to support differentiated instruction based on students' language needs. Speech-language pathologists create metalinguistic approaches to analyze linguistic structure, identify the level of scaffolding needed, and use grammar (syntax and morphology) to enable students to understand meaning. Their role is to engage students in developing knowledge (information they need to understand and use), skills (actions students complete), and strategies (tools to assist in gathering knowledge and skills).

CONCLUDING THOUGHTS

The CCSS represent the culmination of over two decades of focus on raising the achievement levels of all students: those in every geographic region of the United States, students with disabilities, and students who are English language learners. The ultimate goal is for schools to offer rigorous education programs that enable students to be able to create their own meaning out of what they learn, to integrate what they are learning with prior knowledge, and to apply the information to new situations. The standards are fur-

ther explored in the following chapters, first focusing on the language and communication expectations of the standards and strategies for analysis and intervention planning, followed by detailed application of the standards for various special populations. With 69% of school-based speech-language pathologists reporting that they are involved in the CCSS (ASHA, 2014), there is no time like the present for speech-language pathologists to apply their knowledge and skills to enable student success in achieving the standards' language expectations.

REFERENCES

Ainsworth, L. (2013). *Prioritizing the common core: Identifying specific standards to emphasize the most*. Englewood, CO: The Leadership and Learning Center.

American Speech-Language-Hearing Association. (n.d.). *Common Core State Standards: A resource for SLPs*. Retrieved December 21, 2014, from http://www.asha.org/SLP/schools/Common-Core-State-Standards/

American Speech-Language-Hearing Association. (2014). *2014 Schools survey. Survey summary report: Number and type of responses, SLPs*. Retrieved December 31 2014, from http://www.asha.org

Association for Supervision and Curriculum Development. (n.d.). *A whole child approach to education and the Common Core State Standards Initiative*. Retrieved January 5, 2015, from from http://www.ascd.org/ASCD/pdf/site ASCD/policy/CCSS-and-Whole-Child-one-pager.pdf

Blosser, J., Roth, F. P., Paul, D. R., Ehren, B. J., Nelson, N. W., & Sturm, J. M. (2012, August 28). Integrating the core. *The ASHA Leader*. Retrieved September 20, 2014, from http://www.asha.org/publications/leader/2012/120828/integrating-the-core/

Council for Exceptional Children (CEC). (2011). *Common core standards: What special educators need to know. Council for Exceptional Children*

(CEC). Retrieved November 24, 2014, from http://www.broward.k12.fl.us/studentsup port/ese/PDF/CCSS-WhatSPEDShould Know.pdf

Ehren, B. J. (2014). *"Push down" curriculum and the Common Core State Standards—What about developmental appropriateness?"* Presented at the ASHA Schools Conference, Orlando, FL.

Ehren, B. J., Blosser, J., Roth, F. P., Paul, D. R., & Nelson, N. W. (2012, April 3). Core commitment. *The ASHA Leader.* Retrieved September 30, 2014, from http://www.asha.org/ publications/leader/2012/120403/core-commitment/

Holbrook, M. D. (2007, August). *Standards-based Individualized Education Program examples. A seven-step process to creating standards-based IEPs.* Alexandria, VA: National Association of State Directors of Special Education, Inc. (NASDSE). Retrieved from http://nasdse.org /DesktopModules/DNNspot-Store/Product Files/36_a7f577f4-20c9-40bf-be79-54fb510f 754f.pdf

Individuals With Disabilities Education Improvement Act of 2004, Pub. L. No. 108-446, 20 U.S.C. § 1400 et seq. (2004).

Justice, L. (2013, October). From my perspective: A+ speech-language goals. *The ASHA Leader, 19,* 10–11. doi:10.1044/leader.FMP.18102013.10

Kansas University. (n.d.). Dynamic learning maps—essential elements for English language arts. *Dynamic Learning Maps.* Retrieved September 29, 2014, from http://dynamic learningmaps.org

Kendall, J. (2011). *Understanding the common core standards.* Alexandria, VA: Association for Supervision and Curriculum Development (ASCD).

Marzano, R. J., & Haystead, M. W. (2008). *Making standards useful in the classroom.* Alexandria, VA: Association for Supervision and Curriculum Development.

Murza, K. A., Malani, M. D., & Hahs-Vaughn, D. L. (2014, December). Using the Common Core State Standards to guide therapy in the schools: Confidently accepting the challenge. *SIG 16 Perspectives on School-Based Issues, 15,* 125–133. doi:10.1044/sbi15.4.125

National Center and State Collaborative. (n.d.). *National Center and State Collaborative General Supervision Enhancement Grant.* Retrieved February 17, 2014, from http://www.ncscpart ners.org/resources

National Center on Educational Outcomes. (n.d.). *Alternate assessments based on alternate academic achievement standards.* Retrieved February 17, 2014, from http://www.cehd.umn .edu/NCEO/TopicAreas/AlternateAssess ments/aa_aas.htm

National Center on Universal Design for Learning. (n.d.). Retrieved December 31, 2014, from http://www.udlcenter.org/

National Governors Association Center for Best Practices, Council of Chief State School Officers. (2010a). *Application of Common Core State Standards for English Language Learners.* Washington, DC: National Governors Association for Best Practices, Council of Chief State School Officers.

National Governors Association Center for Best Practices, Council of Chief State School Officers, (2010b). *Application to Students with Disabilities.* Washington, DC: National Governors Association for Best Practices, Council of Chief State School Officers.

National Governors Association Center for Best Practices, Council of Chief State School Officers. (2010c). *Common Core State Standards.* Washington, DC: National Governors Association for Best Practices, Council of Chief State School Officers.

National Parent Teacher Association. (2010, April). *Common Core State Standards initiative.* Washington, DC: National Parent Teacher Association.

Partnership for Assessment of Readiness for College and Careers. (2013, September). *PARCC Frequently asked questions.* Retrieved December 31, 2014, from http://PARCConline.org

Peery, A., Wiggs, M. D., Piercy, T. D., Lassiter, C. J., & Cebelak, L. (2011). *Navigating the English language arts common core state standards.* Englewood, CO: The Leadership and Learning Center.

Petrilli, M. J., & McClusky, N. P. (2014). Restarting the common core debate. *The Washington Times.* Retrieved November 24, 2014, from http:// www.washingtontimes.com/news/2014/ sep/1/restarting-the-common-core-debate/

Phillips, V., & Wong, C. (2010, February). Tying together the common core of standards, instruction, and assessments. *Phi Delta Kappan, 19*(5). doi:10.1177/003172171009100511

Power-deFur, L. (2010, August). The educational relevance of communication disorders. *The ASHA Leader, 15,* 20–21.

Power-deFur, L., & Flynn, P. (2012, March). Unpacking the standards for intervention. *SIG 16 Perspectives on School-Based Issues, 13,* 11–16. doi:10.1044/sbi13.1.11

Rudebusch, J. (2012, March). From common core state standards to standards-based IEPs: A brief tutorial. *SIG 16 Perspectives on School-Based Issues, 13,* 17–24. doi: 10.1044/sbi13.1.17

Smarter Balanced. (n.d.). *Smarter balanced states approve achievement level recommendations.* Retrieved December 30, 2014, from http://www.smarterbalanced.org/news/

Thurlow, M. L. (2012, Summer). Common Core State Standards: The promise and the peril for students with disabilities. *The Special Edge, 25*(3), 1, 6–8.

U.S. Census Bureau. (2011). *Geographic Mobility: 2008 to 2009.* Washington, DC: U.S. Department of Commerce.

Wallach, G. (2008). *Language intervention for school-age adolescents.* Maryland Heights, MO: Mosby Elsevier.

CHAPTER 2

Language and Communication Expectations of the Standards

Lissa A. Power-deFur

INTRODUCTION

The four strands of the College and Career Readiness (CCR) Anchor Standards—Reading, Writing, Speaking and Listening, and Language—reflect kindergarten through 12th-grade end-of-year expectations in communication, language, and literacy. The standards presume that language and literacy skills are at the heart of all of the standards, regardless of subject area. Language and literacy skills are richly addressed at the elementary levels and continue to be an emphasis at the middle and high school grades. This chapter explores the communication, language, and literacy expectations of the CCSS.

ROLE OF LANGUAGE AND COMMUNICATION IN THE COMMON CORE STATE STANDARDS

The CCSS are generally considered as rigorous and developmentally appropriate in the area of English Language Arts (Justice, 2013; Marzano & Simms, 2013).

The standards encompass a hierarchy of language skills from phonological awareness to the ability to understand diverse perspectives, from comprehension of discipline-specific vocabulary to syntactic complexity in speech and text (Ehren, Blosser, Roth, Paul, & Nelson, 2012; Rudebusch, 2012). The CCSS emphasize oral language and phonological awareness in the primary grades. In kindergarten, students are to develop skills in counting, pronouncing, blending, and segmenting syllables in spoken words (National Governors Association Center for Best Practices [NGA] & Council of Chief State School Officers [CCSSO], 2010a). The expectations for proficiency in oral language progress with the expectation that students in Grades 9 and 10 are able to present findings and support their evidence clearly and concisely using a style appropriate to the audience and task (NGA & CCSSO, 2010a). In the vocabulary area, students progress from mastering morphology (affixes) for understanding meaning to becoming adept at understanding euphemisms, hyperbole, and paradox prior to graduation. Students' skills in the conventions of Standard

15

English develop from early skills in using nouns, verbs, adjectives, and adverbs to secondary-level skills in using parallel structure in their oral and written communication.

Speaking and Listening Standards

The CCSS have greater emphasis on oral language than most state standards, as noted by the unique section found in the standards devoted specifically to Speaking and Listening. These standards have two sections: Comprehension and Collaboration and Presentation of Knowledge and Ideas. In the area of Comprehension and Collaboration, it is expected that students will participate in a range of conversations with diverse partners. Their conversations are to build upon others' ideas, expressing their own ideas clearly and persuasively. The standards spiral, with the topics of conversation progressing, focusing on grade-level topics and texts, and requiring increasing complexity in students' conversations. In addition, students must demonstrate a growing ability to link their comments to those of others as they apply these skills in higher grade levels.

The Comprehension and Collaboration section is thorough in its recognition of the importance of social communication (pragmatic) skills in conversations. The CCSS call for students to demonstrate independence in pragmatically complex tasks, such as discerning a speaker's key points; requesting clarification; clarifying others' ideas; adapting their communication to the audience, task, and purpose of the communication; and critiquing the communication of others (NGA & CCSSO, 2010a). Beginning in first grade, students are to follow rules for discussion, including listening to others; taking turns;

and speaking one at a time. By Grade 2, students are to demonstrate their ability to respectfully gain the floor in conversations and by Grade 4, students are to carry out these roles in their group discussions. At the upper elementary grade levels, students should pose questions that facilitate discussion through elaborating on specific ideas, connecting the ideas of others, and verifying or challenging communication partners in respectful ways. Students shall participate in academic discussions in class, in small groups, and in one-on-one discussions (NGA & CCSSO, 2010a).

The standards also expect students to develop the pragmatic skill of evaluating a speakers' point of view. This begins in kindergarten with students asking and answering questions to seek help or clarify something that is not understood. By second grade, students' questions are deepening their understanding of a topic; and by fourth grade, students are to identify reasons and evidence for a speaker's point of view. This progression continues into the secondary grades, as students will be identifying fallacious reasoning and assessing speakers' premises, word choice, and tone (NGA & CCSSO, 2010a).

In the area of Presentation of Knowledge and Ideas, students will develop the skill of presenting information in a manner that is appropriate to the audience, task, or purpose of the communication. Third graders will use clear speech with an understandable pace. Fourth graders will create an organized presentation, inserting appropriate facts and details. Prior to graduation, students will be able to present knowledge and information in a range of formal and informal tasks. The standards differentiate between formal English and casual communication, recognizing the importance of both for student learning (NGA & CCSSO, 2010a).

Phonological Awareness

The Foundational Skills (K–5) in the Reading Standards begin with Phonological Awareness (PA). The PA standards are present only for kindergarten and first grade; Phonics and Word Recognition replace PA in second grade. Recognizing the PA skills as fundamental for developing reading skills, the CCSS presents all of the PA elements in these first 2 years. The basic PA skills expect children to be able to demonstrate understanding of phonemes through the following tasks:

- rhyme production;
- counting, blending, pronouncing, and segmenting syllables;
- blending and segmenting onsets and rimes;
- isolating and pronouncing the consonants and vowels in consonant-vowel-consonant words (excluding final [l], [r], and [ks] "x");
- adding and replacing phonemes in words;
- blending phonemes to create consonant blends; and
- segmenting spoken words into their sequence of phonemes (NGA & CCSSO, 2010a).

The ability to produce speech sounds accurately and to understand the rule systems associated with phonological patterns and phonotactics (the rules for the sequential arrangement of speech sounds) are underlying skills for a child's ability to understand the syllable structures in English. Students must have a solid foundation in sound (phoneme) symbol relationships and have the ability to differentiate between various sound relationships (e.g., [i] ee") can be spelled "ee" or "ea" or "ei"). Further, students must have the ability to manipulate phonemes, segmenting and blending them to understand and create new words.

Oral Communication and Fluency

The CCSS in Speaking and Listening and Language require students to use their oral language skills to communicate clearly and fluently. For example, the Speaking and Listening standards in the area of Presentation of Knowledge and Ideas address speaking in a variety of contexts and communicative tasks and demonstrating command of formal English when indicated. At the kindergarten level, this begins with the concept of speaking audibly and clearly (CCSS.ELA-Literacy. SL.K.6). The Foundation Skill for Reading Standard addressing Phonological Awareness in kindergarten speaks to pronouncing phonemes in words (CCSS,ELA-Literacy.RF.K.2.B). These standards expect students to have mastered articulation and phonology, with the ability to produce the English speech sounds and know the underlying phonological rule system.

Students' ability to speak clearly and fluently is further highlighted in fourth grade when students are expected to speak clearly at an understandable pace. In middle school, students should use appropriate eye contact, adequate volume, and clear pronunciation. The Reading Standards also capture the importance of fluency. Students are expected to read with the appropriate rate and expression beginning in first grade, language that remains present in the standards through fifth grade. Similarly, students are expected to read with both accuracy and fluency to support comprehension from first grade through fifth grade. Although the standard is no longer continued, there is the expectation embedded within the CCSS that once a skill is mastered it is retained through graduation (NGA & CCSSO, 2010a).

Reading Standards: Literature, Informational Text, and Foundational Skills

Students need to be skilled at a collection of complex skills in language to be proficient readers. The College and Career Readiness Anchor standards have four sections designed to build a strong reading foundation:

- *key ideas and details* (identifying what the text says; making inferences; determining the main idea or theme; analyzing how and why individuals, events, and ideas develop within the text);
- *craft and structure* (interpreting words and phrases; determining technical, connotative, and figurative meanings; identifying how word choices shape meaning; analyzing text structure, including sentences, paragraphs, sections, or stanzas; assessing how point of view shapes the content and style);
- *integration of knowledge and ideas* (integrate and evaluate content; delineate and evaluate the argument; analyze how two or more texts address similar themes to develop knowledge and compare approaches); and
- *range of reading and level of text complexity* (independently and proficiently reading and comprehending complex text, both literary and informational) (NGA & CCSSO, 2010a).

The standards represent a staircase of increasing complexity in what students should be able to do, capturing the developmental progression of reading. They specifically state, "Students advancing through the grades are expected to meet each year's grade-specific standards and retain or further develop skills and understandings mastered in preceding grades" (NGA & CCSSO, 2010a, p. 11). This highlights the importance of knowing the standards from prior grade levels, as, once it presumed that students have achieved mastery, they are not repeated.

Students are engaged in reading from a broad array of high-quality, increasingly challenging material. They will read a diverse and extensive array of literature, classic and contemporary, national and international, fiction and expository. Their readings will include stories, poems, myths, and dramas from various time periods and cultures. Students will build their skills as readers within specific disciplines by reading. The standards have an increased focus on evidence, expecting students to use the text to answer questions and thus, minimizing students' use of prior knowledge for their responses. Students must have the ability to identify the "main idea" of a text, which requires an understanding of what a "main idea" is. Students need to be able to analyze information from the text and integrate it with their background knowledge in order to generate ideas about the text and to evaluate their predictions. Reading experiences, including reading of texts in the content areas (e.g., history/social studies and sciences), will facilitate students' ability to read independently and meticulously (NGA & CCSSO, 2010a). The standards' increased use of nonfiction better prepares students for college and the workplace. This includes disciplinary literacy—the awareness that disciplines often have a unique way of conveying information (Murza, Malani, & Hahs-Vaughn, 2014).

In the area of key ideas and details, the Reading Standards engage the students in retelling stories. Beginning in first grade, students are to include key information and the central message. By third grade, students are to demonstrate skills in describing characters in a story and explain how the characters' actions contribute to the story sequence. Students must also demonstrate the ability to describe relationships between events, ideas, and steps using language that conveys time and sequence.

Students are to be able to compare texts beginning in kindergarten. The area of integration of knowledge and ideas expects that kindergarten students will be able to identify basic similarities and differences with support. This skill grows throughout the elementary school years as the Craft and Structure standards expect students to be able to compare and contrast by fourth grade. At that time, students should be able to compare and contrast point of view, differentiating between first- and third-person narratives, a skill that relies on the students' comprehension of pronouns.

Students' sophistication in comprehension and use of syntax play a primary role in their ability to understand highly complex texts (Murza et al., 2014; Nelson, 2010; Scott, 2009). By the end of the first grade, students must be able to create simple and compound declarative, interrogative, imperative, and exclamatory sentences on their own. To do so, students require the ability to understand that sentences are a complete thought and that phrases include a noun or a verb plus descriptive words. Creation of compound sentences requires the ability to join thoughts together with conjunctions. Students also should be able to expand and rearrange simple and compound sentences. By third grade, they should be able to demonstrate subject-verb agreement and be able to create complex sentences. Syntactic skills should progress in such a manner that fourth-grade students can demonstrate the ability to order adjectives correctly.

At the syntactic level, readers must have strong skills in identifying parts of speech (e.g., nouns, verbs, adverbs, determiners) and creating a variety of sentence structures (including passive voice). They must be able to segment a sentence into its propositions (ideas) and understand the elements of a complex sentence. Students also need to appreciate cohesion: connecting ideas (e.g., joining words and phrases with linking words, such as because, therefore, also, and since); conveying events in the correct order; making appropriate transitions between thoughts; and providing concluding thoughts. The ability to maintain the appropriate relationships between pronouns and their nouns (e.g., "them" refers to boys, "that" refers to a particular event) is another important skill for maintaining cohesion. Students in fourth grade must have the ability to see connections between ideas, frequently through inference when the ideas are not directly stated. More complex syntactic skills are needed at the higher grade levels as secondary students also need to master embedded clauses (the use of a noun clause as a subject) and nominalization (e.g., demonstrate becomes demonstration).

To fully comprehend the material they read, students need to understand the majority of the words. When students face a number of words they do not know, they are unable to utilize these new words to comprehend the meaning of the passage. Students should analyze new words using context, other information in the passage, presented pictures or diagrams, and/or their morphological awareness skills. Context clues can stem from the adjacent words within the same sentence or from further locations within the text (Nelson, 2010).

Morphological awareness is the ability to consciously consider and manipulate the smallest units of meaning in language (Larsen & Nippold, 2007; Nippold & Sun, 2008; Wolter & Dilworth, 2013). Morphemes, the smallest meaningful units of language, can be either inflectional or derivational in nature (Nelson, 2010). Children first master inflectional morphemes, generally prior to starting school. These are morphemes that modify the base or root word by time, number, aspect, or comparison (e.g., walk to walked; boy to boys; big to bigger). Children then master derivational morphemes during the school years, generally with the support of their language arts instruction. Derivational morphemes modify the base or root word by changing the meaning and/or word class (e.g., fair to unfair, drive to driver, wind to rewind, complete to completion). The ability to analyze derivational morphemes is a critical skill to being able to analyze and comprehend new words (Nelson, 2010; Larsen & Nippold, 2007; Nippold & Sun, 2008).

The Reading Standards further expect that students will be adept at identifying point of view and purpose and at understanding the relationship between characters and themes. These skills require sophistication in perspective taking. To be proficient, readers first need the oral communication skills to understand the perspective of someone else as well as communication in different situations and with different speakers. They must then apply that pragmatic skill to the information on the written page to develop pragmatically the perspective of another.

Additionally, students need a collection of metalinguistic skills to become good readers (Ehren, 2014). Metalinguistic skills—the ability to think about the components of a word to understand its meaning—are essential to the ability to think about language. Morphological awareness is an example of a metalinguistic skill, that ability to think about changes in word meaning as morphemes are added to root words. Metalinguistic skills also include the ability to think about language to determine the meaning of figurative language, such as idioms (e.g., a hot potato), similes (e.g., he is as funny as a monkey), metaphors (e.g., boiling mad), and nuances of meaning (e.g., really vs. truly). These skills are essential for comprehension and creation of higher-level sentences (Nelson, 2010). By Grade 3, the CCSS holds that students must be able to explain the function of nouns, prepositions, verbs, adjectives, and adverbs. Fifth graders need the ability to identify and correct sentence fragments and run-on sentences, another metalinguistic skill, analyzing application of the rules of syntax.

Writing Standards

The Writing Standards expect students to offer and support opinions through writing. The standards focus on using writing to communicate clearly to an external audience, and adapting the form and content of writing as appropriate to the task. Like the Reading Standards, these standards expect students to meet and retain the skills from each year, maintaining the mastery gained at earlier grades. The Writing Standards have four components:

- *text types and purposes* (writing arguments to support claims; writing informative texts to convey ideas; writing narratives);
- *production and distribution of writing* (clear and coherent writing; writing through use of planning, revising, editing, rewriting);
- *research to build and present knowledge* (conducting research projects with focused questions; gathering information from multiple sources; drawing evidence from texts to support analysis); and
- *range of writing* (routine writing that allows for research, reflection, and revision; and responds to various tasks, purposes, and audiences) (NGO & CCSSO, 2010a).

The standards assume students will have focused instruction, with a variety of short- and long-term writing projects. Such projects should enable students to master a range of skills, including vocabulary, syntax, and organization of ideas, and applications in writing, including vocabulary, syntax, and organization of ideas. These standards expect students to write clear logical arguments, using claims they can substantiate, demonstrating sound reasons, and providing relevant evidence (NGA & CCSSO, 2010a). Pragmatic skills are expected from the early grades as students are expected to use different types of writing for different audiences, tasks, and purposes. An additional challenge for students mastering writing is that the rules of composition are not easily deduced, and students may require direct instruction to attain mastery

(e.g., the concept that all ideas in a given paragraph must relate to the same idea). Further, good writing requires organization of thoughts to generate a main idea and its related concepts. Clearly, the meta-linguistic skills students need to be good writers are comparable to those called upon for students to be good speakers and good readers.

Language Standards

The purpose of the Language anchor standards is to ensure that students are able to control the conventions of Standard English grammar, usage, and mechanics; to determine or clarify meaning of grade-appropriate words presented through listening, reading, or the media; and to understand relationships between words, nonliteral meanings, and shades of meaning (NGA & CCSSO, 2010a). The CCSS presents the Language Standards as inseparable from the reading, writing, and speaking and listening standards.

These anchor standards in Language have three components: Conventions of Standard English, Knowledge of Language, and Vocabulary Acquisition and Use. The conventions of Standard English encompass appropriate use of various parts of speech in both speaking and writing and the appropriate use of capitalization, punctuation, and spelling in writing. The Knowledge of Language component focuses on the ability to make effective language choices for meaning or style. Vocabulary standards focus on determining meaning of multiple meaning words, understanding figurative language, and acquiring a range of general academic and domain-specific words and phrases for reading, writing, speaking, and listening. There is an increasing sophistication expected for comprehension and use of multiple meaning words. At the primary levels, students should be able to differentiate the multiple meanings for words such as bark, hard, and stamp. By upper elementary levels, students should master such multiple meaning words as log, stable, and steer. In middle and secondary levels, students should be facile in comprehension and use of the various meanings for words like loom, hamper, and prune.

Conventions of Standard English

The full breadth of English grammar is included in these standards, with kindergarteners demonstrating command of frequently occurring regular plural nouns, question words (e.g., who, what, where, when, why, and how), and prepositions (e.g., to, from, in, out, on, off, for, of, by, and with). The skills progress through elementary and middle school grade levels, with ninth through 12th graders demonstrating the ability to select types of phrases (nouns, verb, adjectival, adverbial, participial, prepositional, absolute) and clauses (independent or dependent) to convey specific meanings and add interest to their communication. These standards address use of formal English in writing and speaking, yet recognize the importance of using informal English when appropriate. The standards also address the pragmatic skill of knowing how to express oneself through language. See Table 2–1 for detailed information about the language skills expected at varying grade levels in the Conventions of Standard English.

Vocabulary

The standards have a strong focus on vocabulary, with the expectation that students will grow vocabulary through conversation, direct instruction, and reading, and then apply that vocabulary to reading, writing, speaking, and listening. The standards address determination of word meanings, comprehension of word nuances, and a steady expansion of vocabulary at the word and phrase level. The Vocabulary Acquisition and Use standards have three components:

- Determine or clarify the meaning of unknown and multiple-meaning words and phrases by using context clues, analyzing meaningful word parts, and consulting general and specialized reference materials, as appropriate.
- Demonstrate understanding of word relationships and nuances in word meanings.
- Acquire and use accurately a range of general academic and domain-specific words and phrases sufficient for reading, writing, speaking and listening at the college and career readiness level; demonstrate independence in gathering vocabulary knowledge when encountering an unknown term important to comprehension or expression (NGO & CCSSO, 2010a).

The standards place emphasis on both "general academic" and "domain-specific" vocabulary. The Anchor standards in language arts speak to the ability to acquire and use a range of academic and domain-specific words and phrases for reading, writing, speaking, and listening (NGO & CCSSO, 2010a). General academic vocabulary, commonly termed *Tier 2* words, are those words commonly used in academic and professional communication (e.g.,

Table 2–1. Progression of Skills in Conventions of Standard English

Convention of Standard English	Grade-Level Expectation	
	Grade	Expectation
Nouns	1	Common, proper and possessive nouns Match singular/plural nouns with verbs
	2	Collective nouns Irregular plural nouns
	3	Regular and irregular plural nouns Abstract nouns Explain function of nouns
Verbs	1	Convey past, present, and future
	2	Create past tense for frequently occurring irregular verbs
	3	Use simple verbs tenses (e.g., walks, walked, will walk) Explain function of verbs
	4	Use progressive, modal auxiliaries (e.g., can, may, must)
	5	Use perfect tense (e.g., had walked, have walked, will have walked) Recognize inappropriate verb tense shifts
	8	Explain functions of verbals (gerunds, participles, infinitives) Use passive voice Use verbs for mood (indicative, imperative, interrogative, conditional, and subjective)
Pronouns	1	Personal, possessive, indefinite
	2	Reflexive Explain function of pronouns
	4	Relative (e.g., who, whose, whom, which, that)
	6	Correct inappropriate shifts in pronoun number and person Correct ambiguous pronouns
Prepositions	K	Frequently occurring (e.g., to, from, in, out, on, off, for, of, by, with)
	1	Frequently occurring (e.g., during, beyond, toward)
	5	Explain function of prepositions
Adjectives and adverbs	1	Use frequently occurring adjectives
	2	Select adjective or adverb appropriately
	3	Use comparative and superlative adjectives and adverbs
	4	Use relative adverbs (e.g., where, when, why)

continues

Table 2–1. *continued*

Convention of Standard English	Grade-Level Expectation	
	Grade	Expectation
Conjunctions	1	Use frequently occurring conjunctions (e.g., and, so, but, or, because)
	3	Use coordinating and subordinating conjunctions
	5	Use correlative conjunctions (e.g., either/or)
		Explain function of conjunctions
Determiners	1	Use determiners (articles, demonstratives)
Phrases	4	Use prepositional phrases
	7	Explain the function of phrases and clauses
		Fix misplaced and dangling modifiers
Produces and expands complete sentences	1	Create simple and compound declarative, interrogative, imperative, and exclamatory sentences (with prompts)
	2	Create and rearrange simple and compound declarative, interrogative, imperative, and exclamatory sentences (without prompts)
	3	Create complex sentences
	4	Recognize and correct sentence fragments and run-on sentences
	9–10	Use parallel structure

Note. Adapted from NGA & CCSSO (2010a).

prevent, imaginative, muscular) but not typically used in conversational speech. (Everyday vocabulary that is common in conversations is termed *Tier 1* vocabulary.) *Tier 3* words, those that are domain specific, are words particular to a certain content or discipline (e.g., geometry, peninsula, vector, and parenthesis) (Marzano & Simms, 2013). Tier 3 vocabulary can be difficult to paraphrase into everyday or common academic language. The standards expect student comprehension and use of both Tier 2 and Tier 3 vocabulary words. These can be seen both in the early Reading and Writing Standards and again in the later Literacy standards for His-

tory/Social Studies, Science, and Technical subjects.

The academic curriculum is rich with diverse vocabulary, with estimates of vocabulary size in 12th grade ranging from 17,000 to 45,000 words. To meet these expectations, students must master from 1,150 to 3,150 new words per year (Marzano, 2004). A majority of these words are Tier 3 words from the discipline-specific areas. Marzano's research informs us that children need six to 10 exposures to a word in context for mastery, and that children with low abilities have only an 8% chance of learning a new word from context alone (Marzano, 2004). Although

Marzano's meta-analysis of the research did not focus on children with speech-language impairments, it is likely that this figure would be typical of a child with a language-processing deficit.

Marzano and Simms remind us that to truly master new vocabulary words, students must not only understand the word, but they must internalize it, remember it, and use it correctly (Marzano & Simms, 2014). Unfortunately, teachers in the content areas typically do not teach vocabulary (Ehren, 2014) as their focus is on teaching content in the sciences, social studies, mathematics, and arts areas. Further, most adolescents are learning six content areas per year, with discipline-specific vocabulary in each subject matter.

At the secondary level, students should be facile in their use of a full complement of figurative language, including idioms, similes, and metaphors, and be able to extend their ability to adages (e.g., a penny saved is a penny earned) and proverbs (e.g., all that glitters is not gold). In middle school literature, students will be exposed to and expected to comprehend personification (e.g., opportunity is knocking at her door), irony, sarcasm, and puns. At the high school level, students will need to understand euphemisms (e.g., between jobs rather than unemployed), oxymoron (e.g., deafening silence), hyperbole (e.g., a million things to do), and paradox (e.g., saving money by spending it). To master these language skills, students must possess a strong vocabulary, good general knowledge, and the ability to draw inferences and conclusions. See Table 2–2 for the progress of vocabulary skills across the grade levels.

The language skills expected in the standards can be challenging for many students. The Virginia Department of Education (VDOE, 2013a, 2013b, 2014) has completed a thorough analysis of student performance on Virginia's Standards of Learning assessments. (Virginia has not adopted the CCSS, but has its own state standards, the Standards of Learning [SOLs].) VDOE gathered these data from student performance on reading assessments in Grades 3 and 4. Student performance on the vocabulary elements of these standards is particularly illustrative. VDOE found that students have difficulty identifying prefixes, roots, and suffixes; using affixes (e.g., comprehending the meaning of the affixes such as "-ly," "-er," or "un"); using synonyms; and comprehending figurative language (e.g., "eyes lit up") (VDOE, 2013a, 2013b). VDOE identified that students will benefit from additional practice with the following skills:

- using affixes and context clues;
- using context to clarify meaning of unfamiliar words; and
- differentiating among multiple meanings of words (VDOE, 2014).

Although these data are specific to Virginia, we can anticipate that students nationwide will have comparable challenges.

The CCSS include a section called, "Language Progressive Skills, by Grade," that details specific language skills that will require continued attention at higher-grade levels (NGO & CCSSO, 2010a). These skills are fundamental to increasingly sophisticated writing and speaking. For example, standard CCSS.ELA-LITERACY.L.3.1.F (ensure subject-verb and pronoun-antecedent agreements) is introduced in Grade 3 and will require continued attention in every grade through 12th grade. Similarly, the CCSS introduces

Table 2–2. Vocabulary Acquisition and Use Standards

Identifying Meaning	
K	Identify new meanings for familiar words (e.g., "duck" as a noun or a verb)
G 1, 2, 3	Use sentence-level context as clue to meaning
G 4	Use context (e.g., definitions, examples, or restatements within text) as a clue to meaning
G 5–12	Use context (e.g., cause/effect relations, comparisons) as a clue to meaning
G 9–12	Use word changes that indicate different meanings or parts of speech (e.g., analyze, analysis, analytical)

Inflections and Root Words	
K	Use the most frequently occurring inflections and affixes (-ed, -s, re-, un-, pre-, -ful, -less) as a clue to meaning
G 1	Use frequently occurring affixes as a clue to meaning
	Identify frequently occurring root words and inflectional forms (e.g., look, looks, looked, looking)
G 2, 3	Determine meaning of new word formed when known prefix/affix is added (e.g., happy/unhappy)
	Use root word as clue to meaning
G 4–8	Use common, grade-appropriate Greek and Latin affixes and roots as clues to meaning

Categories and Attributes	
K, G 1	Sort common objects into categories by one or more key attributes
K	Understand frequently occurring verbs and adjectives by relating them to their antonyms
G 1	Define words by category and one or more key attributes (e.g., a duck is a bird that swims)

Identify Connections With Vocabulary	
K, G 1–3	Identify connections between words and their use (e.g., places in school that are colorful: foods that are spicy)

Distinguish Shades of Meaning	
K	Distinguish among verbs describing the same general actions (e.g., walk, march, strut, prance)
G 1	Distinguish among verbs differing in manner (e.g., look, peek), and adjectives differing in intensity (e.g., large, gigantic)
G 2	Distinguish among closely related verbs (e.g., toss, throw) and closely related adjectives (e.g., thin, slender, skinny)
G 5	Distinguish among related words that describe states of mind or degree of certainty (e.g., knew, believed, suspected, wondered)

Table 2–2. *continued*

Nuances of Meaning	
G 3	Distinguish literal and nonliteral meanings of words and phrases (e.g., take steps)
G 4	Explain meaning of simple similes and metaphors (e.g., pretty as a picture)
	Relate words to their antonyms and synonyms
G 4, 5	Explain meaning of common idioms, adages, and proverbs
G 5	Interpret figurative language (e.g., similes and metaphors) in context
	Use relationship between words (synonyms, antonyms, homographs) to understand words
G 6–12	Interpret figures of speech
G 6	Understand personification
G 8	Understand verbal irony and puns
G 9, 10	Understand euphemisms, oxymoron
G 11, 12	Understand hyperbole, paradox
Acquire and Use Tier 1, 2, and 3 Words	
K	Use words and phrases acquired through conversation, being read to, and reading
G 1	. . . including frequent conjunctions
G 2	. . . including adjectives and adverbs
G 3–5	Use grade-appropriate conversation, general academic and domain-specific words and phrases
G 3	. . . including those for spatial and temporal and relationships (e.g., after dinner)
G 4	. . . including those that signal precise actions, emotions, or states of being (e.g., quizzed) and are basic to a particular topic (e.g., wildlife)
G 5	. . . including those that signal contrast, addition, and other logical relationships (e.g., however, similarly)
Use Relationship Between Words to Better Understand Words	
G 6	Understand cause–effect, part–whole, and item–category
G 7	Understand synonym–antonym, analogy
G 6–8	Distinguish between connotations (associations) of words with similar denotations (definitions)

Note. Adapted from NGA & CCSSO (2010a).

standards for producing complete sentences and choosing words and phrases to convey ideas precisely in fourth grade and expects students to retain these skills in later years. As the Language Standards move into the secondary level, standards are introduced in sixth grade that are to continue into the high school years: recognizing and correcting inappropriate shifts in pronoun number and person; recognizing pronouns with unclear antecedents; and varying sentence patterns for meaning, reader/listener interest, and style. The concept of selecting language that expresses ideas with concise precision is introduced in seventh grade and is a continued focus for the following five years. This longer-term focus on this skill ensures that students have the ability to recognize and eliminate wordiness and redundancy. Table 2–1 highlights the spiraling nature of skill acquisition and use as students must not only learn a skill at one level, but must continue to demonstrate this skill at later grade levels.

Literacy in History/Social Studies, Science, and Technical Subjects, 6–12

At the middle and secondary levels, the College and Career Readiness' Literacy standards focus on grade spans (6–8, 9–10, and 11–12) and complement the demands of specific content areas (NGA & CCSSO, 2010b). Students' reading becomes more specific to certain disciplines, for example, students look for evidence in the areas of science and history. They must be able to understand increasingly complex domain-specific words and phrases and develop the skills to analyze arguments and to synthesize complex information. Students will differentiate between primary and secondary sources of material as they use these in their research and writing (NGA & CCSSO, 2010b).

During the middle and high school years, students will develop a collection of complex language and metalinguistic skills. These skills include drawing logical inferences from the text, analyzing the

structure of the text, identifying central ideas or themes, and analyzing the development of the idea or theme. Additionally, students must be able to identify how individuals, events, and ideas develop and interact throughout the whole of a text. Further, students must be able to interpret meanings of words, including both technical and figurative meanings. And finally, students must be able to delineate and evaluate arguments (NGA & CCSSO, 2010b).

Mathematics Standards

The CCSS designed the Mathematics Standards to raise the standard for academic achievement, stressing both key mathematical concepts and basic mathematical principles with standards for mathematical practice and content (NGA & CCSSO, 2010c). Mathematics is not without its own language challenges. Mathematics is rich with Tier 2 (e.g., addition, subtraction, multiplication) and Tier 3 (e.g., denominator, spheres) vocabulary. In addition, the directions associated with mathematics frequently use challenging vocabulary (e.g., "count forward beginning at . . . "). Students need to understand interrogative concepts such as "how many," and they must have the ability to compare and contrast information. From the structure of mathematical equations to the structure of math problems, the language of mathematics includes syntactic expectations, problems that frequently begin with clauses rather than directly ask the question (e.g., If the number of miles to the next city is 520, and it takes him 7 hours to get there, how fast is he driving). Table 2–3 provides selected examples of language skills that are expected on the Mathematics Standards.

Table 2–3. Selected Language Expectations of Mathematics Standards

Grade Level	Concept
Kindergarten	Ones (counting from 11–19) Describe length and weight More of/less of Comparative (larger/smaller) Prepositions (e.g., above, below, beside, in front of, behind, next to) Two- and three-dimensional shapes (e.g., flat, solid) Corners and sides (geometry)
G 1	Understand meaning of equal sign Less than and greater than concepts Tens (place value) Classify items into three categories Shapes (e.g., rectangles, squares, trapezoids, triangles, half-circles, quarter-circles, cubes, prisms, cones, cylinders) Words of partition (e.g., halves, fourths, quarters, half of, fourth of, quarter of)
G 2	Hundreds (place value) Understand meaning of less than and greater than symbols Measurement units and tools (rulers, yardsticks, meter sticks, measuring tapes; inches, feet, yards, centimeters, meters) Understand word problems beginning with "If . . . " Create picture and bar graphs Shapes (e.g., quadrilaterals, pentagon, hexagon, cube) Rows and columns Words of partition (e.g., third, a third of)
G 3	Understand word problems beginning with "Find . . . ," "How many more . . . ," "how many less . . . " Even, odd Perimeter Polygon Understand "partition" as a verb

LANGUAGE AND COMMUNICATION EXPECTATIONS FOR STUDENTS WITH MORE SIGNIFICANT DISABILITIES

A consortium of states developed the Dynamic Learning Maps (DLM) (Kansas University, n.d.) to address the academic expectations for students with more significant disabilities. The consortium developed Essential Elements that correspond to the CCSS, delineating expectations for students with significant disabilities. Table 2–4 presents a comparison of selected CCSS standards and their aligned Essential Elements from the DLM.

Table 2–4. Comparison of Selected CCSS Standards With DLM Essential Elements

Reading	
CCSS Standards	**Dynamic Learning Map Essential Elements**
Phonics and Word Recognition CCSS.ELA-LITERACY.RF.K.3. Know and apply grade-level phonics and word analysis skills in decoding word.	EE.RF.K.3. Demonstrate emerging awareness of print. With guidance recognize first letter of own name in print and recognize environmental print.
Fluency CCSS.ELA-LITERACY.RF.K.4. Read emergent-reader texts with purpose and understanding.	EE.RF.K.4. Engage in purposeful shared reading of familiar text.

Writing	
CCSS Standards	**Dynamic Learning Map Essential Elements**
Text Types and Purposes CCSS.ELA-LITERACY.W.K.1. Use a combination of drawing, dictating, and writing to compose opinion pieces . . . tell or read the topic/book . . . and state an opinion or preference.	EE.W.K.1. With guidance and support select a familiar book and use drawing, dictating, or writing to state an opinion about it.
Production and Distribution of Writing CCSS.ELA-LITERACY.W.5.5 With guidance and support from peers and adults, develop and strengthen writing as needed by planning, revising, editing, rewriting, or trying a new approach.	EE.W.5.5 With guidance and support from adults and peers, plan before writing and revise own writing.

Speaking and Listening	
CCSS Standards	**Dynamic Learning Map Essential Elements**
Comprehension and Collaboration CCSS.ELA-LITERACY.SL.1.1 Participate in collaborative conversations; following agreed upon rules for discussion.	EE.SL.1.1 Participate in conversations with adults; multiple-turn exchanges with supportive adults, uses one or two words to ask questions.
Knowledge and Ideas CCSS.ELA-LITERACY.SL.4.4 Report on a topic or text, tell a story, or recount an experience with appropriate facts and relevant, descriptive details, speaking clearly at an understandable pace.	EE.SL.4.4. Retell a story or personal experience or recount a topic with supporting details.

Table 2–4. *continued*

Language	
CCSS Standards	**Dynamic Learning Map Essential Elements**
Conventions of Standard English CCSS.ELA-LITERACY.L.1.1 Demonstrate command of conventions of standard English grammar and usage when writing or speaking. Prints all upper- and lowercase letters. Use of common, proper, and possessive nouns; singular/plural nouns and matching verbs; personal, possessive, and indefinite pronouns; past, present, and future tense; frequently occurring adjectives, conjunctions, and prepositions; determiners.	EE.1.1 Demonstrate emerging understanding of letter and word use. Write letters from own name. Use of frequent nouns and plurals, frequent present tense verbs, and common prepositions. With guidance and support uses familiar personal pronouns, familiar adjectives, and simple question words.
Knowledge of Language CCSS.ELA-LITERACY.L.3.3 Use knowledge of language and its conventions when writing, speaking, reading, or listening. Chooses words and phrases for effects and observes differences between spoken and written standard English.	EE.L.3.3 Use language to achieve desired outcomes when communicating. Use language to make simple requests, comment, or share information.
Vocabulary Acquisition and Use CCSS.ELA-LITERACY.L.5.5 Demonstrate understanding of figurative language, word relationships, and nuances in word meanings. Interpret figurative language, including similes and metaphors. Explain common idioms, adages, and proverbs Use synonyms, antonyms, and homographs to better understand words.	EE.L.5.5 Demonstrate understanding of word relationship and use. Use simple common idioms (e.g., *You bet*) Demonstrate understanding of words that have similar meanings.

A complete alignment is found at http://dynamiclearningmaps.org/. Another resource for speech-language pathologists (SLPs) working with students with more significant disabilities is the Learning Progression Framework designed to support these students through a progression of learning opportunities across the CCSS domains (Hess & Kearns, 2011), This information and additional curriculum and instructional resources are available at National Center and State Consortium wiki (https://wiki.ncscpartners.org/index.php/Main_Page). SLPs working with students with significant cognitive impairments will find both of these to be valuable resources in their work to ensure that these students are included in division-wide initiatives to link intervention with the expectations of the CCSS. See Chapters 7 (Students With Visual Impairment or Deaf-Blindness) and 9 (Students With Severe Disabilities at the Secondary Level) for further application of DLM's Essential Elements.

CONCLUDING THOUGHTS

The expectations for student performance in reading, writing, speaking and listening, language, mathematics, and literacy found in the Common Core State Standards' build upon students' successful development of language and communication skills. Beginning with skills in speech sound production and fluent oral communication and building through the students' acquisition of derivational morphemes and complex syntactic structures, these standards rely on a students' successful acquisition of oral and written language milestones during their educational career. The previous discussion highlights the importance of having skills in a variety of aspects of communication to meet the standards at each grade level. The following skills are necessary for students to access and be successful in the standards:

- Articulation and fluency are needed for clear speaking.
- Articulation and phonological skills are necessary for phonological awareness, a fundamental reading skill.
- Language skills in morphology and syntax are necessary for the conventions of standard English, reading and writing.
- Morphological awareness and semantic skills are necessary for vocabulary standards, reading and writing.

- Pragmatic skills are needed to exhibit the social communication skills associated with varying communication for the audience, purpose, and task for speaking and listening, reading, and writing.

Students with deficits in any of these areas will be challenged to meet the standards without support. These students will often be expected to have skills acquired at prior grade levels, placing them behind as they are approaching later level standards. By gaining an understanding of the language implications of these standards, SLPs and their collaborators in education can analyze the standards, compare with students' strengths and needs, and tailor instruction and intervention to enable student success. The following chapters provide in-depth discussion of the role of language, literacy, and communication skills in mastering the standards for students with various types of communication disorders.

REFERENCES

Ehren, B.J. (2014). *"Push down" curriculum and the Common Core State Standards—What about developmental appropriateness?"* Presented at the ASHA Schools Conference, Orlando, FL.

Ehren, B. J., Blosser, J., Roth, F. P, Paul, D. R., & Nelson, N. W. (2012, April). Core commitment. *The ASHA Leader, 17*, 10–13.

Hess, K. K., & Kearns, J. (2011). *Learning progressions frameworks designed for use with the Common Core State Standards in English Language Arts and Literacy K–12. National Center for the Improvement of Educational Assessment (NCIEA).* Dover, NH: Author.

Justice, L. (2013, October). From my perspective: A+ speech-language goals. *The ASHA Leader, 19*, 10–11. doi:10.1044/leader.FMP.18102013.10

Kansas University. (n.d.). Dynamic learning maps—essential elements for English language arts. *Dynamic Learning Maps*. Retrieved September 29, 2014, from http://dynamic learningmaps.org

Larsen, J. A., & Nippold, M. A. (2007). Morphological analysis in school-age children: Dynamic Assessment of a word learning strategy. *Language, Speech and Hearing Services in Schools, 38*, 201–212.

Marzano, R. J. (2004). *Building background knowledge for academic achievement: Research on what works in schools*. Alexandria, VA: Association for Supervision and Curriculum Development.

Marzano, R. J., & Simms, J. A. (2013). *Vocabulary for the common core*. Bloomington, IN: Marzano Research Laboratory.

Murza, K. A., Malani, M. D., & Hahs-Vaughn, D. L. (2014). Using the Common Core State Standards to guide therapy in the schools: Confidently accepting the challenge. *SIG 16 Perspectives on School-Based Issues, 15*, 125–133. doi:10.1044/sbi15.4.125

National Center and State Collaborative. (n.d.). *Curriculum resources*. Retrieved February 26, 2015, from https://wiki.ncscpartners.org/index.php/Main_Page

National Governors Association Center for Best Practices, Council of Chief State School Officers. (2010a). *Common Core State Standards*. Washington, DC: National Governors Association for Best Practices, Council of Chief State School Officers.

National Governors Association Center for Best Practices, Council of Chief State School Officers. (2010b). *Common Core State Standards for English Language Arts and Literacy in History/Social Studies, Science, and Technical Subjects*. Washington, DC: Author.

National Governors Association Center for Best Practices, Council of Chief State School Officers. (2010c). *Common Core State Standards for Literacy in History/Social Studies, Science, and Technical Subjects 6–12*. Washington, DC: Author.

National Governors Association Center for Best Practices, Council of Chief State School Officers. (2010d). *Common Core State Standards for Mathematics*. Washington, DC: Author.

Nelson, N. W. (2010). *Language and literacy disorders: Infancy through adolescence*. New York, NY: Allyn & Bacon.

Nippold, M. A., & Sun, L. (2008). Knowledge of morphologically complex words: A developmental study of older children and young adolescents. *Language, Speech and Hearing Services in Schools, 39*, 365–373.

Rudebusch, J. (2012, March). From common core state standards to standards-based IEPs: A brief tutorial. *SIG 16 Perspectives on School-Based Issues, 13*, 17–24. doi:10.1044/sbi13.1.17

Scott, C. (2009). A case for the sentence in reading comprehension. *Language, Speech, and Hearing Services in Schools, 40*, 84–91.

Virginia Department of Education. (2013a). *Spring 2013 Student Performance Analysis: Grade 3 reading standards of learning test*. Richmond, VA: Author.

Virginia Department of Education. (2013b). *Spring 2013 Student Performance Analysis: Grade 4 reading standards of learning test*. Richmond, VA: Author.

Virginia Department of Education. (2014). *Spring 2014 Student Performance Analysis: 3rd, 4th, and 5th Grade Reading Standards of Learning Tests*. Richmond, VA: Author.

Wolter, J. A., & Dilworth, V. (2013). The effects of a morphological awareness approach to improve language and literacy. *Journal of Learning Disabilities, 47*, 76–85. doi:10.1177/0022219413509972

CHAPTER 3

Analyzing Students' Ability to Meet the Expectations of the Standards

Lissa A. Power-deFur

Students with disabilities, English language learners, and other students at risk will need a scaffolded approach to mastering the expectations of the standards. These students will not progress at the same rate or with the same support system as children who are progressing well in the general education classroom. To enable student success for all children, educators need a comprehensive understanding of the language and communication skills underlying the standards. This understanding extends not only to the standards at the child's current grade level, but also to prior grade levels. Additionally, speech-language pathologists (SLPs) and their education partners will need to identify the foundational language skills needed for success. SLPs will find that they are most successful in meeting the needs of their students with disabilities if they collaborate with a wide variety of education partners. These include, but are not limited to, general education teachers, special education teachers, reading specialists, psychologists, occupational therapists, physical therapists, guidance counselors, transition specialists, principals, special education directors, and paraprofessionals. This analysis should be a systematic unwrapping of the standards at each grade level, and the preceding grade levels, to create a framework of skills needed to master the standard. When paired with a thorough understanding of students' strengths and needs in language and communication, this analysis facilitates planning for effective, meaningful intervention.

Analysis of Student Achievement Data

The standards movement brought an increased focus on using student achievement data to support instructional decision making (Institute of Education Sciences [IES], 2009). Analysis of student achievement data enables the assessment of what students are learning and identification of how students are progressing toward meeting their goals. Individualized Education Programs (IEPs) now include a statement of student progress toward meeting goals with a variety of vehicles available for assessment (e.g., curriculum-based assessments, chapter tests, standardized assessments, and checklists). Reliance on one data source can lead to overalignment of instructional and remediation approaches with the assessments based upon the standards, often termed "teaching to the test." According to IES, educators (which include SLPs) should collect data from a variety of sources throughout the year and use these sources to gauge the success of their instructional (and intervention) strategies. Educators should also investigate nonachievement data, such as attendance.

Educators can use this variety of data they have gathered to prioritize instructional time, target individual instruction, adapt lessons or assignments, alter classroom instruction, and/or modify student groupings to enhance student achievement (IES, 2009). In its analysis of the literature regarding use of achievement data for instructional decision making, IES (2009) recommended certain steps for educators, including the following specific actions:

- Make data part of an ongoing cycle of instructional improvement. This involves collecting a variety of data, interpreting data, developing hypotheses about improving student learning, and modifying instruction to test hypotheses and increase student learning.
- Teach students to examine their own data and set learning goals.
- Provide supports to foster a data-driven culture within the school. This recommendation involves allocating structured time for staff collaboration and providing

targeted professional development to support data-driven decision making.

IES acknowledges the challenge of managing and analyzing large volumes of student data, making it difficult to focus attention on particular students or their needs (IES, 2009). IES recommends addressing the magnitude of data through collaboration among educators. They further recommend collaborating to create interim assessments, used by multiple educators in multiple settings, to gauge student progress and, therefore, the development of interventions tailored to specific needs.

Standards–Based IEPs

Many states and localities moved to a standards-based approach to IEP development after the reauthorization of the Individuals with Disabilities Education Improvement Act (IDEA) in 2004, because the Act increased its focus on accountability for the performance of students with disabilities. The standards-based approach recognizes that students with disabilities must engage in and progress in the general curriculum; however, many IEPs do not sufficiently link student performance and intervention to the expectations of the general curriculum. Further, IEPs often result in lowered expectations for students with disabilities by using a separate curriculum, a curriculum minimally related to the academic expectations of the general curriculum. With the advent of standards-based education, special educators have the ability to better align planned intervention with the general curriculum. The purpose of this approach is to develop IEPs that link to the general curriculum and enable students to demonstrate academic achievement linked to grade-level content (Holbrook, 2007; Rudebusch, 2012). Standards-based IEPs are aligned with state academic grade-level content standards (Holbrook, 2007). Such use of a standards-based IEP process facilitates unpacking the standards for pertinent intervention.

Analysis of the Common Core State Standards

Larry Ainsworth (2013) advocates prioritizing the CCSS to identify the specific standards that matter most and recommends district-wide engagement of educators in the needs assessment. His approach enables educators to identify the key standards, not by eliminating any standards, but rather by suggesting that educators focus on those standards that are most important for students to successfully enter the next grade. Ainsworth identified four criteria for selecting the priority standards: (a) *endurance*, a standard that lasts beyond one grade and/or a concept that is needed in life; (b) *leverage*, a standard that applies to multiple content areas; (c) *readiness*, a standard that represents prerequisite skills that support a new grade level; and (d) *relationship to external exams*, a standard linked to state assessments and college entrance exams.

Although Ainsworth's approach is designed for district-level prioritization (Ainsworth, 2013), the principles are equally applicable to the work of SLPs and their education partners working with students with disabilities and English language learners. Floyd (2014); Ehren (2014); Murza, Malani, and Hahs-Vaughn (2014); Blosser, Roth, Paul, Ehren, Nelson, and Sturm (2012); Power-deFur

and Flynn (2012); and Rudebusch (2012) describe the importance of analyzing standards in comparison with the performance of children with speech-language impairment(s). Such an analysis process enables SLPs and their collaborators in the schools to align the intervention with both the students' specific needs and the expectations of the CCSS.

Given the importance of the standards nationwide, it is likely that each school district has teams of professionals who have already analyzed the standards. (This would equally apply to states that have not adopted the CCSS but are implementing their own state-level standards.) SLPs are valuable members of these teams, based upon their in-depth knowledge of language and its development. In some cases, districts may have completed their analysis of the CCSS (or state-level standards). If these analyses were completed without an individual with a rich background in language and literacy, SLPs will want to conduct an additional level of analysis. Morgan et al. (2013) created education teams to analyze the standards. These researchers noted that although educators found the task to be laborious at first, as they continued to work through the standards in teams, the unwrapping and analysis process became easier. Participants felt the analysis process worked best in a group, which was a combination of general and special education personnel. Morgan et al.'s data and Ainsworth's experience further highlight the value of a team approach for CCSS analysis.

A Team Approach

SLPs and other educators with whom they will be collaborating are encouraged to gather either within the district or across multiple districts to collaborate on analyzing the standards (Power-deFur & Flynn, 2012; Schraeder, 2012). SLPs and their colleagues will find it most efficient to complete this analysis in teams. The collaborative team approach minimizes the workload on any one professional, facilitates brainstorming, and produces a more comprehensive product. By working together, it is more likely that professionals will have a more all-inclusive view of the standards, based on the rich brainstorming that occurs in collaborative groups.

The teams will review the standards and identify those standards that are a priority to address. With 45 pages of standards in the English Language arts and Literacy in History/Social Studies, Science, and Technical subjects K–5 alone, the analysis can become a behemoth task. A first step is to identify the expertise of each team member and then to distribute the analyses accordingly. For example, a person who focuses on children at the primary level would focus on kindergarten, first grade, and second grade standards. Persons who are particularly adept at literacy would work through Reading and Writing Standards, whereas those who have expertise in supporting students in their social language would address speaking and listening standards and the pragmatic expectations in reading and writing. The team should also consider the mathematic standards, as there are also rich language expectations in mathematics.

An effective way to build on the expertise of the various team members is to pair individual ratings with group discussion. Team members should individually rate the standards that are most important to address due to the challenges they present to children with speech-language impairment. Team members may wish to use Ainsworth's prioritization approach

to identify those standards that represent endurance (cross grade levels), leverage (cross content areas), and readiness (prerequisite skills). Following completion of the individual rating, team members should discuss their viewpoints, sharing their rationale for selecting particular standards. The team should reach consensus on a collection of standards that the team will then analyze in detail.

ANALYSIS OF THE STANDARDS

An analysis model is provided, adapted from the Power-deFur and Flynn model (2012), to guide SLPs and educators in analyzing the standards and developing appropriate interventions for the child. The model includes five steps:

- *Step 1. Review relevant standards to identify skills needed for success.* The team reviews current grade level standards to identify those standards that would be challenging for a child with a speech-language impairment, a child with a disability, or an English language learner. Comparable standards from prior grade levels are also reviewed to ensure that readiness skills are identified. It is also valuable to review standards from upcoming grades to appreciate future expectations for student performance.
- *Step 2. Identify the language and communication skills needed for success.* Each standard is analyzed to identify the language and communication skills needed for mastery. The analysis addresses the areas of phonology, morphology, syntax, semantics, and pragmatics,

as well as metalinguistic skills (the ability to analyze language) and general oral communication skills (including speech sound production and fluency).

■ *Step 3. Identify the student's current skills and needs.* Information from recent standardized and informal assessments, observation of the child in the classroom, and specific probes are reviewed (or generated) to identify needed areas for intervention.

■ *Step 4. Review classroom materials and activities.* As texts and classroom activities generally include vocabulary and syntax that can be challenging, a review of these will assist in forming a picture of the challenges the child faces in the classroom.

■ *Step 5. Design and implement intervention.* Effective intervention will be both direct, with the SLP in individual or small group settings, and in collaboration with the teacher(s) in the classroom in small or whole groups to facilitate transfer and mastery.

Steps 1 and 2 can be completed by teams of SLPs and educators without a specific student in mind. Steps 3 to 5 are completed with a focus on a particular student. Each of these steps is discussed in depth in the remainder of this chapter, with an analysis worksheet in Appendix 3–A.

Step 1: Review Relevant Standards to Identify Skills Needed for Success

For children with speech-language impairments, the analysis begins by reviewing the CCSS for the child's current grade level to identify those standards that have language and communication expectations that may be challenging. Due to the spiraling nature of the CCSS, many readiness skills are assumed to have been mastered at prior grade levels. It is highly likely the children with disabilities and English language learners will not have met all of these skills; therefore, a thorough review of prior grade levels is necessary. As the skills represented in each grade level build upon those acquired in earlier grade levels, this review of prior grade levels is critical to gain a full understanding of the hierarchy of skills the students will need to master. SLPs will also want to look at upcoming expectations in the standards to help them prepare students for future needs, as appropriate.

One approach to analysis of the standards is to identify both the verbs and nouns. Verbs tend to reflect the skills needed, and nouns tend to reflect the concepts expected. By identifying and then sorting in this fashion, educators will have thoroughly attained the necessary information to identify what students need to know for mastery and how they will demonstrate these skills. Table 3–1 demonstrates this approach for the Language Standard, Conventions of Standard English, in Grade 3. The nouns are underlined, and the verbs are bolded.

Frequent employment of the verb "use" in the standards makes it clear that students need to not only demonstrate that they can create these grammatical forms but also incorporate those forms into their everyday oral and written communication. Similarly, the analysis of nouns informs us that students need to (a) know the relationship between nouns and their verbs and pronouns and (b) have the ability to check that relationship for accurate agreement.

Table 3–1. Analysis of Standards by Coding Nouns and Verbs

CCSS.ELA-LITERACY.L.3.1 "**Demonstrate** command of the conventions of standard English <u>grammar</u> and usage when writing or speaking.

Explain the function of <u>nouns</u>, <u>pronouns</u>, <u>verbs</u>, <u>adjectives</u>, and <u>adverbs</u> in general and their functions in particular <u>sentences</u>.

Form and **use** regular and irregular plural <u>nouns</u>.

Use abstract <u>nouns</u> (*e.g., childhood*).

Form and **use** regular and irregular <u>verbs</u>.

Form and **use** the simple (e.g., *I walked, I walk, I will walk*) <u>verb tenses</u>.

Ensure subject-verb and pronoun-antecedent <u>agreement</u>.

Form and **use** comparative and superlative <u>adjectives</u> and <u>adverbs</u>, and choose between them depending on what is to be modified.

Use coordinating and subordinating <u>conjunctions</u>.

Produce simple, compound, and complex <u>sentences</u>." (NGO & CCSSO, 2010)

Note: Nouns are <u>underlined</u> and verbs are **bolded**.

Step 2: Identify the Language and Communication Skills Needed for Success

The next step engages the SLP and the team in analyzing the standards to identify the foundational language and communication skills needed for mastery. By utilizing their strong background in language and literacy, SLPs pinpoint the specific skills students need to acquire to meet the expectations of the standards. A good question to ask is, "What language skills do my students need to have to successfully meet this standard?" This backward chaining approach enables the SLP and the team to develop a fuller understanding of the skills the student needs to achieve prior to being able to master the grade-level skills. Peery, Wiggs, Piercy, Lassiter, and Cebelak (2011) refer to this as "circling backward to bring students forward." The student needs a repertoire of skills to demonstrate mastery of a con-

cept (Morgan et al., 2013). These include the following: (a) explain what the concept is (e.g., name); (b) explain the concept (e.g., characteristics, examples); (c) identify the concept through practical experiences (e.g., what to look for when identifying the concept, comparing with other experiences); and (d) explain how the concepts connect to other concepts the students understand. SLPs and their collaborating education partners would be wise to refer to Morgan's list when evaluating the skills needed for a particular standard.

SLPs will then use their rich background in language and communication to unpack the standards in order to identify the communication skills needed for success (Power-deFur & Flynn, 2012). The SLP should explore each aspect of language: phonology, morphology, syntax, semantics, pragmatics, and metalinguistics. See Table 3–2 for an analysis of various standards.

Table 3–2. Analysis of Language Skills Needed for Selected Standards

CCSS Standard	Underlying Language Skills Needed for Mastery
Reading. Literature. Craft and Structure. CCSS.ELA-LITERACY.RL.K.4 Ask and answer questions about unknown words in a text.	• Appropriate way to ask questions (understanding rules of conversation related to turn-taking, interrupting, register for asking question of adult, appropriate presupposition, providing listener with necessary background information) • Ability to correctly relate pronouns to the noun reference and use noun as needed for clarification • Ability to identify when misunderstood and to reframe question spontaneously • Ability to maintain appropriate eye contact, volume • Ability to create syntactically and morphologically appropriate interrogative • Possession of foundation of Tier 1 vocabulary and ability to use any Tier 2 vocabulary from story
Reading. Literacy. Grade 3. CCSS.ELA-LITERACY.RL.3.3. Describe characters in a story (e.g., their traits, motivations, or feelings) and explain how their actions contribute to the sequence of events.	• Understanding of vocabulary to describe characters • Ability to take another's perspective to understand character's motivations • Ability to create syntactically and morphologically correct sentences • Ability to use sequencing words (e.g., first, then, finally) • Ability to use coordinating and subordinating conjunctions, and relative clauses • Ability to use morphological markers to identify possession and past tense • Understanding of Tier 2 vocabulary (e.g., traits)
Speaking and Listening. Comprehension and Collaboration. Grade 4. CCSS.ELA-LITERACY.SL.4.2. Paraphrase portions of a text read aloud or information presented in diverse media and formats and formats, including visually, quantitatively, and orally.	• Ability to determine meaning from information presented auditorily • Ability to deduce the topic • Possession of a rich vocabulary of synonyms • Ability to create grammatically complete and appropriate sentences (correct syntax and morphology) • Ability to sequence information and stay on topic • Ability to add one more idea to the topic to make comments

continues

Table 3–2. *continued*

CCSS Standard	Underlying Language Skills Needed for Mastery
CCSS.ELA-LITERACY.L.3.1. Demonstrate command of the conventions of standard English grammar and usage when writing or speaking. a. Explain the function of nouns, pronouns, verbs, adjectives, and adverbs in general and their functions in particular sentences. b. Form and use regular and irregular plural nouns. c. Use abstract nouns (e.g., *childhood*). d. Form and use regular and irregular verbs. e. Form and use the simple (e.g., *I walked, I walk, I will walk*) verb tenses. f. Ensure subject-verb and pronoun-antecedent agreement. g. Form and use comparative and superlative adjectives and adverbs, and choose between them depending on what is to be modified. h. Use coordinating and subordinating conjunctions. i. Produce simple, compound, and complex sentences	• Understanding of the function of various parts of speech (nouns, pronouns, verbs, adjectives, and adverbs). • Understanding of the concept of plurality and plural morphemes. • Understanding of the concept of how verb tenses convey time and morphemes that code these concepts. • Understanding of the relationship between the number represented by a noun (e.g., cat, cats) and verb (walks, walk). • Understanding of the relationship between a pronoun and the noun to which it refers and how to maintain number and gender concepts constant. • Understanding of how comparative and superlative forms enhance the meaning of adverbs and adjectives and how to use the appropriate morpheme. • Understanding of how coordinating and subordinating conjunctions influence meaning. • Understanding of how to combine simple sentences and phrases into compound sentences. • Understanding of how to combine sentences and phrases into complex sentences.
Language Standards. Vocabulary Acquisition and Use. Grade 3. CCSS.ELA-LITERACY.L.3.6. Acquire and use accurately grade-appropriate conversational, general academic, and domain-specific words and phrases, including those that signal spatial and temporal relationships (e.g., *After dinner that night we went looking for them*).	• Understanding of the difference between spatial and temporal meaning of words (e.g., after, before). • Understanding and use of Tier 1 vocabulary (conversational), Tier 2 vocabulary (general academic), and Tier 3 vocabulary (domain specific). • Ability to create grammatically appropriate sentences, using appropriate syntax and morphology.
Mathematics. Content. Operations and Algebraic Thinking. Grade 2. CCSS.MATH.CONTENT.2.OA.A.1. Use addition and subtraction within 100 to solve one- and two-step word problems involving situations of adding to, taking from, putting together, taking apart, and comparing, with unknowns in all positions (e.g., by using drawings and equations with a symbol for the unknown number to represent the problem).	• Comprehension of Tier 2 and 3 vocabularies associated with mathematics • Comprehension of coordinating and correlative conjunctions (e.g., neither, nor) • Comprehension of inflectional morphemes in word problems

Note. Adapted from NGA & CCSSO (2010).

Step 3: Identify the Student's Current Skills and Needs

With a thorough analysis of the standards in hand, SLPs will next turn to understanding how particular children will be able to meet the standards. The first step is to develop a comprehensive view of the child's current skills and needs. The team will complete a thorough analysis of student-specific data. The present level of academic achievement and functional performance (PLAAFP) found on the student's IEP (or a comparable section on the child's 504 Plan or another planning document) is the first source of information. These summaries include recent standardized and nonstandardized assessments, which provide data on the students' performance in comparison with age peers. Standardized assessments are generally designed to diagnose rather than plan intervention; therefore, SLPs need to gather additional data to gain a full understanding of the child's ability to meet the standards. Reliance on standardized assessments alone has the potential to misdirect instruction and remediation.

Informal Data Collection Sources

SLPs and their colleagues should use a variety of informal measures such as curriculum-based assessments, classroom work samples, classroom observations, writing samples, and projects for additional information. Data from criterion-referenced assessments (e.g., the state assessments or benchmarks) are valuable if the clinician can review actual performance on test items.

Use of probes is another valuable component to track student progress and identify areas that will require tailored instruction. These clinician or teacher-made tools probe a child's ability on selected skills. The probes serve as valuable baselines to gauge the effectiveness of instruction or intervention. SLPs may create their own probes tailored to a particular language or communication skill or to specific curricular skills. Probes could include analyzing the child's ability to follow multistep directions with complex syntax; probing the student's ability to describe Tier 2 and Tier 3 words; or using a morphological awareness probe to understand the student's ability to analyze new word skills (Larsen & Nippold, 2007). Schultz (2014) created a series of skill-based probes for the K–2 CCSS language skills that investigate specific skills in the domains of language and speaking and listening (e.g., phonological awareness skills, presentation of knowledge and ideas, conventions of standard English). The completion of the Type-Token Ratio (Templin, 1957) is another useful analysis tool, as is elicitation and analysis of oral or written language samples.

A review of the child's response to various academic approaches and the effectiveness of accommodations and modifications will identify strategies that facilitate success as well as instructional approaches that are particularly challenging. Teacher, parent, and specialist checklists can be valuable sources of information. Schraeder (2012) reported on the effective use of a variety of checklists in the area of listening and speaking for kindergarten and first grade. Many state departments of education, such as the Virginia Department of Education (VDOE), have a variety of checklists for teachers and parents that focus on a variety of communication and language skills (VDOE, 2011).

Completion of structured observations in the classroom by the SLPs, specialists, and teachers will facilitate the gathering of a full picture of the student's strengths and needs, especially with respect to the language demands found in the classroom. Many state education agencies and local districts have observation forms for use as part of the special education eligibility process. For example, the VDOE and the North Carolina Department of Public Instruction have observation forms that focus on the linguistic demands of the classroom and the child's response to various instructional strategies. In addition, these observations should attend to the auditory and visual stimulation in the classroom and the effect on the student's attention and distractibility.

The focus of the data collection is to identify patterns in the students' communication needs as they engage with the academic curriculum. By triangulating the data from a variety of sources, the SLP can verify the students' skills and needs. The combination of standardized assessments, observations, classroom data, and SLP data gives the SLP and colleagues the information needed for a thorough analysis. This information will then influence the acquisition of the language and communication skills needed for the general curriculum.

Identify the Student's Current Educational Goals, Accommodations, and Modifications

After gaining a complete picture of the child's current abilities, the SLP and fellow team members will next review the IEP or 504 Plan for the child's current goals, accommodations and modifications, and supports. The team will review the goals to determine how they relate to the language and communication skills needed for success on the standards. These goals will make clear those skills the last IEP team identified as most crucial. After completing this detailed review of the child's performance, the SLP and the IEP team may identify that additional and/or different goals may be in order. This will result in scheduling an IEP meeting to discuss the information and constructing an amended IEP, following pertinent state and district procedures.

The SLP will also attend to the accommodations and modifications section of the IEP or 504 Plan, looking for typical accommodations (e.g., extended time, quiet seating, use of note takers or teacher notes, use of assistive technology). SLPs may also identify the need to update accommodations and modifications on the IEP (following appropriate procedures), based on the thoroughness of the information gathered about the child in this process. Certain accommodations and modifications might be in order to facilitate the success of children with communication disorders in the classroom:

- Stand facing bright light (rather than in front of it, making it difficult to see the speaker's face).
- Reduce classroom noise (e.g., turn off equipment, hang soft materials on the walls, place soft tips on the bottoms of chairs and tables, minimize use of open classrooms, avoid use of centers that involve using the computer while other groups are working quickly).
- Provide both verbal and written instruction for lessons and homework.
- Use gestures to gain a students' attention.
- Provide target specific feedback, using both verbal and nonverbal feedback.

- Adjust pace, with slower rate and more pauses.
- Use auditory cues for recall of vocabulary, directions, and descriptions (e.g., associated word, beginning sound, category, context).
- Organize the schedule to place the most rigorous tasks earlier in the day.
- Post written and pictorial of the schedule for the day.
- Use visual prompts such as color coding, gestures, and icons.
- Use advance organizers.

The guide, *RTI in Action: Oral language activities for K-2 classrooms*, by Roth, Dixon, Paul, and Bellini (2010), is a helpful resource for identifying appropriate accommodations and modifications in the classroom and instruction.

The team will want to consider the types of supports provided to educators. This section of the IEP encourages the team to consider how specialists can collaborate with the classroom teacher(s) to provide necessary supports for the student's benefit. This becomes an excellent opportunity for collaboration amongst professionals as they plan how the SLP can assist the teachers in working with students within the classroom. Supports may include demonstrations, development or rubrics or modified classroom materials, or in-services tailored to students' specific needs.

Step 4: Review Classroom Materials and Activities

It is not sufficient to simply understand the language and communication expectations of the standards. In addition, the SLP needs an understanding of the day-to-day language and communication skills required in the student's classroom. The sources will be the texts, supplemental instructional materials, teachers' instruction, and communications of teachers, specialists, and paraprofessionals. SLPs can use their classroom observations to gather information on the linguistic demands in the classroom. It may be useful to transcribe certain teacher and teacher assistant statements to capture the linguistic complexity of the oral language. Statements such as those found in Table 3–3 may be particularly challenging.

A review of student textbooks will reveal highly complex language and a variety of scaffolds to support understanding. It is important to look at the variety of supports that the texts provide to the reader and those texts that challenge comprehension. See Table 3–4 for illustrative examples.

The SLP's understanding of the linguistic complexity of the classroom and the materials used for instruction will enable better tailoring of intervention to meet student-specific needs. Failure to gain this information can result in intervention that does not sufficiently address the environment the students face on a daily basis, denying students the ability to gain the skills necessary to be productive and participating members in the classroom.

Step 5: Design and Implement Intervention

The completed analysis becomes a map to guide student intervention. The SLP and the student's teacher(s) will work together to differentiate interventions to address each student's individual learning needs. Instruction should target those foundational skills that the student has not yet mastered. SLPs need to design interven-

Table 3–3. Linguistic Complexity of Illustrative Teacher or Paraprofessional Statements

Illustrative Teacher or Paraprofessional Statement	Linguistic Skills Students Need for Comprehension
Before we start our test, we might as well do a little warm-up	• Ability to identify two propositions (ideas) • Knowledge of temporal relationship ("before") means that the order of action is the reverse of the order of the words • Understand the modal "might"
If you have a mirror, go put it on that table (without gesture)	• Ability to identify two propositions (ideas) • Understand a sentence with the dependent clause first • Understand what table is referenced
When we go over this, you can fill this out	• Understand sentence that begins with subordinating conjunction introducing a dependent clause
Eight over one-thousand, how do we write that as a decimal?	• Understand sentence that begins with the object of the sentence • Understand what the pronoun "that" refers to

Table 3–4. Linguistic Complexity of Illustrative Text Language

Illustrative Text Features That Facilitate Comprehension	Illustrative Text Features That Challenge Comprehension
Pair nonlinguistic representation (pictures, diagrams, icons) with new vocabulary	Syntax: use of passive voice, embedded clauses, nominalization
Use of advance organizers and diagrams	Use of humor and satire
Highlighting key vocabulary/concepts with (e.g., bold, larger font; subheadings)	Lengthy text; multiple propositions (ideas)
Review of information learned previously	Use of Tier 2 and Tier 3 words without explanation

tion to address the readiness skills that the students need for success, those for which mastery was assumed to have been achieved in prior grade levels.

For maximum effectiveness, the SLP's intervention on communication skills should integrate with classroom instruction. Provision of strategies and supports for mastering a skill are best when paired with application of that skill within the classroom. Intervention may be appropriate with direct intervention from the SLP, typically in a pull-out setting. Ideally, the intervention will also involve collaboration between the SLP and the classroom teacher(s) with some services provided in an integrated fashion in the classroom. The SLP and the classroom teacher(s) should jointly determine the intervention that is best provided via direction/instruction by the SLP in a separate setting and that which is best provided in a collaborative fashion within the classroom. Collaborative classroom activities may include conducting whole class instruction on topics related to speaking and listening, demonstrating strategies that support the learning of students with communication impairments, and/or leading certain small groups or centers with a focus on intervention and support for certain students with speech-language impairments.

Regardless of where the intervention occurs, the SLP should use instructional materials as a foundation for intervention (Power-deFur, 2010). Use of classroom-based materials enables the child to immediately see the connection between his speech-language services and classroom expectations and facilitates generalization to real-world situations. In addition, this practice ensures that the clinician will not spend time using materials that are not relevant to the academic expectations of the general curriculum.

Data Collection

Intervention should plan for multiple data collection points to ensure the student is mastering the material. These data points should occur at pre-set scheduled times to confirm that intervention continues to be relevant, targeting students' areas of need. The probes used when identifying students' needs are also valuable measures of progress, comparing baseline performance with the results gathered during and after intervention. SLPs should also probe areas of need not yet addressed to determine if the existing interventions are supporting student growth in other areas, as it would be a poor use of time to develop an intervention for a skill the child has mastered since data were first gathered.

Students at all grade levels need to be engaged in gathering and analyzing data regarding their performance, as IES recommends (IES, 2009). In addition to motivating the student to improve, the gathering of data can provide incidental experiences with math skills such as graphing or calculation of percentages. This creates an additional opportunity to link with the general curriculum, giving students opportunity to practice these mathematical concepts.

CONCLUDING THOUGHTS

The process of analyzing the standards enables education professionals to identify the component skills needed for mastery and to develop a systematic plan for instruction and intervention for specific students. In addition, it empowers the teams of professionals who work together in standards analysis to develop a common core knowledge and deep understanding of the skills and concepts needed for achievement. The five-step analysis approach described here is the foundation for determining appropriate intervention. Each of the following chapters uses this five-step approach in the case histories of the children.

REFERENCES

Ainsworth, L. (2013). *Prioritizing the common core: Identifying specific standards to emphasize the most*. Englewood, CO: The Leadership and Learning Center.

Blosser, J., Roth, F. P., Paul, D. R., Ehren, B. J., Nelson, N. W., & Sturm, J. M. (2012, August). Integrating the Core. *The ASHA Leader, 17*, 12–15.

Ehren, B. J. (2014). *"Push down" curriculum and the Common Core State Standards—What about developmental appropriateness?"* Presented at the ASHA Schools Conference, Orlando, FL.

Floyd, S. (2014). *Aligning speech-language assessment and treatment with the Common Core State Standards*. Presentation at the ASHA Convention, Orlando, FL.

Holbrook, M. D. (2007, August). *Standards-based individualized education program examples*. Alexandria, VA: National Association of State Directors of Special Education, Inc. (NASDSE). Retrieved from http://nasdse.org/Desktop Modules/DNNspot-Store/ProductFiles/36_a7f577f4-20c9-40bf-be79-54fb510f754f.pdf

Institute of Education Sciences (IES). (2009, September). *Using student achievement data to support instructional decision making*. Washington, DC: U.S. Department of Education.

Larsen, J. A., & Nippold, M. A. (2007). Morphological analysis in school-age children: Dynamic assessment of a word learning strategy. *Language, Speech and Hearing Services in Schools, 38*, 201–212.

Morgan, J. J., Brown, N. B., Hsiao, Y., Howerter, C., Juniel, P., Lidia, S., & Castillo, W. L. (2013, September 10). Unwrapping academic standards to increase the achievement of students with disabilities. *Intervention in School and Clinic, 49*(3), 131–141. doi:10.1177/1053451213496156

Murza, K. A., Malani, M. D., & Hahs-Vaughn, D. L. (2014, December). Using the Common Core State Standards to guide therapy in the schools: Confidently accepting the challenge. *SIG 16 Perspectives on School-Based Issues, 15*, 125–133. doi:10.1044/sbi15.4.125

National Governors Association Center for Best Practices, Council of Chief State School Officers. (2010). *Common Core State Standards*. Washington, DC: National Governors Association for Best Practices, Council of Chief State School Officers.

North Carolina Department of Public Instruction. (2006). *North Carolina Guidelines for Speech-Language Pathology Services in Schools*. Raleigh, NC: Author.

Peery, A., Wiggs, M. D., Piercy, T. D., Lassiter, C. J., & Cebelak, L. (2011). *Navigating the English Language Arts Common Core State Standards*. Englewood, CO: The Leadership and Learning Center.

Power-deFur, L. (2010, August). The educational relevance of communication disorders. *The ASHA Leader, 15*, 20–21.

Power-deFur, L., & Flynn, P. (2012, March). Unpacking the standards for intervention. *SIG 16 Perspectives on School-Based Issues, 13*, 11–16. doi:10.1044/sbi13.1.11

Roth, F. P., Dixon, D. A., Paul, D. R., & Bellini, P. I. (2010). *RTI in action: Oral language activities for the K–2 classrooms*. Rockville, MD: American Speech-Language-Hearing Association.

Roth, F. P., Dixon, D. A., Paul, D. R., & Bellini, P. I. (2013). *RTI in action: Oral and written language activities for the common core state standards Grades 3–5*. Rockville, MD: American Speech-Language-Hearing Association.

Rudebusch, J. (2012, March). From common core state standards to standards-based IEPs: A brief tutorial. *SIG 16 Perspectives on School-Based Issues, 13*, 17–24. doi:10.1044/sbi13.1.17

Schraeder, T. (2012, March). Literacy, common core state standards and the school-based speech/language pathologist: Making sense of it all: A pilot project conducted by the ASHA special interest group 16 ad hoc committee on literacy assessment. *SIG 16 Perspectives on School-Based Issues, 13*, 3–10. doi:10.1044/sbi13.1.3

Schultz, J. (2014). *Skill-based assessment of core communication standards K–2*. Indiana, PA: Dynamic Resources, LLC.

Templin, M. C. (1957). *Certain language skills in children*. Minneapolis, MN: University of Minnesota Press.

Virginia Department of Education (VDOE). (2011). *Speech-language pathology services in schools: Guidelines for best practice*. Richmond, VA: Author.

Analysis of Common Core State Standards for Students With Special Needs

Step 1: Review relevant standards to identify skills needed for success.

Review current grade-level standards.		Review preceding grade-level standards for prerequisite skills.	
Grade, Standard, Number	Key Concepts	Grade, Standard, Number	Key Concepts

Step 2: Identify the language and communication skills needed for success (consider phonology, morphology, syntax, semantics, pragmatics, and metalinguistic skills).

Skill Area	Specific Skills Needed

Step 3: Identify the student's current skills and needs (consider the present level of academic achievement and functional performance [PLAAFP] from Individualized Education Program [IEP], standardized and curriculum-based assessments, observations, checklists).

Child's current skills and needs (consider PLAAFP from IEP, standardized and curriculum-based assessments, observations, checklists).	Child's instructional goals (consider IEP, 504 plan).

Step 4: Review classroom materials and activities related to the student's skills and needs.

Step 5: Design and implement intervention to address the student's needs.

Need #1		
Need #2		
Need #3		
Need #4		
Need #5		

CHAPTER 4

Students With Communication Disorders

Lissa A. Power-deFur

CHARACTERISTICS OF CHILDREN WITH COMMUNICATION DISORDERS

Special education programs in public schools include children with communication disorders who are eligible for specially designed instruction under the disability category of speech-language impairment. This category of exceptionality under the Individuals with Disabilities Education Improvement Act (IDEA, 2004) is defined as "a communication disorder such as stuttering, impaired articulation, a language impairment, or a voice impairment that adversely affects a child's educational performance" (IDEA 20 U.S.C. § 1401 [2004]). This federal definition, initially crafted with the first passage of the Education of All Handicapped Children Act (EHA) in 1975, includes the major components of speech-language impairment that will have an influence on a child's educational performance. According to data reported by states to the U.S. Department of Education (USDE), approximately 18% of children in special education received services identified with the disability of speech-language impairment

(USDE, 2014). As these data only reflect students whose primary disability is speech-language impairment (SLI) and thus do not capture students with secondary or tertiary disabilities of SLI (those students whose primary disability is in another area, such as learning disabilities), this 18% under-represents the population of students with SLI. Analysis of information in Virginia revealed that the federal figures represent approximately 45% of students receiving speech-language services as a primary disability or as a related service (Power-deFur, 2011). Therefore, it is likely that approximately 35%–40% of students eligible for special education are receiving services for SLI.

CHARACTERISTICS OF SPEECH-LANGUAGE IMPAIRMENTS IN CHILDREN

The federal definition of SLI includes articulation, language, and fluency. In addition, speech-language pathologists (SLPs) in schools are increasingly working with students with swallowing disorders with 13.9% of SLPs in 2014 reporting working with students with dysphagia. That population is beyond the scope of this book, as swallowing and feeding issues are less directly related to the general curriculum (the Common Core State Standards [CCSS]) than articulation, language, and fluency disorders. The caseload of the public school SLP typically includes two subgroups: students who are receiving "speech only" or students who are receiving "speech as a related service." The students commonly referred to as "speech only" are those with only a SLI. This is their primary and only disability under IDEA. Students who are receiving speech as a related service have another primary disability (or disabilities) and receive speech-language services as a related service (Power-deFur, 2011). As such, IDEA intends for speech-language services to support special education services to enable the child to be successful and progress in the general curriculum. This population of students in-cludes students with primary disabilities such as autism, deaf-blindness, deafness/hearing loss, emotional disability, intellectual disability, orthopedic impairment, other health impairment, specific learning disability, and/or traumatic brain injury. See Chapters 5 (autism), 6 (deaf and hard of hearing), 7 (blindness and deaf-blindness), 8 (specific learning disabilities), and 9 (intellectual disabilities) for discussion of these populations and the roles of SLPs and their education partners in supporting students as they meet the CCSS.

A recent survey of school-based SLPs conducted by the American Speech-Language-Hearing Association (ASHA, 2014) revealed that children with articulation and language disorders represent the majority of students on their caseloads. For example, 92.7% of respondents

reported serving children with articulation/phonological disorders (and 62.9% reported serving children with childhood apraxia of speech). In the area of language, 89.1% reported serving children with pragmatic/social communication disorders and 92.2% reported serving children with semantic, morphological, or syntactic disorders. Fewer SLPs reported serving children with fluency (67.6%) or voice (22%) disorders. School-based SLPs also reported serving children with auditory processing disorders, swallowing and feeding disorders, cognitive communication disorders, literacy disorders, and traumatic brain injury (ASHA, 2014a).

This chapter presents the effect of various communication disorders on students' ability to achieve success on the CCSS. This chapter presents four students to elucidate the process of analyzing the CCSS in comparison with students' learning needs and developing appropriate interventions (see box below).

Speech Sound Disorders

The term "speech sound disorder" encompasses any combination of difficulties with speech perception, speech motor production, and phonological rules related to speech sounds and speech segments that adversely affect speech intelligibility (ASHA, n.d.b). When Congress passed EHA in 1975, the prevailing term was "articulation disorder." Currently, the term *articulation disorder* describes errors affecting the form of speech sounds (e.g., production of an interdental or lateral lisp) and may be associated with structural or motor deficits (e.g., cleft lip or palate, childhood apraxia of speech). In contrast, the term "phonological disor-

Mariah is a first grader who loves to dance. She enjoys all forms—hip-hop, ballet, and jazz—and goes to dance class weekly. She has been receiving speech-language services since she entered school in kindergarten. She has a severe speech sound disorder and concomitant difficulty with phonological awareness. Dance is a particularly good outlet for her, because it allows her to express herself without the difficulty she experiences when using speech.

Antonio is in third grade and is the youngest of three children. He enjoys playing most any kind of ball, especially baseball. He follows his favorite local team and goes to games with his dad and older brother. He often has his mitt in his backpack. He is very social and readily participates in classroom activities. He has been receiving speech-language services since he was in kindergarten, first with a primary focus on his speech sound disorder, but more recently focusing on his comprehension and use of syntax and morphology, now that he has only a few speech sound distortions.

Joe is a fourth-grade student who takes karate lessons, enjoys comic books, and likes to illustrate stories he writes for himself. After his newborn hearing screening at the hospital, he received a diagnosis of bilateral moder-ate to severe hearing loss. He was fitted for bilateral hearing aids at 4 months of age and has received speech-language services through early intervention from 6 months of age. Joe wears his hearing aids all day. Joe has a vocabulary deficit secondary to his hearing loss. Joe began wearing glasses approximately 1 year ago and wears them all day. After school, Joe is usually tired and tends to hang out in his room by himself, not doing much of anything. Joe is the second child with an older sister who is in seventh grade and achieves well in school.

Sam is a fifth-grade student who has a fluency disorder. He is the second of three boys in his family. One of his brothers and his father also stutter. He is on the robotics team, where he thrives. They are going to a competition this fall at the state fair, and Sam is already getting ready. Sam has been receiving speech-language services since first grade. He tends to avoid speaking in class in whole-group and small-group discussions. When he does speak, he pauses at inappropriate places in the communication and frequently uses a low volume. He generally avoids eye contact when speaking. Sam sits with some friends at lunch and is observed to be a regular participant in lunchtime conversations.

der" describes disorders stemming from impairments in the phonological representation of phonemes and speech segments, including phonotactic rules governing syllable shape, structure, and stress (ASHA, n.d.b).

Children with speech sound disorders generally lag their age peers in producing words with the appropriate phonemes. They may demonstrate substitution, deletion, distortion, or addition of phonemes, either due to difficulties in placement of the articulators or due to difficulty with the phonological rules associated with producing phonemes and words. Differences in production of speech sounds (phonemes) that are attributable to dialect or non-English language influences are not considered speech sound disorders (ASHA, n.d.b; Bleile, 2015). The development of an accurate speech sound system relies on motor control for articulatory performance, knowledge of the phonology of language, and the ability to perceive phonemes in running speech (Nelson, 2010). Approximately 8%–9% of children have a speech sound disorder. This falls to 5% for first graders (National Institute of Deafness and Other Communication Disorders [NIDCD], 2010), which is likely a combination of the child's maturation and intervention received from SLPs. There is a higher prevalence for boys than girls and a low positive correlation with socioeconomic status (ASHA, n.d.b). These figures include children with one or two phoneme errors (commonly [s] and [r], articulation disorders) or multiple error patterns. Children with multiple error patterns generally have errors on phonological rule systems. Other children with multiple error patterns may exhibit childhood apraxia of speech due to a neurological deficit in which the child is unable to exhibit voluntary control over the articulators for speech production in the absence of neuromuscular deficits (Bleile, 2015). In either situation, the presence of multiple error patterns drastically impacts the child's intelligibility and can make it difficult to identify if there is a concomitant language production issue.

As many as 50%–70% of children with speech sound disorders experience general academic difficulty through their high school years (Bernthal, Bankson, & Flipson, 2013; Bleile, 2015). An initial impact is the reduced clarity of the students' speech. Many students with speech sound disorders avoid speaking in class, not wanting to draw attention to their speech. This behavior may result in social isolation, limiting the students' ability to learn from peers.

The presence of speech sound disorders is associated with lower performance on phonological awareness tasks (Bernthal, Bankson, & Flipson, 2013; Justice, Gillon, & Schuele, 2013). Children with phonological disorders are more likely to have difficulty with phonological awareness and literacy than children with articulation disorders. Children's performances on phonological awareness tasks are consistently associated with reading ability, so it is not surprising that children with severe speech sound disorders tend to have poorer reading skills (Anthony et al., 2011), especially if the errors persist after the age of 6 years, 9 months (Nathan, Stackhouse, Goulandris, & Snowling, 2004). Further, the presence of reduced speech intelligibility adversely affects teachers' perceptions of students, as they frequently perceive such students as having less academic potential (Bleile, 2015).

The presence of a speech sound disorder of any degree of severity can adversely affect a child's ability to master a variety of the standards in the CCSS, especially those in Phonological Awareness (Reading Foundation standards) and in Speaking and Listening. The Speaking and Listening standards hold the expectation that students will be able to report on a topic, tell a story, or recount an experience, speaking clearly at an understandable pace (CCSS.ELA-LITERACY.SL.4.4) (NGA & CCSSO, 2010). In addition, the entirety of the Phonological Awareness standards (spanning kindergarten and first grade) may be challenging for students with speech sound disorders. The effect of a speech sound disorder on acquisition of the standards is further explored in the following case study.

Speech Sound Disorder Case Study

Mariah is receiving speech-language services for the second year, focusing on her severe speech sound disorder. The SLP has focused on improving her intelligibility but is also aware of the need to address phonological awareness to support Mariah's acquistion of foundational skills in reading.

Step 1: What Are the Relevant Standards?
All of the Phonological Awareness (PA) standards from the CCSS Reading Foundational Skills in first grade are relevant, as Mariah's speech sound disorder has seriously affected her ability to understand and manipulate phonemes:

- Demonstrate understanding of spoken words, syllables, and sounds (phonemes).
- Orally produce single-syllable words by blending sounds (phonemes) including consonant blends.
- Isolate and pronounce initial, medial vowel, and final sounds (phonemes) in spoken single-syllable words.
- Segment spoken single-syllable words into their complete sequence of individual sounds (phonemes) (CCSS.ELA-LITERACY.RF.1.2, A–D) (NGA & CCSSO, 2010).

A review of the kindergarten standards reminds the SLP and teacher that Mariah had not mastered the following standards prior to entering first grade:

- Demonstrate an understanding of spoken words, syllables, and sounds (phonemes).
- Recognize and produce rhyming words.

- Count, pronounce, blend, and segment syllables in spoken words.
- Blend and segment onsets and rimes of single-syllable spoken words.
- Isolate and pronounce the initial, medial vowel, and final sounds (phonemes) in three phoneme (consonant-vowel consonant, or CVC) words. (This does not include CVCs ending with /t/, /r/, or /x/.)
- Add or substitute individual sounds (phonemes) in simple, one-syllable words to make new words (CCSS.ELA-LITERACY.RF.K.2) (NGA & CCSSO, 2010).

Step 2: What Are the Necessary Language Skills Required for Success With These Standards? For Mariah to be successful in meeting these phonological awareness standards, the SLP determines that she will need to have the following communication skills:

- Produce all phonemes clearly.
- Produce all syllables in multisyllable words.
- Identify and separate onset and rime in words.
- Identify rhyming and alliteration when presented by others.
- Produce alliteration.
- Create rhyming words with single and multisyllabic words.
- Count, segment, and blend syllables.
- Count, segment, and blend phonemes.

Step 3: Analyze the Child's Current Skills.
The SLP and the teacher meet together to identify Mariah's current skills and identify how her speech sound disorder

is influencing her prereading skills. They note that Mariah does not speak up in class or in small groups. She does not ask questions of the teacher or peers, and she does not attempt to clarify her speech if she is misunderstood. Together they identified that Mariah has the following challenges in PA:

- Although Mariah could identify words that do not rhyme, she cannot consistently identify a rhyming word with greater than 50% accuracy. She has particular difficulty with two-syllable words and words ending in consonant clusters.
- Mariah can identify alliteration in words but has difficulty producing alliteration, especially with words beginning with affricates.
- Mariah can blend two-syllable words but has difficulty blending words of three or more syllables.
- Mariah is able to accurately complete syllable deletion with two-syllable compound words but has difficulty deleting morphemes (e.g., prefixes or suffixes) and phonemes.
- Mariah is able to blend phonemes for consonant (C) vowel (V) (CV), VC and CVC words but makes errors when consonant clusters or multisyllable words are introduced.

The SLP reviewed Mariah's IEP and identified the following from the present level of academic achievement and functional performance (PLAAFP):

- On the Diagnostic Evaluation of Articulation and Phonology (DEAP) (Dodd, Hua, Crosbie, Holm, & Ozanne, 2002), Mariah exhibited consonant cluster

reduction, stopping, deaffrication, final consonant deletion in multisyllabic words, and weak syllable deletion in words of three or more syllables. Mariah was stimulable for all phonemes in isolation and continues to stop fricatives in consonant CV, VCV, and VC combinations.
- A Percentage of Consonants Correct (calculated from a spontaneous speech sample of 50 utterances) was 63%. Error patterns noted on the speech sample were consistent with those on the DEAP.
- Mariah's hearing was found to be within normal limits on the kindergarten screening.

Mariah's IEP includes these goals:

- include final consonants and weak syllables in multisyllabic words in 90% of opportunities;
- replace phonological process of stopping (e.g., "s" becomes "t") with frication (e.g., creating the airstream for the consonant "s") in 80% of opportunities in words;
- identify and create one- and two-syllable words that rhyme in 90% of opportunities;
- accurately blend syllables in three or more syllable words and phonemes in one- and two-syllable words in 75% of opportunities; and
- accurately delete morphemes and phonemes in two-syllable words in 75% of opportunities.

Step 4: Review Classroom Instructional Materials. The SLP's review of the first-grade reading materials revealed extensive reliance on students' PA skills. For example, students will read directions that involve exchanging one letter for another and understand the sound-symbol relationship to be able to create new rhyming words. Further, she is expected to read a new word and be able to pronounce it and generate a rhyming word.

Step 5: Design Intervention. The SLP and classroom teacher met to discuss intervention approaches. They decided that the SLP would focus on Mariah's speech sound disorder in direct intervention, and she would join the teacher in the classroom in whole and small group activities related to phonological awareness.

Direct Intervention: The SLP decides to use a minimal pairs approach for Mariah's speech sound disorders (Bernthal, Barnkson, & Flipson, 2013; Bleile, 2015). She will select words with the same onset but different rime, facilitating rhyming skills. Similarly, words for minimal pairs addressing final consonant deletion will include the same phoneme in the initial position, facilitating alliteration skills. Classroom reading materials are used for target words. The SLP will address final consonant deletion with minimal pairs of words that contrast inclusion or deletion of plural, possessive, and past tense markers.

Collaborative Classroom-Based Intervention: The SLP and the teacher identified a small group of students who are having difficulty with phonological awareness skills of rhyming, sound and syllable blending, and segmentation. During the center time during Language Arts, 2 days/week, the SLP leads the small group in activities such as the following:

- Create the first and last names of a person/animal in a photo, both with the same first phoneme.
- Pass a beanbag, and when you get the beanbag, say a word that

rhymes with a word given by the SLP.
- When playing a matching game, find words that rhyme.
- Play "Talk Like an Alien," changing all words to begin with a certain phoneme from the planet [x] (planet name is sound of phoneme).
- Create "Hink pinks," word pairs that rhyme (e.g., overweight pet is a "fat cat," a laughing rabbit is a "funny bunny").

Appendix 4–A includes a completed CCSS Analysis Worksheet applied to Mariah. The SLP and the teacher notice that Mariah begins to become more engaged in the class after the SLP has been present during the centers. As Mariah increases her engagement, she begins to participate more in class instructional activities, gaining more opportunities for participation and increasing her mastering of PA concepts. In addition, the increase in opportunities for oral communication increase the generalization of her work on her speech sound disorder.

Language Disorders

ASHA identifies spoken/oral language disorders as "a significant impairment in the acquisition and use of language across modalities (e.g., speech, sign language, or both) due to deficits in comprehension and/or production across any of the five language domains (i.e., phonology, morphology, syntax, semantics, pragmatics" (ASHA, n.d.c). When a spoken language disorder is present without another disability (e.g., intellectual disability, hearing loss), it is generally termed "specific language impairment." The abbreviation for specific language impairment (SLI) is the same as that for the federal definition of speech-language impairment (SLI), which can cause confusion when using abbreviations in education settings.

Language disorders may occur in the presence of other conditions such as autism spectrum disorder, intellectual disabilities, developmental disabilities, attention deficit disorder, traumatic brain injury, emotional disabilities, and hearing loss. Approximately 6%–8% of kindergartners have specific language impairment (ASHA, n.d.c; NIDCD, 2013; Nelson, 2010).

Language disorders may affect any of the domains of language: phonology, morphology and syntax, semantics, and pragmatics. The previous section on speech sound disorders discussed phonological disorders. Deficits in morphology and syntax include restricted mean length of utterances (MLU) in morphemes and shorter utterances in general. Students with deficits in morphology and syntax display errors in comprehending and using the various parts of speech (nouns, pronouns, verbs, determiners, adjectives, adverbs, and prepositions). These children display deficits in comprehending and using morphemes, both derivational (e.g., prefixes and suffixes) and inflectional morphemes (e.g., tense markers). They use simple sentences with minimal use of subordinating clauses.

In the area of semantics, children with language disorders often have slower rates of vocabulary development. They have difficulty learning new vocabulary and often display word-finding difficulties. Academically, they have difficulty comprehending and using synonyms and antonyms, multiple meaning words, and figurative language. They have difficulty with comprehension of narrative or expository text, and their own narratives are often poorly organized.

Children with social communication and pragmatic impairments will have difficulty with conversations, both structured and unstructured. They typically have difficulty with conventional rules of conversation (initiating, turn-taking, maintaining appropriate eye contact), may offer inappropriate comments, and have difficulty expressing ideas, feelings, and experiences. As these children frequently have difficulty understanding the perspective of another, they may also show difficulties with tailoring language to a listener and repairing communication breakdowns.

Children with language disorders may experience social and/or behavioral problems secondary to the language disorder. These can affect social interactions with peers and adults and the students' academic performance. Children may exhibit withdrawal or shyness and have difficulty forming and maintaining close relationships. As children with language disorders often have difficulty understanding the expression of emotions in communication, they may have difficulty regulating and expressing their own emotions. Poor self-esteem has also been identified in children with language disorders. These children are at risk for bullying (ASHA, n.d.c).

Due to the relationship between spoken and written language, children with language disorders frequently will have difficulty with both reading and writing. Approximately 40%–65% of children with language impairment receive a diagnosis of reading disability during the elementary grades (Catts, Fey, Tomblin, & Zhang, 2002). Language disorders may be diagnosed as learning disabilities, especially during the later elementary years.

Children with language disorders are most at risk for mastering the academic expectations of the CCSS due to the heavy reliance on language throughout the standards, as discussed in detail in Chapter 2. High expectations are present in the areas of Reading, especially Foundational Skills, Language (especially in the Conventions of Standard English and Vocabulary Acquisition and Use components), and Speaking and Listening (with the subsections of Comprehension and Collaboration and Presentation of Knowledge and Ideas). Specific standards are discussed in the cases of Antonio and Joe, explored below.

Syntax, Morphology, and Vocabulary Case Study

Antonio has been receiving speech-language services since he was in kindergarten. His IEP team shifted his goals over time to focus more attention on his language deficits, specifically his comprehension and use of syntax and morphology, now that he no longer has speech sound errors.

Step 1: What Are the Relevant Standards? Antonio's SLP reviewed the third-grade CCSS standards in Language Arts, the grade in which Antonio is currently enrolled, and identified a number of challenging standards in the Convention of Standard English section of the Language Standards:

- Explain the function of nouns, pronouns, verbs, adjectives, and adverbs in general and their functions in particular sentences.
- Form and use regular and irregular plural nouns.
- Use abstract nouns (e.g., childhood).
- Form and use regular and irregular verbs.
- Form and use the simple (e.g., I walked, I walk, I will walk) verb tenses.

- Ensure subject-verb and pronoun-antecedent agreement.
- Form and use comparative and superlative adjectives and adverbs, and choose between them depending on what is to be modified.
- Use coordinating and subordinating conjunctions.
- Produce simple, compound, and complex sentences (CCSS.ELA-Literacy.L.3.1. A to I) (NGA & CCSSO, 2010).

The SLP then turned to standards from the prior grade levels, knowing that Antonio had not yet met some of these standards. Her review revealed that Antonio has not yet mastered a number of the standards in the same area. These standards at the second-grade level are still challenging:

- Use reflexive pronouns (e.g., myself, ourselves).
- Form and use the past tense of frequently occurring irregular verbs (e.g., sat, hid, told).
- Use adjectives and adverbs, and choose between them depending on what is to be modified.
- Produce, expand, and rearrange complete simple and compound sentences (e.g., The boy watched the movie; The little boy watched the movie; The action movie was watched by the little boy) (CCSS.ELA-LITERACY.L.2.1.C – F).

The SLP also identified first-grade standards that have not been mastered:

- Use verbs to convey a sense of past, present, and future (e.g., Yesterday I walked home; Today I walk home; Tomorrow I will walk home).

- Use frequently occurring adjectives.
- Use frequently occurring conjunctions (e.g., and, but, or, so, because).
- Use frequently occurring prepositions (e.g., during, beyond, toward).
- Produce and expand complete simple and compound declarative, interrogative, imperative, and exclamatory sentences in response to prompts (CCSS.ELA-LITERACY.L.1.1.E - I) (NGA & CCSSO, 2010).

Step 2: What Are the Necessary Language Skills Required for Success With These Standards? Antonio's SLP reviewed the standards he identified and recognized that Antonio needed the following syntactic and morphologic skills to be successful:

- Understand and identify parts of speech.
- Understand and use reflexive pronouns.
- Understand concept of plurality and strategies to create plural nouns and their verbs.
- Understand and use morphological markers to mark comparatives and superlatives.
- Understand and use morphemes to mark verb tense by time (past and present) and number.
- Understand and use conjunctions to create compound sentences.

Step 3: Analyze the Child's Current Skills. When the SLP reviewed Antonio's IEP, she noticed that his most recent speech-language evaluation is described in the PLAAFP. On the Oral and Written Language Scales II (Carrow-Wolfolk, 2011), Antonio had standard scores between 78 and 80 in all sections. He has strengths in

naming pictures and finishing sentences (a cloze set), and he had weaknesses in understanding and using prefixes and suffixes, in formulating sentences, and in punctuation. Antonio's performance on the Expressive Vocabulary Test 2 (Williams, 1997) was comparable, with a standard score of 80 and weaknesses in identifying synonyms. The SLP reported Antonio's articulation, voice, and fluency to be within normal limits. His hearing was found to be within normal limits on the third-grade hearing screening.

The SLP and teacher both observed Antonio in the classroom within the last 6 weeks, with the following observations about Antonio:

- Antonio has difficulty following directions in class and seldom completes assignments without prompting.
- He responds well to having a friend whom he can ask for clarification about teacher directions and to being given additional time on assignments.
- He has greater difficulty learning new vocabulary than do other students.

The SLP also noticed that Antonio loses focus if other students are speaking or if there is noise in the room, and his responses are often unclear when asked to respond promptly. He responds well to using a graphic organizer for identifying main ideas in oral and written stories but is unable to do so independently. The SLP also observed that the teacher and paraprofessional often speak rapidly using many complex sentences in their oral directions without visual support.

The SLP conducted a few informal assessments to gather more information on Antonio's skills. Antonio had varying accuracy when responding to questions about two-paragraph stories read aloud (75% accuracy with who, what, when, where, and which questions; 40% accuracy with how and why questions). Antonio used predominantly simple and compound sentences with coordinating conjunctions and simple (unelaborated) noun and verb phrases in oral narratives. He did not use subordinating conjunctions, superlatives, or adverbs. When given multiple-step directions, Antonio had difficulty with three-step directions when the elements were unrelated. For example, "pick up your pencil, open the window, and get your coat," as opposed to "pick up your pencil, take out a piece of paper, and write your name."

The SLP identified Antonio's IEP goals:

- Independently follow three-step directions in nine out of ten opportunities in multiple locations.
- Independently explain nine out of ten classroom vocabulary words via description (identification of synonym or antonym, or create a nonlinguistic representation) in the classroom.
- Independently retell a story in the classroom from the reading text, correctly identifying the main idea, maintaining the correct sequence of events, and using correct verb tense and adjectives/adverbs in compound sentences, with fewer than three errors.

The IEP includes two accommodations and modifications: that Antonio will sit away from noise sources in the classroom and receive additional time on class assignments.

Step 4: Review Classroom Instructional Materials. The SLP and teacher reviewed the current Language Arts texts and found a number of expectations of students' language skills that would be problematic for Antonio. These include relying on the student's comprehension of morphemes that denote verb tense, understanding story sequence, and understanding the contrast between past, present, and future tense.

Step 5: Design Intervention. The SLP and teacher collaborated to plan interventions that would support Antonio and decided how to differentiate the interventions between direct intervention and collaborative classroom-based activities.

Direct Intervention: The SLP will work with Antonio to answer and create who, what, when, where, and which questions about stories read by the clinician. Antonio will select the wh- question word to answer or create from a card deck. The stories will increase in length and complexity as Antonio develops his skills.

Collaborative Classroom-Based Intervention: The SLP and teacher decide that the SLP will join the classroom during center time. The SLP will work with Antonio and other students on a variety of vocabulary activities that support development of story narratives and comprehension of the functions of the various parts of speech. The students will use templates for silly stories that the SLP and teacher create using current vocabulary. Each sentence will have one or more blanks to be filled in by asking another student for a particular part of speech. The students will read their stories aloud to each other and then will retell the stories in their own words. Students will play a "Simon Says" game with three-step directions involving cards with current vocabulary words written on them (e.g., "Put the noun on the verb, put the adjective next to the adverb, and put the preposition below the noun.").

As a result of these interventions, the SLP and teacher notice that Antonio's oral and written narratives are beginning to include more compound sentences and greater variety of nouns, verbs, adjectives, and adverbs. In addition, he is using verb tense to denote story sequences more effectively.

Vocabulary Case History

Joe has been receiving speech-language services since being enrolled in early intervention, after being first fitted with hearing aids at 4 months of age. Although he has progressed well in the past 10 years, he continues to have a vocabulary deficit.

Step 1: What Are the Relevant Standards? The SLP reviewed the CCSS Language Standards, Vocabulary Acquisition and Use for Grade 4 and identified the following standards for which Joe will need additional support to achieve mastery:

- Determine or clarify the meaning of unknown and multiple-meaning words and phrases based on Grade 4 reading and content, choosing flexibility from a range of strategies.
- Use common, grade-appropriate Greek and Latin affixes and roots as clues to the meaning of a word (e.g., telegraph, photograph).
- Use context as a clue to meaning.
- Explain the meaning of simple similes and metaphors (e.g., pretty as a picture).
- Demonstrate an understanding of words by relating them to their opposites (antonyms) and to words with similar but not identical meanings (synonyms).

- Use grade-appropriate conversation, general academic and domain-specific words and phrases, including those that signal precise actions, emotions, or states of being (e.g., quizzed), and are basic to a particular topic (e.g., wildlife) (CCSS.ELA-LITERACY.L.4.4 and 4.5) (NGA & CCSSO, 2010).

She also looked at the same Language strand of the CCSS for prior grade levels and recognized that Joe has not yet mastered these standards from third grade:

- Determine the meaning when a known affix is added (e.g., agreeable/disagreeable, care/careless) (CCSS.ELA-LITERACY.L.3.4).
- Distinguish the literal and nonliteral meanings of words and phrases in context (e.g., take steps) (CCSS.ELA-Literacy.L.3.4 and 3.5).

Step 2: What Are the Necessary Language Skills Required for Success With These Standards?. As the SLP studied the standards, she identified that Joe would need to have the following skills to understand and use new vocabulary:

- Use context: comprehend definitions as opposed to examples or descriptions; use knowledge of syntax to identify the word's part of speech;
- Morphological awareness skills: recognize affixes; isolate the affix from the root; identify morphological constraints (what affixes can be joined to what roots; which affixes are prefixes and which are suffixes); and
- Phonological skills: adjust phoneme and stress as new word is produced.

Step 3: Analyze the Child's Current Skills. The SLP reviewed Joe's IEP and found the PLAAFP included his most recent test data. On the Oral and Written Language Scale (Carrow-Woolfolk, 1997), Joe's language skills are scattered, showing age-level performance in syntax but significant weaknesses in understanding and using abstract vocabulary and figurative language. The classroom teacher reports that Joe is attentive in the classroom but seldom asks questions and frequently completes reading and writing tasks after his classmates. He notices that Joe generally masters vocabulary when new vocabulary is taught in the classroom but has difficulty with relatively common vocabulary that is generally understood by other students. Joe always completes his classwork and homework. The SLP reviewed one of Joe's recent writing assignments and noticed that it was filled with simple, concrete vocabulary. His written answers to questions about material he has read reflect misunderstanding of terminology and misapplication of new vocabulary learned in the classroom.

After noticing that Joe had difficulty identifying affixes and roots in selected vocabulary from third- and fourth-grade textbooks, the SLP conducted a morphological analysis probe based on the work of Larsen and Nippold (2007). Joe had difficulty explaining words that included affixes, although he was able to select the correct meaning of the word if given choices. When given a selection of affixes, Joe had difficulty identifying affixes that were suffixes.

The SLP identified the following relevant goal from his IEP:

■ Joe will demonstrate mastery of 80% vocabulary words from the Grade 4 reading, social studies, science, and math content.

The accommodation identified on the IEP is that Joe is able to use an online dictionary program on his classroom computer when reading a word he does not understand or when writing narratives. A second accommodation is additional time on in-class writing assignments, which gives him time to use this dictionary.

Step 4: Review the Classroom Instructional Materials. A review of his Language Arts texts reveals some vocabulary words that may be difficult for Joe to master independently. The social studies and science texts have a heavy use of Tier 2 words, many of which Joe should have mastered in prior grades. All texts have the expectation that Joe is able to determine meaning by using the glossary and within-text clues. However, his teacher noted that Joe does not use cues within the text to aid his comprehension (e.g., descriptions of new words, underlined/italicized words).

Step 5: Design Intervention. The SLP and teacher have recently participated in a division-wide workshop on Marzano and Simms' work on vocabulary instruction which speaks to the importance of frequent and systematic vocabulary instruction (2013). Marzano and Simms' meta-analysis of the research revealed that direction instruction in targeted vocabulary enables students to learn new words and gain the knowledge of vocabulary they need for success in school. Given the weakness Joe has in the area of vocabulary, especially his ability to analyze new Tier 2 and 3 words for comprehension, the SLP and teacher decide that direct instruction in vocabulary is a needed component in their intervention. They decide that the SLP will pre-teach the meanings of common affixes in an individual session with Joe and then reinforce his comprehension in a small group setting in the classroom with Joe and other children who are at risk for mastering vocabulary. In addition, the SLP will conduct occasional vocabulary activities for the entire class.

At the beginning of each 6-week marking period, the SLP and teacher review vocabulary from the Language Arts readings. The teacher identifies the vocabulary he will be teaching the entire class, and the SLP focuses on vocabulary that may be difficult for Joe, but will not be the focus of the class instruction.

Direct Intervention: The SLP will teach Joe to use the "Word Detective" organizer (Appendix 4–B) for learning new vocabulary. This incorporates a description of the word, identification of the part of speech of the word, synonyms and antonyms, and etymology of the word (as appropriate). It also includes creation of a picture, and the SLP will demonstrate how to create simple, nonlinguistic representations of the words.

The SLP creates a variety of activities to uncover the meaning of affixes. For example, she identifies the word "absorption" in the text as an opportunity to teach the meaning and use of the suffix "-tion." This common suffix means "act or process." During the one-on-one time with Joe, they review the various meanings of "-tion" and apply it to the verb "absorb." Joe completes a word web with "-tion" in the middle and identifies six other words that include the suffix "tion" with a comparable meaning.

Collaborative Classroom Intervention: The SLP joins the class during center time, and she works with a small group, including Joe, on a "Rehit" task, in which the students will select an affix from one pack of cards and a root from another and create new words. (The words are not intended to be real words.) The students will explain the meaning of the word, pronounce it, and place it in a sentence.

Later that week, the SLP and teacher agree on a whole-class activity to address the terms "settlement," "territory," and "neighborhood" in the story about New York City firefighters then and now. The SLP leads the students in creating an "antonym scale" (Diamond & Gutlohn, 2009) for these terms with "country" at one end and "neighborhood" at the other, filling in the scale with various terms that describe geographic groupings of people (e.g., settlement, neighborhood, territory, precinct, city, subdivision, state). In a second activity, the clinician creates a timeline from the 1600s to 2012 and asks the class to place the terms "settlement," "territory," and "city" on the timeline to enable the students to understand the terms by their historical context.

The intervention with Joe enables him to have more confidence, as he no longer felt foolish when he did not understand what was apparently clear to other students. He is beginning to show independence in his ability to analyze new words by their roots and affixes and to look for clues for meaning within the text.

Fluency Disorders

Fluency refers to the feature of speech that reflects its continuity, smoothness, rate, and effort. Fluency disorders are characterized by an interruption of the flow of oral language, generally a disruption in rate, rhythm, smoothness, effort, or automaticity. Stuttering is the most common fluency disorder, a disruption in speech production that may take the form of repetitions and prolongations of sounds, blockage of airflow, interjections, and revision. Stuttering may also include secondary behaviors, physical tension, avoidance, and reduced communication. Stuttering can co-occur with a speech sound disorder and/or a language disorder. Children who stutter often have a tendency to avoid speaking, resulting in fewer opportunities to develop linguistic complexities, and demonstrating an expressive language disorder (ASHA, n.d.a).

Cluttering is another fluency disorder that causes a reduction in speech clarity and fluency due to a perceived rapid or irregular speech rate. It may include collapsing syllables and deletion of word endings, syntactically inappropriate pauses, and unusual prosody. Some persons with cluttering lack awareness of the effect on communication and do not attempt to repair the communication breakdown caused by their rate of speech, resulting in a pragmatic language disorder (ASHA, n.d.b; Justice, 2010).

Approximately 5% of people will stutter at some time in their lives with higher incidence rates in preschool years (e.g., 8.5%–11%). The incidence is greater in males than in females. There are limited data regarding the incidence of cluttering (ASHA, n.d.b).

Students who stutter will also exhibit challenges with reading fluency tasks, as they cannot change words to avoid moments of stuttering during reading tasks. ASHA's Ad Hoc Committee on Reading Fluency for School-Age Children Who Stutter found that 36.1% of students who stutter took oral reading assessments (ASHA Ad Hoc Committee, 2014). A typical oral reading assessment is a measure of reading fluency that captures the student's grade-level reading rates with appropriate prosody, phrasing, and effortless decoding (Reutzel, 2009). The committee also identified that many SLPs did not fully understand whether accommodations would be necessary. Without attention to the effect of stuttering on this oral reading measure, the results may indicate that the child who stutters has a reading deficit due to the effect of stuttering on rate. SLPs can advocate for students on their caseload who stutter to participate in alternative methods for assessing reading fluency. For example, a more accurate measure for students who stutter would be a test of silent reading fluency for children (ASHA Ad Hoc Committee, 2014). At a minimum, however, assessment results should not be used for educational placements or determinations regarding the students' reading abilities.

Students who stutter will have difficulty with many of the Speaking and Listening aspects of the CCSS. The standards elevate the importance of clear speech across all grade levels with expectations regarding appropriate use of eye contact, volume, and clear pronunciation (NGA & CCSSO, 2010b).

Students' ability to speak clearly and fluently is further highlighted in the Speaking and Listening Standard (4.3), Presentation of Knowledge and Ideas, speaking clearly at an understandable pace. In middle school, students are to use appropriate eye contact, adequate volume, and clear pronunciation. The Reading Standards also capture the importance of fluency. Students are expected to read with appropriate rate and expression beginning in first grade and continuing through fifth grade. Similarly, the standards expect students to read with both accuracy and fluency to support comprehension from first grade through fifth grade (NGA & CCSSO, 2010).

Fluency Case Study

Sam has been receiving speech-language services since first grade. He uses strategies learned in therapy (e.g., easy onset) on occasion with family and teachers. He tends to avoid speaking in class in whole-group and small-group discussions. When he does speak, he pauses at inappropriate places in the communication and frequently uses a low volume. He generally avoids eye contact when speaking.

Step 1: What Are the Relevant Standards? The SLP investigated the CCSS to identify those Speaking and Listening standards that rely on effective oral fluency and identified this Literacy standard from fifth grade:

- Report on a topic or text or present an opinion, sequencing ideas logically and using appropriate facts and relevant, descriptive details to support main ideas or themes; speak clearly at an understandable pace (CCSS.ELA-LITERACY.SL.5.4) (NGA & CCSSO, 2010).

The SLP then reviewed the standards for the third and fourth grades and found comparable language regarding logical sequence and clarity of speech. She also looked ahead to middle school standards and found that the expectations for effectiveness in making oral presentations increase, thereby increasing the urgency for addressing Sam's abilities in this area. (Present claims and findings, sequencing ideas logically and using pertinent descriptions, facts, and details to accentuate main ideas or themes; use appropriate eye contact, adequate volume, and clear pronunciation [CCSS.ELA-LITERACY.SL.6.4] [NGA & CCSSO, 2010].)

Step 2: What Are the Necessary Language Skills Required for Success With These Standards? The SLP reflected on the CCSS related to oral fluency and identified that students with fluency disorders will need to be skilled at a variety of oral communication tasks. These include maintaining appropriate rate with pauses at appropriate phrase boundaries; logical sequence to information presented, rather than altering due to circumlocution; and appropriate eye contact and volume for the speaking situation.

Step 3: Analyze the Child's Current Skills. The SLP reviewed Sam's IEP and found the following description of his stuttering behaviors: whole word repetitions (monosyllabic words); syllable and phoneme repetitions; prolongations of phonemes; and silent blocking. Sam's stuttering behavior increases during oral narratives in comparison with conversation with known speakers. He exhibits secondary behaviors of throat clearing when initiating a conversational exchange and of clenching his fist. He exhibits phoneme and word avoidances, inserting unnecessary words, and circumlocution.

Sam's IEP goals are as follows:

- Speak with fewer than five stuttered words and two stuttering secondary behaviors per minute during conversations with adults in the therapy room or in the classroom.
- Maintain eye contact for at least 50% of the communication while speaking to adults and peers in all settings.

■ Decrease pauses within phrases to less than two per minute when speaking in class in small groups or class presentations.

In addition, the SLP conducted an observation of Sam's oral narratives in the classroom and in the therapy room. She noticed that his oral narratives reveal fewer overall words and fewer different words in comparison with his age peers. He exhibits numerous phrase repetitions, revisions, and interjections. A probe of his written narratives reveals that he exhibits similar, but less pronounced, patterns of fewer overall and different words. He does not exhibit the same performance of repetitions, revisions, and interjections in his written narratives. Sam's teacher reports that his oral reading fluency performance is below expectations for his grade.

Step 4: Review Classroom Instructional Activities. Oral presentations are expected in content area topics (e.g., history, geography, science) every 9 weeks. Currently, the teacher does not use a rubric, and she is wondering whether she should exclude Sam from the requirement to give oral presentations.

Step 5: Design Intervention. Sam is able to use speech modification strategies taught over the last 4 years consistently in pull-out speech-language sessions. He effectively controls his rate, and he uses continuous phonation and easy onset to manage his stuttering. The SLP is now working on production of oral narratives to address his use of these strategies in conjunction with strategies to organize his comments and maintain appropriate eye contact and volume. Because the SLP has identified that Sam works to avoid words in his oral narratives, a key focus is on reducing word avoidances.

Direct Intervention: The SLP will continue to work with Sam on increasing his spontaneity in communication. She uses the following activities, using vocabulary and concepts that Sam is working on in the classroom:

■ The SLP writes Grade 5 Tier 2 and Tier 3 vocabulary words that have been introduced in class on index cards. Sam selects a card and explains the word to the SLP. They have set a goal of being able to produce a complete explanation within 60 seconds.

■ Using a selection of photographs describing historical events reviewed in Grades 3 through 5, Sam selects a photograph and generates a three-sentence narrative about the event. The SLP counts the number of total words, number of different words, and number of fillers used in each narrative. Sam and the SLP established a goal of producing the narrative with no more than two fillers, a minimum of 25 total words and 15 different words.

Collaborative Classroom-Based Intervention: Sam, the SLP, and the classroom teacher met to establish expectations for Sam's participation in class activities. They jointly agreed to the following:

■ The teacher will alert Sam that he will be asked to respond with some advance warning. She will use strategies to minimize the focus on Sam, such as
  □ calling on all students at a certain table in a clockwise order;

□ calling on one student and alerting another student that he/she will be next; and

□ before initiating think-pair-share activities, she will inform the students which person in the pair will be sharing the information.

■ The SLP will provide instruction to the entire class on effective oral presentation strategies. These strategies include the effective use of eye contact, stance, volume, rate, and pauses. The SLP also discusses how the meaning of the presentation is altered by changing any of these features. The SLP will note that many persons have fears of speaking publicly and have challenges with these strategies. When the students meet in small groups for practice, the SLP will meet with a group that includes Sam.

■ The teacher will assign oral presentation topics 2 weeks in advance, so Sam can develop his presentation and practice it with the support of the SLP.

■ The SLP and teacher will jointly develop a rubric that they will use for evaluation of oral presentations by all students, including Sam. The SLP will use this with Sam in one-on-one speech sessions and then work with the teacher to identify any needed modifications to the rubric for Sam's presentation to the entire class. In addition, the teacher agrees that all students will conduct their oral presentations to half the class, while the other students engage in a silent reading activity at centers.

■ To address the challenges that Sam's fluency disorder has on reading fluency measures, the SLP and the teacher agreed to use a silent reading fluency measure (rather than an oral reading fluency measure), as this would eliminate the adverse effects of his stuttering on his oral reading fluency.

This collaboration between the SLP and Sam's teacher enables Sam to experience more success in oral communication activities in the classroom, developing more confidence in his ability to participate in classroom discussion and conduct oral presentations.

Voice Disorders

The ASHA School Survey revealed that 22% of school-based SLPs report working with children with voice disorders, with an average of 1.5 children per caseload (ASHA, 2014a). Although the National Institute for Deafness and Other Communication Disorders (NIDCD) reports that 7.5 million Americans have voice disorders (NIDCD, n.d.), according to Hooper (2004), accurate prevalence and incidence data on voice disorders in children are not clear. A voice disorder is generally characterized by abnormal pitch, loudness, and/or vocal quality that is a result of disordered respiratory, laryngeal, or vocal tract functioning (ASHA, n.d.d.; Hooper, 2004). Voice disorders in children are primarily due to vocal hyperfunction, with or without other speech or language disorders, and may also be related to medical conditions (Hooper, 2004). Hooper points out that treatment of voice disorders in children is warranted, as the voice disorder tends to persist without intervention. Children's voice adversely affects adults' perception, as listeners perceive these students more negatively (Hooper, 2004).

The analysis of the CCSS and intervention applied for Sam, who has a fluency disorder, are applicable to a child with a voice disorder. The same Speaking and Listening standards will apply as will the classroom activities associated with oral communication and presentations. The SLP will similarly collaborate with the classroom teacher(s) on those activities that require effective oral communication in the classroom, with the SLP providing direct intervention to implement effective voice treatment and collaborate with the teacher on classroom activities. In addition, because prevention is an important part of the management of vocal hyperfunction, the collaborative partnership between the SLP and teachers will be important to develop strategies to reduce the student's use of his/her voice in ways that contribute to vocal trauma (shouting incorrectly, screaming, making vocal noises, excessive throat clearing) (Hooper, 2004).

CONCLUDING THOUGHTS

Students with speech-language impairments can be successful in achieving the CCSS. Many of the standards will be challenging for students on the SLP's caseload. By applying the analysis model, the SLP can develop and understand the standards that will be affecting his or her students' performance (Power-deFur & Flynn, 2012). After review of his or her students' performance, through analysis of the IEP, informal probes, and classroom observations, the SLP can identify specific areas of focus. Finally, by collaborating with classroom teachers, the SLP can develop appropriate intervention, both directly with the SLP and collaboratively in the classroom with the teacher. This approach will enable students' success in achieving the expectations of the CCSS.

REFERENCES

ASHA's Ad Hoc Committee on Reading Fluency for School-Age Children Who Stutter (2014, July). Quick: Talk Fast & Don't Stutter! The perils of oral-reading fluency assessments for children who stutter led a group of SLPs to investigate the issue and call on colleagues to change their school districts' policies. *The ASHA Leader, 19,* 44–48. doi:10.1044/leader .FTR2.19072014.44

American Speech-Language-Hearing Association. (n.d.a). *Childhood fluency disorders.* Retrieved December 30, 2014, from http://www .asha.org/Practice-Portal/Clinical-Topics/ Childhood-Fluency-Disorders/

American Speech-Language-Hearing Association. (n.d.b). *Speech sound disorders: Articulation and phonological processes.* Retrieved October 28, 2014, from http://www.asha .org/public/speech/disorders/SpeechSound Disorders/#signs_artic

American Speech-Language-Hearing Association. (n.d.c). *Spoken language disorders.* Retrieved December 30, 2014, from http://www.asha .org/Practice-Portal/Clinical-Topics/Spoken -Language-Disorders/

American Speech-Language-Hearing Association. (n.d.d). *Voice disorders.* Retrieved from http://www.asha.org/public/speech/dis orders/voice/

American Speech-Language-Hearing Association. (2014). *2014 Schools survey. Survey summary report: Number and type of responses, SLPs.* Retrieved from http://www.asha.org

Anthony, J. L., Aghare, R. G., Dunkelberger, M. J., Anthony, T. I., Williams, J. M., & Zhang, Z. (2011, May). What factors place children with speech sound disorders at risk for reading problems? *American Journal of Speech-Language Pathology, 20,* 146–160.

Bernthal, J. E., Bankson, N. W., & Flipson, P. (Eds.) (2013). *Articulation and phonological disorders: Speech sound disorders in children* (6th ed.). Boston, MA: Pearson.

Bleile, K. M. (2015). *The manual of speech sound disorders: A book for students and clinicians.* Stamford, CT: Cengage Learning.

Carrow-Woolfolk, E. (2011). *Oral and written language scales* (2nd ed.). Torrance, CA: Western Psychological Services.

Catts, H. W., Fey, M. E., Tomblin, J. B., & Zhang, X. (2002). A longitudinal investigation of reading outcomes in children with language impairments. *Journal of Speech, Language, and Hearing Research, 45,* 1142–1157.

Diamond, L., & Gutlohn, L. (2006). *Vocabulary handbook: Core literacy library.* Berkeley, CA: Consortium on Reading Excellence, Inc. (CORE).

Dodd, B., Hua, Z., Crosbie, S., Holm, A., & Ozanne, A. (2002). *Diagnostic evaluation of articulation and phonology.* San Antonio, TX: Psychology Corporation.

Hooper, C. R. (2004). Treatment of voice disorders in children. *Language, Speech, and Hearing Services in Schools, 35,* 320–326.

Individuals With Disabilities Education Improvement Act of 2004, Pub. L. No. 108-446, 20 U.S.C. § 1400 et seq. (2004).

Justice, L. M. (2010). *Communication sciences and disorders: A contemporary perspective.* Boston, MA: Pearson Education.

Justice, L. M., Gillon, G. T., & Schuele, C. M. (2013). *Phonological awareness: Description, assessment, and intervention.* In J. E. Bernthal, N. W. Bankson, & P. Flipson (Eds.), *Articulation and phonological disorders: Speech sound disorders in children* (6th ed., pp. 355–382). Boston, MA: Pearson.

Larsen, J. A., & Nippold, M. A. (2007). Morphological analysis in school-age children: Dynamic assessment of a word learning strategy. *Language, Speech and Hearing Services in Schools, 38,* 201–212.

Marzano, R. J., & Simms, J. A. (2013). *Vocabulary for the Common Core.* Bloomington, IN: Marzano Research Laboratory.

Nathan, L., Stackhouse, J., Goulandris, N., & Snowling, M. J. (2004). The development of early literacy skills among children with speech difficulties: A test of the "critical age hypothesis." *Journal of Speech, Language, and Hearing Research, 47,* 377–391.

National Governors Association Center for Best Practices and Council of Chief State School Officers. (2010). *Common Core State Standards for English Language Arts.* Washington, DC: Authors. Retrieved December 15, 2014, from http://www.corestandards.org/ELA-Literacy/

National Institute of Deafness and Other Communication Disorders (NIDCD). (n.d.). *Statistics on voice, speech and language.* Retrieved February 26, 2014, from http://www.nidcd.nih.gov/health/statistics/Pages/vsl.aspx

National Institute of Deafness and Other Communication Disorders (NIDCD). (2010). *Statistics on voice, speech, and language.* Retrieved October 24, 2014, from http://www.nidcd.nih.gov/health/statistics/pages/vsl.aspx#2

National Institute of Deafness and Other Communication Disorders (NIDCD). (2013). *Specific Language Impairment.* Retrieved November 14, 2014, from http://www.nidcd.nih.gov/health/voice/pages/specific-language-impairment.aspx

Nelson, N. W. (2010). *Language and literacy disorders: Infancy through adolescence.* New York, NY: Allyn & Bacon.

Power-deFur, L. (2011, April). Special education eligibility: When is a speech-language impairment also a disability? *ASHA Leader, 16,* 12–15.

Power-deFur, L., & Flynn, P. (2012, March). Unpacking the standards for intervention. *SIG 16 Perspectives on School-Based Issues, 13,* 11–16. doi:10.1044/sbi13.1.11

Reutzel, D. R. (2009, April). Reading fluency: What every SLP and teacher should know. *ASHA Leader, 14,* 10–11.

U.S. Department of Education. (2014). *36th annual report to Congress on the Individuals with Disabilities Education Act (2014).* Retrieved February 17, 2015, from http://www2.ed.gov/about/reports/annual/osep/2014/parts-b-c/36th-idea-arc.pdf

Williams, K. T. (1997). *Expressive vocabulary test* (2nd ed.). Minneapolis, MN: NCS Pearson.

Appendix 4–A. Analysis Worksheet for a Child With Speech Sound Disorder

Analysis of Common Core State Standards for Students With Special Needs

Step 1: Review relevant standards to identify skills needed for success.				**Step 2:** Identify the language and communication skills needed for success (consider phonology, morphology, syntax, semantics, pragmatics, and metalinguistic skills).	
Review current grade-level standards.		Review preceding grade-level standards for prerequisite skills.			
Grade, Standard, Number	Key Concepts	Grade, Standard, Number	Key Concepts	Skill Area	Specific Skills Needed
RF.1.2	Blending phonemes Produced phonemes Segment words into their individual phonemes	RF.K.1.	Producing rhyming words Segment words into syllables Isolate and pronounce phonemes in CVC words	Produce phonemes Produce syllables Identify rhyming and alliteration Blend and segment phonemes	Produce all phonological processes accurately, including syllable processes Identify rhyming and alliteration Produce rhyming in one and multiple syllable words Produce alliteration Blend syllables Segment syllables Blend phonemes Segment phonemes

Step 3: Identify the student's current skills and needs (consider present level of academic achievement and functional performance [PLAAFP] from Individualized Education Program [IEP], standardized and curriculum-based assessments, observations, checklists).		**Step 4:** Review classroom materials and activities.	**Step 5:** Design and implement intervention.
Child's current skills and needs (consider PLAAFP from IEP, standardized and curriculum-based assessments, observations, checklists).	Child's instructional goals (consider IEP, 504 Plan).		

continues

Appendix 4–A. *continued*

Need #1 Eliminate phonological processes of final consonant deletion, weak syllable deletion, stopping	Include final consonants and weak syllables Produce fricatives in place of stops	Must produce all phonemes and syllables	Direct intervention: minimal pairs with focus on alliteration, final consonants that mark plurals, possessives, and verb tense
Need #2 Identify and produce words that rhyme	Identify and create rhyming words	Need to create rhyming words from print and oral stimuli	Collaborative classroom intervention: Rhyming activities and games
Need #3 Manipulate phonemes and morphemes in words	Blend and delete phonemes and morphemes in single and multisyllabic words	Need to manipulate syllables and phonemes from print and oral stimuli	Phoneme and syllable (morpheme) blending and segmentation

Appendix 4–B. Word Detective

Word:			
Prefix	Root Word	Suffix	Part of Speech
Description:			
Word History:			
Synonym	Antonym	Example	Picture

CHAPTER 5

Students With Autism Spectrum Disorder

Peggy C. Agee

INTRODUCTION

Sarah stands behind the fish tank in her fourth-grade classroom watching the children in her collaborative group as they complete their assignment nearby. She twists her hair into a tight knot and begins to sway from side to side. Periodically, she calls out, "No, not like that." Her group does not respond but continues with their discussion.

Sammy sits at the lunch table with other 7-year-olds in his class. As Halloween is approaching, the children are excitedly talking about their costumes and plans for trick-or-treating. Sammy frequently interrupts the speaker with a description of the train pictures he methodically collects and carries in his backpack. Even when the children try to return to their conversation, Sammy continues to interject descriptions of the trains, apparently unaware of their annoyed expressions.

Dale enters his special needs classroom and heads for his usual seat, the first seat in the third row. Usually, Dale enters the classroom early enough so that he can select that seat without competition. Today, however, another boy has sat in Dale's chair. As soon as Dale sees the boy in his chair, he begins to

scream and flail his arms and throw books and papers until two adults remove him from the classroom to a "cooldown" room next door.

What do all of these students have in common? They belong to the heterogeneous group of children who share the diagnosis of autism spectrum disorder (ASD).

NATURE AND DESCRIPTION OF ASD

ASD is a complex collection of neurodevelopmental changes to brain development before and after birth. These disorders are characterized by impairments of social interaction, verbal and nonverbal communication, and also restricted interests, inflexibility, and/or stereotypical or repetitive behaviors.

The publication of the fifth edition of the *Diagnostic and Statistical Manual* (*DSM-5*) by the American Psychiatric Association (APA) in May 2013 merged the previous diagnoses of autistic disorder, childhood disintegrative disorder, pervasive developmental disorder not otherwise specified (PDD-NOS), and Asperger syndrome under one umbrella diagnosis, that of ASD, with varying severity levels and the need for increasing levels of support (APA, 2013). In other words, the characteristic impairments of ASD will fall on a continuum such that some individuals will evidence milder impairments with a lesser need for supports and accommodations, while others will have more severe impairments with a much greater need for support and accommodations. Yet all of these individuals will be diagnosed with ASD. In summary, the change in the diagnosis of ASD has now mandated a change in the language used by both general and special educators to label and describe the disability.

In public school settings, eligibility determination under the disability category of ASD is based upon the definition of autism found in the Individuals with Disabilities Education Improvement Act of 2004 (U.S. DOE, 2004). This definition follows:

> Autism means a developmental disability significantly affecting verbal and nonverbal communication and social interaction, generally evident before age 3, which adversely affects a child's educational performance. Other characteristics often associated with autism are engagement in repetitive activities and stereotyped movements, resistance to environmental change or change in daily routines, and unusual responses to sensory experiences. The term does not apply if a child's educational performance is adversely affected primarily because the child has an emotional disturbance as defined by Individuals with Disabilities Education Improvement Act (IDEA) criterion.

> A child who manifests the characteristics of "autism" after age 3 could be diagnosed as having "autism" if the criteria in the preceding paragraph are met (34 C.F.R. § 300.7 [c] [1]).

Diagnostic Criteria for ASD

The *DSM-5* (APA, 2013) has described two critical, diagnostic features of ASD. The first of these diagnostic criteria is communication deficits that impact the development of both language and nonverbal communication, such as reading signals and cues and responding appropriately. These communication deficits are such that the individual is less able to form relationships appropriate for his or her age. The second diagnostic feature is an intense or unusual preoccupation or an overdependence on established routines. This criterion is evidenced through a demand for sameness of routine or context, reduced flexibility and adaptability, and difficulty transitioning from one activity or interaction to the next. Both of the diagnostic criteria must have been present since early childhood even though they may not be identified until a later time (APA, 2013). ASD, then, is an early onset, lifelong disability that impacts all aspects of everyday function. How ASD manifests for a particular individual is likely to change over time as the demands for and expectations of communication change over time and across contexts (ASHA, 2006b).

The National Autism Center has further explained both of these diagnostic features by describing specific characteristics that are most often demonstrated by children and adults with ASD. The deficits in social interaction and social communication are shown through a reduced interest in making friends or a significant difficulty in making and maintaining friendships. Communication purposes are often restricted to those instrumental purposes, those communicative initiations that serve to obtain wants and needs (e.g., to obtain a preferred food or object). Inviting others to share in one's accomplishments or experiences is most often absent. Other characteristic features may include reduced use of eye contact to connect and engage with communication partners and a reduction in the frequency and variety of use of conventional gestures and the presence of atypical gestures as in using another's hand as a tool for opening a jar or milk container. For some children with ASD, parents or caregivers will report the loss of early language (National Autism Center, n.d.).

An explanation of the second diagnostic feature may be summarized as restricted interests and/or repetitive behaviors (National Autism Center, n.d.). For example, a child with ASD may demonstrate repetitive motor movements like hand flapping or finger flicking. Similarly, this repetitive behavior may extend to the use of objects (repetitive stacking or sequencing) or a component of an object as in spinning the wheels of toy cars or repeatedly flicking a switch on and off. A child may be overly fixated on a single idea such as the identification and labeling of trains. Frequently, the child will experience significant difficulty in transitioning from one situation to the next as shown through frequent temper tantrums and/or aggressive or self-injurious behaviors.

Incidence and Prevalence

The number of children diagnosed with ASD has shown a steady, though largely unexplained, increase in the last two decades. In March 2014, the Centers for Disease Control and Prevention (CDC) announced that the prevalence of ASD had increased to one in 68 children, with five times as many boys affected as girls (CDC, 2014). In 2003, little difference across racial and ethnic groups was observed (Frombonne, 2003). As recently as 2000, the prevalence was reported to be one in 150 children (CDC, 2015). In that year, 94,000 children were identified with ASD; by 2011–2012, 417,000 children were receiving services for autism (National Center for Education Statistics, 2013). This remarkable increase has prompted the CDC to describe ASD as a critical and urgent issue of public health (CDC, 2014).

Research has suggested multiple factors as the cause of the increasing numbers of persons with ASD. Both genetics and environmental factors have been implicated in the changes to early brain development that are characteristic of ASD (Grafodatskaya, Chung, Szatmari, & Weksberg, 2010). A multiple factor influence as the cause of autism is also supported by the National Institute of Environmental Health Sciences (NIEHS) (2014). NIEHS' hypothesis is that autism is caused by an interaction of genetic and environmental factors, most likely triggered at the time of prenatal developmental by environmental exposures during pregnancy. Though multiple environmental contributors are currently under examination as causes of ASD, none has been determined to be definitive (NIEHS, 2014).

This significant change in the number of children with the ASD diagnosis has also increased the need for special education services in schools. Of all the children ages 3 to 21 years of age served under the IDEA, those with ASD comprised 7.1% in 2011–2012, an increase of almost

6 percentage points since 2000–2001 (U.S. Department of Education, 2013). In the 2014 Schools Survey, the American Speech-Language-Hearing Association (ASHA) reported that 89.8% of certified speech-language pathologists (SLPs) in all school settings and facility types regularly served an average of 8.5 clients with the diagnosis of ASD.

The increase in prevalence of ASD has also been felt in regular education classrooms. The U.S. Department of Education (2013) reported that during 2010, 38.5% of all public school children with a diagnosis of autism spent 80% or more of their school day in a general education classroom. An additional 18.1% of children with ASD were served in regular classrooms between 40% and 79% of their school day.

Age of Diagnosis

The diagnosis of ASD can occur, in most cases, close to the time of a child's second birthday (Chawarska, Klin, Paul, Macari, & Volkmar, 2009). The CDC's most recent data revealed that 44% of the 8-year-olds in the 2010 study with a diagnosis of ASD had received the diagnosis by a qualified professional on or before age 3; an additional 36% were assigned the diagnosis by age 4 (Baio, 2014). Therefore, most children with autism will arrive at their preschools and kindergarten programs with a predetermined diagnosis. What are the unique challenges that children with ASD will encounter in their classrooms? How will school programs respond?

Challenges Imposed by ASD in the Classroom

The classroom is a complex, dynamic environment which requires students to navigate a sea of rapid-fire, constantly changing interactions with both peers and adults. This environment poses significant challenges for learning and interaction for the child or adolescent with ASD.

One of these challenges is that of the "hidden curriculum," the unwritten, unstated rules for engagement and participation which are assumed and not taught (Bieber, 1994). These rules include teacher and student expectations, assumed rules of conduct, and often-employed figurative language as in "get on the ball" (Myles, 2014). Understanding the hidden curriculum can be difficult for all children. However, the social and interactional challenges imposed by ASD can make comprehension and application of the hidden curriculum especially difficult (Myles & Simpson, 2001). Myles, Trautman, & Shelvan (2004) summarized a brief listing of the hidden curriculum skills that are likely to be challenging for children and adolescents with ASD. A summary of this list follows:

- Treat all adults, even those who are unfamiliar, with respect.
- Not all unfamiliar people are strangers who cannot be trusted. For example, teachers and bus drivers are there to help.
- Some behaviors are acceptable at home (e.g., leaving the room when you desire) but are not acceptable at school.
- Peers do not always want to hear an honest answer when they ask a question (e.g., a friend does not want to hear that she looks fat in her new dress).
- Different teachers in different classrooms may have different rules. One teacher may demand that a student request permission to

go to the restroom; another teacher may expect the student to leave and return to the room quietly without interrupting his or her teaching.

■ Teachers expect students to follow the sometimes unique script for their classroom which may include such expectations as sitting down when the bell rings or placing homework in a bin without a reminder.

■ When a teacher says, "This is a warning," the teacher means that he or she wants the behavior to stop and that, if it does not, there will be an unpleasant consequence.

■ Unless there is an emergency, it is always impolite to interrupt someone who is talking.

■ Acceptable slang may be spoken to peers but may not be acceptable to use with adults.

■ If the teacher is correcting or disciplining another student, that is not the best time to ask him or her a question.

■ If the teacher tells a student to stop talking or wait his or her turn, that is not an appropriate time for you to begin talking.

■ Many times, people should not speak what they are thinking but should keep those thoughts to themselves.

There are three theories that attempt to explain why children and adolescents have difficulty recognizing and operationalizing the hidden curriculum. Such cognitive difficulties stem from the difficulty in understanding the minds of others (Theory of Mind), conceptualizing the whole by assembling perceptual parts (Weak Central Coherence), and processing the higher-order thinking processes

that permit planning, organizing, and executing behavior in order to achieve a specific goal (Executive Dysfunction) (Winner, 2007).

Impairment of Theory of Mind

The failure to appreciate *that* others are thinking, often differently from oneself, and *what* those thoughts might be has been described as a Theory of Mind (Baron-Cohen, 1990). A Theory of Mind permits perspective taking, the ability to put oneself "into someone else's shoes." Taking into account another's perspective is central to many of the social uses of language (pragmatic skills) (Happé, 1994). These skills will include the development of a conversation (including turn taking and reciprocity, topic initiation, and topic development and maintenance), responding to the intent of another's message and not the literal wording, providing sufficient information but not more than that, framing relevant questions and comments, reading nonverbal and contextual cues, recognizing and interpreting others' emotions, and using appropriate proximity and body orientation (Johnson, Johnston, & Weinrich, 1984; Tager-Flusberg, 1996).

In 1996, Lunday published a checklist of communication skills considered to be essential to classroom and occupational success. This checklist was a delineation of skills in the following language areas: vocabulary use, function, organization, form, and pragmatics. To further explain necessary pragmatics, Lunday (1996) identified these specific skills:

■ differentiate speech/register when interacting;

■ use language appropriate to a variety of settings;

■ give and respond to nonverbal cues;

- listen for content importance transmitted by prosody;
- modify communication based on feedback;
- initiate, take turns, and terminate interactions;
- display responsive and appropriate language behavior;
- handle concerns, complaints, and criticism appropriately; and
- provide and support an opinion.

Impairments in the development of a conversation are observed in all learners with ASD across all ages with a varying degree of severity and effects on communication (Tager-Flusberg, n.d.). In fact, the pragmatic deficit appears to be the primary communication deficit in ASD, uniquely differentiating ASD from other communication impairments (ASHA, 2006a, 2006b; Tager-Flusberg, 1996). Even so, the pragmatic deficit will also have a rippling effect on the development of other components of language including semantics and syntax; difficulty with the functional use of language will interfere with the extraction of meaning at the word, sentence, and text levels, particularly when the *intended* message differs from the surface meaning of the words themselves. Another area of language impacted by a pragmatic deficit is the development of more complex sentence structure that explains, describes, and elaborates (Tager-Flusberg, 1996).

Developing and maintaining a conversation is more than an issue of word choice and sentence construction. Individuals with autism often find it challenging to read and accurately interpret the nonverbal cues (facial expressions, body movements, gestures) which create a window of understanding into the speaker's thoughts, feelings, beliefs, and communicative intents (ASHA, 2006b). Equally problematic is the lack of understanding of how one's own behavior affects others and influences what others think about him or her (Constable, Grossi, Moniz, & Ryan, 2013; Winner, 2007). Such a disability negatively affects conversational development and exchange as well as the enacting of appropriate behavioral responses. Problems with interpreting cues will also have implications for reading literature and analyzing character intentions and motivations.

In summary, students with ASD demonstrate unique difficulties with appreciating and interpreting the minds of others. Theory of Mind partially explains many of the pragmatic deficits that are at the core of the communication-learning differences for learners with ASD. Pragmatic deficits will also present significant challenges to successful participation in all of the interactions, oral and written, demanded for effective, efficient classroom participation. ASHA has identified the need for SLPs to be able to observe and describe these pragmatic behaviors in order to accurately diagnose and treat the communication-language-speech disorders that are the consequences of ASD (ASHA, 2006a, 2006b).

Weak Central Coherence

Central coherence explains the ability to assemble details in order to construct a meaningful, unified whole. This cognitive skill set will support a myriad of tasks which include deducing the main idea, drawing conclusions and making inferences, and reading the social context for relevant cues to construct an appropriate response. Individuals with ASD have been described as having weak central coherence with a reduced ability to integrate visual elements (Joliffe & Baron-Cohen, 2001) and an increased propensity for engaging in a piecemeal focus on perceptual features, placing individuals with ASD at a disadvantage with making full use of contextual cues (Baron-Cohen & Swettenham, 1997). Learners with ASD can appear to have a relative strength with attending to details and yet have pronounced difficulty with appreciating the gestalt (Frith & Happe, 1994).

Executive Dysfunction

Executive function can be defined as those skills that permit people to monitor and control their own thoughts and behaviors (Carlson & Moses, 2001). These controls will include a broad collection of frontal-lobe governed processes: planning, prioritizing, self-monitoring (including error detection and correction), self-regulation and response inhibition, behavior organization, cognitive flexibility, and resistance to interference (Carlson & Moses, 2001). Collectively, both response organization and self-regulation will depend on three subtypes of frontal lobe activity, including working memory, mental flexibility, and self-control (Center on the Developing Child, 2015). The three types of skills are highly interrelated, as each skill set will depend upon and pull from the others; similarly, successful application of all executive function skills will demand the effective coordination of the individual skills (Center on the Developing Child, 2015). Working memory can be described as the ability to retain and manipulate discrete pieces of information in the short term. Mental flexibility permits learners to shift attention from one stimulus to a competing stimulus and/or to apply different guidelines or expectations to different contexts. Self-control is the ability

to prioritize behavioral responses and to resist those responses that are impulsive or predicted to be nonproductive (Center of the Developing Child, 2015).

Executive dysfunction, then, will be an impairment in any of these higher-order thinking processes such that goal-directed behavior is negatively affected. The consequences of executive dysfunction will include reduced planning, initiation, and sustaining of behavior to achieve an identified goal while incorporating feedback and making adjustments in the process. Children and adolescents with ASD demonstrate varying effects on executive function, particularly with regard to behavioral regulation and behavioral inhibition (Carlson & Moses, 2001).

Individuals with ASD frequently demonstrate immature patterns of self-regulation, for example, rocking or chewing on clothing (ASHA, 2006b). Additionally, children with ASD may use repetitive behaviors like finger flicking or manipulating objects during times of stress or emotional dysregulation. Because of the challenges of selectively attending to and deducing the intent of a communication partner and the ensuing increased likelihood of misinterpretations, children or adolescents with ASD may respond by shutting down, acting out, having tantrums, demonstrating aggression toward others, or self-injurious behaviors (ASHA, 2006b). Hypersensitivities (to environmental noise, unexpected touch, strong or unusual smells, increased visual stimuli) have been frequently described in the descriptive profiles of individuals with ASD and may also precipitate dysregulated behavioral responses (Anzalone & Williamson, 2000) like bolting from the social setting, screaming, kicking, or biting.

Other areas of executive function have also been described as problematic for individuals with ASD (ASHA, 2006b). Day-to-day activities, especially those which occur in the typical classroom, require organization and formulation of thoughts, problem solving to attack and complete assignments and projects, and planning for future activities. Likewise, managing complex information as in math, science, or social studies demands the understanding of novel concepts, demonstration of cognitive flexibility for the application of those concepts in new contexts or new ways of thinking, and new applications of previously learned guidelines or strategies. All present significant challenges for the child or adolescent with ASD (Goldstein, Johnson, & Minshew, 2001; Minshew, Meyer, & Goldstein, 2002; Ozonoff & McEvoy, 1994; Ozonoff, Pennington, & Rogers, 1991).

DEMANDS OF THE CCSS

The Common Core State Standards (CCSS) are a comprehensive, hierarchical organization of expectations in math and English language arts and literacy which are necessary for success in college, a vocation, and life (National Governors Association [NGA] and the Council of Chief State School Officers [CCSSO], 2010). The standards are not a curriculum but were designed to ensure educational consistency and quality across the country. The CCSS are grade-level expectations with each set of expectations building on assumed mastery of the expectations at the previous level. Because the standards were developed to clearly define the expectations for what students should know and be able to do at each grade level, the CCSS are the current lens through which the performance of *all* students, including those with ASD, is viewed.

Though the CCSS are not a federal curriculum, they have been developed as academic content standards that meet the high expectations for student performance under the Individuals with Disabilities Education Improvement Act (U.S. DOE, 2004) and No Child Left Behind (U.S. DOE, 2002). Under these federal mandates, all children including those with disabilities, like ASD, must be challenged to excel within the general education curriculum through development and provision of supports and related services that will address their unique learning needs.

Meeting the demands of the CCSS will pose significant challenges for children and adolescents with ASD. For example, in order to master the grade-level standards, students will need to demonstrate progressively more complex proficiencies with comprehension and construction of complex language, analysis and explanation of problem solving, presenting an organized and logical line of reasoning, and pragmatic skills (Dodd, 2014). The metacognitive and metalinguistic processes demanded by the CCSS directly tap into the core deficits of students with ASD.

Impacts of ASD on Reading Standards

The CCSS's Reading Standards (NGA & CCSSO, 2010) will demand higher-level language and thinking skills from students with autism. For example, in kindergarten, children are expected to ask and answer questions about unknown words in a text (CCSS.ELA.LITERACY. RL.K.4) (NGA & CCSSO, 2010). To demonstrate mastery of this skill, children with ASD will be required to "think about my thinking." "Which of the words that I just read don't I know?" To answer that question, children must first pay attention to the relevant details of the text and then use the available details to assemble a big picture idea about the vocabulary, drawing conclusions or making inferences about the word-level meanings. These skills will tax both executive function and central coherence.

In second grade, students will be expected to determine the meaning of words and phrases in a text that is relevant to a Grade 2 topic or subject area (CCSS.ELA.LITERACY.RL.2.4) (NGA & CCSSO, 2010). Underlying this expectation is the assumption that students can pull together the details of the story in order to conceptualize what is likely to be an unstated, implicit meaning. Students with ASD with weak central coherence are going to find this a challenging task. Additionally, readers will find it necessary to consider the perspective of the character or author. What does this character or author *mean* in choosing that particular word and in having that particular discussion? Answering that question will pose challenges to Theory of Mind. Finally, organizing thoughts in order to express a cogent response about a word's meaning will tap into the planning and organizational skills of executive function.

In fifth grade, students must determine the meaning of words and phrases as they are used in a text, including figurative language such as metaphors and similes (CCSS.ELA.LITERACY.RL.5.4) (NGA & CCSSO, 2010). Just as in the word-meaning expectations at lower grade levels, the expectations here tax the cognitive processes that have been implicated in ASD. However, the expectations have upped

the ante to include figurative language. Because of their cognitive challenges, children and adolescents with ASD tend to be very literal thinkers. In order to accurately interpret what the author means when describing a character as having a "bee in his bonnet," the child must appreciate that the meaning is beyond that of any of the individual words and can only be appreciated by interpreting the situational context, the character's behaviors and intents, and by creating the "whole."

By seventh grade, students are expected to determine the meaning of words and phrases as they are used in a text, including figurative and connotative meanings, analyzing the impact of rhymes and other repetitions of sounds (e.g., alliteration) on a specific verse or stanza of a poem or a section of a story or drama (CCSS.ELA.LITERACY.RL.7.4) (NGA & CCSSO, 2010). At this level, the metacognitive and metalinguistic demands have increased significantly to target attention to and analysis of the prosodic features of orally read text and the relationship between the features and meaning. Requirements for selective attention, consideration of author's perspective (why did the author choose rhyme or alliteration to make this point?), planning and organization, and conceptualizing the whole from its parts have increased exponentially and are likely to pose significant challenges for learners with ASD.

By 12th grade, students must cite strong and thorough textual evidence to support analysis of what the text says explicitly as well as inferences drawn from the text, including determining where the text leaves matters uncertain (CCSS.ELA. LITERACY.RL.11-12.1) (NGO & CCSSO, 2010). Awareness of uncertainty requires a high level of thinking about thinking (my own *and* the author's), a challenge to all cognitive processes implicated in ASD.

The conclusion drawn from an examination of this one skill in the Reading Standard of Literature (word, phrase, text meaning) across several grade levels is that children with ASD will struggle to meet the increasing metalinguistic/metacognitive demands of the Reading Standards of the CCSS.

Impacts of ASD on Speaking and Listening Standards

The CCSS also include a focus on speaking and listening (NGA & CCSSO, 2010). To meet the needs of children and adolescents with ASD, educators must consider the impact of ASD on the mastery of these standards.

For example, in kindergarten, students will be expected to ask and answer questions in order to seek help, get information, or clarify something that is not understood (CCSS.ELA.LITERACY.SL. K.4) (NGA & CCSSO, 2010). Many young children with ASD can answer simple who, what, and where questions but are often less able to answer the more abstract kinds of questions (how and why) that require higher-level thinking and planning. Additionally, though children with ASD may answer simple questions, they may not ask assistance-seeking or information-seeking questions. The ability to initiate a conversation is often observed to be an area of deficit. Seeking clarification requires an awareness of what the speaker knows that I do not—a high level of perspective taking. Children with weak Theory of Mind will find this a challenging task.

In second grade, the expectation for comprehension and expression of question-types increases. Students at this level must ask and answer questions about what a speaker says in order to clarify comprehension, gather additional information, or deepen understanding of a topic or issue (CCSS.ELA.LITERACY.SL.2.3) (NGA & CCSSO, 2010). This expectation requires a significant level of perspective taking (What did the speaker mean by that? What does this speaker know that I do not?), central coherence (What do all of the details that I currently know mean?), and executive function (What details am I missing? What's the best way to frame the question so that I find out?).

By fifth grade, the expectations have increased to target effective topic development. At this level, students must pose and respond to specific questions by making comments that contribute to the discussion and elaborate on the remarks of others (CCSS.ELA.LITERACY.SL.5.1c) (NGA & CCSSO, 2010). All of the cognitive processes that have been implicated in ASD are underpinning success with this standard. Selective attention to the speaker, assembling the details of the speaker's argument into a gestalt, determining the topic of discussion, analyzing the speaker's thoughts and feelings about the topic, responding to the speaker with relevant information that extends the topic (and is not tangential or unrelated), considering how much information to share, and appreciating how to frame a comment versus asking a question are all demanded by this standard and are likely to be problematic for children with ASD.

In seventh grade, the relevant standard for speaking and listening demands that students pose questions that elicit elaboration and respond to other's questions and comments with relevant observations and ideas that bring the discussion back on topic as needed (CCSS.ELA.

LITERACY.SL.7.1c) (NGA & CCSSO, 2010). This standard builds on all of the underpinnings for the previous standards and adds the expectation that students will thoughtfully employ conversational strategies for acquiring additional details (How can I get the speaker to tell me more?). Additionally, students must conduct a real-time analysis of the current discussion, peer into the speaker's thinking and make predictions about where the conversation is headed, and evaluate the appropriateness of that direction. Evaluation, prediction, and hypothesizing are high levels of cognitive processing which will be difficult for many children and adolescents with ASD.

By 12th grade, students will initiate and participate effectively in a range of collaborative discussions (one-on-one, in groups, and teacher-led) with diverse partners on Grades 11–12 topics, texts, and issues, building on others' ideas and expressing their own clearly and persuasively (CCSS.ELA.LITERACY.SL.11-12.1) (NGA & CCSSO, 2010). Because of the inflexibility that is most often inherent in ASD, learners may have a very difficult time adjusting to the styles of different conversational partners. Likewise, understanding and demonstrating different communication purposes (e.g., persuasion) and then organizing complex ideas in a clear and cogent manner will make high demands of cognitive systems that are likely to have weak central coherence, impaired Theory of Mind, and executive dysfunction.

This analysis demonstrates that the Speaking and Listening standards of the CCSS will offer many obstacles for youngsters with ASD. Identification of these unique obstacles will be a critical factor in assisting students to meet and achieve the standards.

Impacts of ASD on Writing Standards

The CCSS emphasize progressive, increasingly complex changes in written expression as part of the English Language Arts Standards (NGA & CCSS, 2010). For example, in kindergarten, children must use a combination of drawing, dictating, and writing to compose informative/explanatory texts in which they name what they are writing about and supply some information about the topic (CCSS.ELA.LITERACY.W.K.2) (NGA & CCSSO, 2010). Drawing and writing are both symbolic representations—the simple line drawings and invented spellings that characterize early writing are symbols for the ideas they represent. Many children with ASD are less able to develop and use a symbol system which will cause this standard to be challenging.

In second grade, children must write informative/explanatory text in which they introduce a topic, use facts and definitions to develop points, and provide a concluding statement or section (CCSS.ELA.LITERACY.W.2.2) (NGA & CCSSO, 2010). The writing process is very complex. For many children with ASD, a challenge with writing is in initiating (How do I begin?) and organizing the information (What ideas go together? What ideas do not belong?), stemming from problems with executive function.

By fifth grade, children are expected to refine the development of a written topic through including relevant facts, definitions, concrete details, quotations, or other information and related examples (CCSS.ELA.LITERACY.W.5.2b) (NGA & CCSSO, 2010). This standard assumes that children are able to adjust their writing to meet the needs of the audience. What does my reader know? What is unknown? How can I fully inform my reader? How much detail do I need to include? What might be unclear to my reader? How can I explain and clarify? What written conventions will clearly inform my reader about who is talking? This self-talk will be critical in meeting the expectations of this standard but will most certainly tax the perspective-taking, gestalt-building, and executive function capabilities of the child or adolescent with autism.

By seventh grade, children must write arguments to support claims with clear reasons and relevant evidence (CCSS.ELA.LITERACY.W.7.1) (NGA & CCSSO, 2010). All of the prior demands for Theory of Mind, cognitive coherence, and executive function underpin this standard, as well. But to this standard is added an understanding of the variety of purposes of written communication. Understanding how to develop an argument and how that communication purpose differs from others (informing, describing, etc.) and engaging in discussions about that process during instruction will be important subskills that will place high demands on executive function, perspective taking, and conceptualizing the whole.

By 12th grade, students must write arguments to support claims in an analysis of substantive topics or texts, using valid reasoning and relevant and sufficient evidence (CCSS.ELA.LITERACY.W.11-12.1) (NGA & CCSSO, 2010). This expectation demands the awareness of how to construct an argument, how to use language to persuade without offending, how to "analyze" and "evaluate," how to differentiate credible from less-credible evidence, and how to assemble the available evidence into a unified, cogent whole. For the learner with ASD, the challenges will be extraordinary.

Impacts of ASD on Math CCSS

The impacts of ASD on mathematical thinking may be less easy to discern. For the many children and adolescents with less severe ASD, mathematical calculation may not be problematic. However, the CCSS Mathematics Standards that demand high levels of part-to-whole reasoning and decoding of word problems written from a unique perspective may present significant challenges. For example, in kindergarten children must demonstrate mastery of solving addition and subtraction word problems, and adding and subtracting within 10, by using objects or drawings to represent the problem (CCSS.MATHCONTENT.K.OA.A.2) (NGA & CCSSO, 2010). By second grade, students must put together, take apart, and compare unknowns and use drawings and equations with symbols to represent the problem (CCSS.MATH CONTENT.2.OA.A.1) (NGA & CCSSO, 2010). Even at this level, we can begin to see the critical demands on executive function (What is "unknown"?). Yet those demands increase.

By fifth grade, students must record calculations with numbers and interpret the numerical expressions (CCSS.MATH CONTENT.5.OA.A.2) (NGA & CCSSO, 2010), a process that will often require switching symbol sets (e.g., words to numbers), evaluating one's own accuracy, and determining and correcting thinking errors. By seventh grade, children will be expected to analyze proportional relationships and use them to solve real-world mathematical problems (CCSS.MATHCONTENT.7.RP.A.1) (NGA & CCSSO, 2010). Children with ASD may have difficulty creating the "big picture" so as to appreciate the writer's purpose and the ultimate goal of the mathematical problem and then deconstructing the "goal" or final solution into the necessary steps for reaching the goal.

A critical evaluation of this small sample of Common Core Mathematical Standards reveals that "math" is more than just calculation. The metacognitive demands for planning and prioritizing, initiating, predicting, evaluating, analyzing, and responding to internal feedback place a heavy burden on executive function, central coherence, and Theory of Mind. These challenges directly intersect with the unique learning differences of children with ASD.

Unpacking the CCSS

From the previous discussion, it is clear that any one of the CCSS has more than surface value. In other words, each of the standards is a complex statement that overarches a set of subskills and expectations (e.g., planning, organization, conceptualization, and perspective taking). Moreover, any one of the standards assumes mastery of all of the standards on which it is built. When a sixth-grade student encounters the sixth-grade Speaking and Listening standard CCSS.ELA-LITERACY.SL.6.1.B, that student can only master the expectation for following rules for collegial discussions *if* that student has previously mastered the Grades 1 through 5 standards in the same strand. Therefore, educators and SLPs alike must unpack the CCSS in order to assist the student with ASD to build the necessary knowledge and skills that underpin the current grade-level standards and will promote future success (Morgan et al., 2013). Without this systematic unpacking, students with disabilities are very likely to struggle with meeting grade-level expectations because they lack the necessary foundational skills (Haager & Vaughn, 2013). See Chapter 3 for an approach to unpacking the standards.

CASE STUDIES

With the previous information in mind, it is now time to return to the case studies introduced at the beginning of this chapter. Two of these cases are presented individually to mine each for relevant grade-level standards that the students will be expected to meet and which are likely to be challenging because of ASD. Additionally, it will be important to examine the standards from the child's previous grade levels by proceeding backward through the hierarchy until the student's point of success is determined. Finally, treatment strategies are identified and briefly described for the purpose of designing an evidence-based intervention that meets the child's individual learning needs.

Case Study: Sarah

Sarah is a 10-year-old girl in the spring of her fourth-grade year. She was diagnosed with Asperger syndrome at age 5 under the *DSM-IV*. At that time, her parents' concerns included the child's extreme rigidity and demand for the same routine. Those concerns continue to persist as she consistently demonstrates difficulty with transitioning from one activity to the next (e.g., playtime to homework time to bath time) and from one setting to the next (home to dance class and back to home). These transitions are stressful for both the child and the family. Her current diagnosis under the *DSM-5* would be described as Autism Spectrum Disorder, Level 1, requiring support. In other words, without specific supports in place, her deficits in social communication would result in noticeable difficulties (Autism Speaks, 2015).

Currently, Sarah earns acceptable grades in math but low average grades in reading. Though she is a voracious reader and an exceptionally strong decoder, she is characterized as a weak comprehender; she easily recalls details that are clearly referenced in the text but has significant difficulty with comprehension of deeper information. For example, when asked to draw conclusions or make inferences, pulling together underlying but unstated information, she most often responds, "I don't know" while becoming agitated and fidgety. Likewise, she has great difficulty responding to questions about what a story character might be thinking or planning or why the character behaved as described.

Her greatest challenges, however, revolve around peer interactions—a difficulty that causes her significant anxiety. Her mother reports that Sarah often tearfully complains, "No one likes me. I don't have any friends." The difficulties she experiences frequently surface on the playground. Daily attempts to direct and control the behavior of the other children around the same theme of princesses, castles, and fiery dragons most often result in tears and shouts and end with Sarah stomping to a corner of the playground where she sits and icily observes. Other children describe her as "bossy" and "weird."

Challenges with peer interactions have also created difficulties during small group collaborations within the classroom because of Sarah's insistence on directing and controlling the behaviors of others in the group and her failure to acknowledge

and consider their ideas and suggestions. This insistence on forcing her own perspective can also be seen in her persistence with a preferred topic of conversation even when her communication partner is no longer interested in or responding to the topic. Such problems suggest that Sarah does not accurately read and interpret the nonverbal messages of others.

Discussion of Sarah and CCSS

Sarah is a bright child who is struggling in her academic curriculum because of significant pragmatic issues which are at the heart of her failure to enter into and maintain peer relationships. The emphasis of the CCSS on peer-to-peer collaborations and interactions for learning will continue to create major challenges for her. See Table 5–1. For example, a fourth-grade standard for speaking and listening requires her to engage effectively in collaborative discussions with diverse partners, building on others' ideas. Taking a backward walk through that same standard at prior grade levels identifies the earlier skills that she is missing. Sarah does not gain the floor in respectful ways or listen to others with care (Grade 3). She does not build her conversation by linking her comments to others' ideas (Grade 2) or contribute easily to a discussion topic established by someone else (Grade 1). This backward march identifies the starting place for Sarah's work on this standard: she will need to develop proficiency with taking turns in a conversation about a topic of discussion established by a communication partner (kindergarten level). She will not become competent with the fourth-grade standard until she masters the underlying skills for the kindergarten standard followed, in turn, by mastery of each of the progressive competencies in the hierarchy.

Table 5–1. Unpacking the CCSS for Sarah

Current Grade–Level Standards	Standards at Preceding Grade Levels	Present Level of Performance	Observed Classroom Behaviors	Interventions to Promote Success
CCSS.ELA.LITERACY.RL.4.1 Refer to details and examples in a text when explaining what the text says explicitly and when drawing inferences from the text.	CCSS.ELA.LITERACY.RL.3.1 **Ask and answer questions to demonstrate understanding of a text, referring explicitly to the text as the basis for the answers.**	Voracious reader; excellent decoder; successfully answers recall questions; has difficulty answering questions whose answers are not specifically stated on text; has difficulty generating questions for peers about the text.	Poor inferencing from text. Difficulty with drawing conclusions from text.	**Teacher-Implemented Strategies:** **Questioning Techniques** **Anaphoric Cuing** (a text-based strategy in which the teacher underlines all pronouns and assists learner to locate and name the noun referent for each pronoun)
CCSS.ELA.LITERACY.SL.4.1 Engage effectively in a range of collaborative discussions (one on one, in groups, and teacher led) with diverse partners on *Grade 4 topics and texts*, building on others' ideas and expressing their own clearly.	CCSS.ELA.LITERACY.SL.3.1.B Follow agreed-upon rules for discussions (e.g., gaining the floor in respectful ways, listening to others with care, speaking one at a time about the topics and texts under discussion). CCSS.ELA.LITERACY.SL.2.1.B Build on others' talk in conversations by linking their comments to the remarks of others.	Prefers completing assignments and activities alone; when assigned to a small group, wants to control the group and dictate group's response; does not listen to the ideas of others or include them in her decision making;	Difficulty with entering into and maintaining peer interactions. Difficulty with reading and interpreting nonverbal behaviors of others.	**Speech-Language Pathologist (SLP)-Implemented Strategies (in therapy room for explicit teaching and in classroom for application):** **Cognitive/Behavioral Approach** (to invite thinking/talking about others' thinking and behavior) **Role Play** (Peer Interactions) **Social Scripts** (to support entry into and maintenance of peer interactions)

continues

89

Table 5-1. *continued*

Current Grade-Level Standards	Standards at Preceding Grade Levels	Present Level of Performance	Observed Classroom Behaviors	Interventions to Promote Success
	<u>CCSS.ELA.LITERACY.SL.1.1.A</u> Follow agreed-upon rules for discussions (e.g., listening to others with care, speaking one at a time about the topics and texts under discussion). **<u>CCSS.ELA.LITERACY.SL.K.1.A</u> Follow agreed-upon rules for discussions (e.g., listening to others and taking turns speaking about the topics and texts under discussion).**	rigid in expectations of group roles and outcomes; similar behaviors are observed on the playground.	Difficulty with listening to/ responding to the stated ideas of others. Rigid persistence with topic of conversation.	**Comic Strips** (to develop perspective taking) **Video Modeling** (to support the development of appropriate playground behavior) **Peer Training** (to facilitate the development of knowledgeable and supportive communication partners)
<u>CCSS.ELA.LITERACY.W.4.3.B</u> Use dialogue and description to develop experiences and events or show the responses of characters to situations.	**<u>CCSS.ELA.LITERACY.W.2.3</u> Write narratives in which they recount a well-elaborated event or short sequence of events; include details to describe actions, thoughts, and feelings; use temporal words to signal event order; and provide a sense of closure.**	Writes narratives from her perspective only; does not address another character's thinking or motivations and uses only generic emotion words (happy, sad, mad).	Difficulty with perspective taking. Difficulty with reporting a character's thoughts, plans, or motivations.	Integrating spoken and written language by using Questioning Techniques, a Cognitive Behavioral Approach, and Comic Strips during conversations which precede writing.

Note. Standards in bold have been selected as targets by Sarah's education team.

To support Sarah's access to the general curriculum, the SLP at her school and her regular education teacher have elected to collaborate. During an initial meeting, the professionals discuss the deficit language skills and their shared concerns for Sarah's success in meeting the challenges of her curriculum. Sarah's teacher voices her concerns for Sarah's difficulty with participating in and completing required group projects and difficulty with answering inferencing questions drawn from assigned literature. Following a review of the CCSS, the teacher and the SLP decide to target three of the grade-level standards: CCSS.English Language Arts-Literacy, Reading.4.1, CCSS.English Language Arts-Literacy, Speaking and Listening.4.1, and CCSS.English Language Arts-Literacy, Writing.4.3. For each of the targeted standards, the teacher and the SLP use artifacts and direct observations to march backward through the CCSS until Sarah's current level of function is identified. They then meet with Sarah's parents to share their observations and concerns, enlist their support and ideas, and create the final draft of the IEP.

The American Speech-Language-Hearing Association (ASHA) has posted Evidence Maps, online tools to assist language interventionists by providing research summaries needed to make evidence-based treatment decisions (National Center for Evidence-Based Practices in Communication Disorders [NCEB-PCD], n.d). A review of the Evidence Map for ASD suggests a variety of strategies appropriate for facilitating Sarah's success with the standard, CCSS.ELA.LITERACY. SL.4.1 (NGA & CCSSO, 2010). A cognitive behavioral approach would assist her to develop essential social thinking skills and strategies (Winner, 2007). Video Mod-

eling would provide opportunities for her to observe successful peer interactions that she could then emulate in real life (Buggey, 2012). Comic Strips are picture panels of a situation arranged in a comic strip format which offer opportunities to reflect on and create character dialogue and actions as part of an adult-supported discussion (Hutchins & Prelock, 2006). Role-plays of problematic interactions used in conjunction with a prepared social script also offer opportunities to try out social thinking and social skills (Ganz, Cook, & Earles-Vollrath, 2006). Finally, Peer Training equips a small group of peers to support Sarah's development of more appropriate conversational and interactional skills (Carter, Sisco, & Chung, 2012). Taken together, these intervention strategies have as their purpose to facilitate Sarah's ability to read nonverbal cues, take another person's perspective, reflect on her own behavior, and develop a topic of conversation that builds upon the listener's contributions.

Sarah's pragmatic challenges are also affecting reading comprehension. While Sarah has no difficulty recalling explicitly stated facts, she does experience problems with making implicit connections. The work of drawing conclusions and making inferences frequently requires perspective taking—viewing the situation through the character's eyes or reading the character's mind. The fourth-grade standard (CCSS.ELA.LITERACY.RL.4.1) (NGA & CCSSO, 2010) expects that students will develop competency with making both explicit text connections and with making inferences. As this will be a challenge for Sarah, it will be necessary to determine the grade-level standard at which she can be successful and the missing skills between those two points. Sarah appears to have mastered the third-grade standard as she can ask and answer questions that are explicitly related to the text. What she is missing are strategies for triangulating the situational context, character behaviors, and effects of those behaviors in order to see into the minds of both the characters and the author.

Effective reading comprehension strategies are not disability specific. A strategy that results in improved comprehension may need to be modified for students with ASD in order to meet their unique learning challenges but can be successfully implemented (Zein, Solis, Vaughn, & McCulley, 2013). ASHA's Evidence Map (NCEBPCD, n.d) for ASD reports that Questioning Techniques, when implemented along with adult think-aloud, are likely to support Sarah's ability to make connections and draw conclusions. For example, during a discussion of a reading, Sarah could highlight all of the emotion words in a paragraph and then, with adult questioning and conversational support, construct a sentence using the word "because" to explain the connection between the character's emotion and the character's behavior.

Anaphoric Cueing is a suggested strategy to promote reading comprehension (Waylon, Otaiba, & Delano, 2009). In this strategy, a teacher or language interventionist will underline all of the pronouns in a reading passage and then ask the student to locate and name the noun referent for each pronoun. Supported dialogue and adult think-aloud during the Anaphoric Cueing task will be critical to Sarah's success with making unstated, implicit connections.

The writing challenges that Sarah faces are also impacted by specific pragmatic disabilities. Like speaking, writing is another mode for the use of language. By integrating spoken and written language,

pragmatic challenges can be addressed and remediated in both modes of language. Therefore, Sarah's intervention program should include the use of supported writing tasks within the previously identified strategies which will target the standard CCSS.ELA.Literacy.W.4.3b (NGA & CCSSO, 2010). For example, after using Anaphoric Cueing to target reading comprehension, Sarah could be taught to use the visual support of a story grammar map to create her own story. Checking that story for cohesion by underlining each of the pronouns, labeling its referent, and making revisions when the referent is not clearly stated would then follow. This activity, along with an adult-led discussion about the needs and perspective of the writer's audience, would assist Sarah to refine written language pragmatic skills.

To bring Sarah's intervention plan to life, each of the collaborators will assume both an individual and a shared role. The teacher will pre-print the story passage that will be the topic of group discussion and underline each of the pronouns. The SLP will train a small group of peers to use a script that will assist Sarah with determining who or what is named by each pronoun. This script will make use of focal questions and also peer think-aloud. To facilitate positive interactions on the playground, the SLP will construct a brief homemade video showing a child of Sarah's age who first observes the play of others, then requests to join in, and also makes positive affirmations to peers ("That's a good idea!"). The teacher will provide an opportunity for Sarah to view the video each day for 2 weeks prior to recess and will make anecdotal comments about Sarah's playground behavior during that period. The SLP will pull Sarah out of her classroom once weekly. During pull-out sessions, the SLP will use a Cognitive Behavioral Approach to assist Sarah to talk through playground and classroom challenges related to peer interactions. Sessions will also include the introduction of Comic Strips to identify and discuss the nonverbal language of others, to identify peer's emotions and predict behavioral responses, and to discuss and predict peer responses to one's own behavior. Additionally, Sarah will be introduced to a social script that can be implemented in the classroom which targets listening to and responding to the comments of others by adding one more idea and incorporating peer ideas into her own comments as a way of participating in a small group discussion. At least once weekly, the SLP will enter the classroom to support Sarah with implementing the social script during a small-group collaboration. A system of graduated and fading prompts and cues will be implemented so that Sarah can internalize and own the script. Both the SLP and the classroom teacher will take data on each of Sarah's targeted standards for progress monitoring. They have agreed to meet briefly every 2 weeks to review their data and make any necessary changes in the intervention plan.

Case Study: Dale

Dale is a ninth grader and spends most of his school day in a self-contained, special education classroom for students with significant learning needs. Dale takes his lunch in the school cafeteria and is included in a ninth-grade physical education activity class. There are six other students in his self-contained classroom.

When Dale was 2 years old, his parents took him to his pediatrician because Dale was not talking but was having frequent outbursts and meltdowns. Also, Dale's mother reported that "he didn't look at you" and "he didn't want to play with or be around any other kids." She described him as being "lost in his own world." At that time, Dale's parents were encouraged by the pediatrician to wait and give the child more time to develop. At age 3, he accompanied his older brother to a kindergarten registration where he was observed by the school SLP who encouraged the family to bring Dale to a speech-language screening session. Subsequent to this visit, Dale and his family were referred by the SLP to a developmental psychologist who diagnosed Autistic disorder under the *DSM-IV*. Currently using the *DSM-5* (2013) diagnostic categories and criteria, Dale is described as an adolescent with ASD, Level 3, Requiring Very Substantial Support. In other words, severe deficits in verbal and nonverbal social communication skills cause severe impairments in all aspects of everyday functioning (Autism Speaks, 2015).

The SLP has only recently been assigned to Dale's high school. At the request of Dale's teacher, the SLP has entered into the classroom to complete an observation. The following descriptive information resulted. Dale works best when he is overly familiar with the routine. Dale's work area is set up in one corner of the classroom, facing the wall to limit distractions. A sequence of picture cards, arranged in a longitudinal array, currently functions as a sequential calendar of daily events which includes "Work Time." As Dale completes an activity during his Work Time, he places it in his "finished" box. Activities in the work box include work sheets for picture-to-text matching, and object or picture sorting and categorizing activities. When his work box is empty, he moves a clothespin to the next pictured activity which may be physical education, computer, or lunch. Infrequently, he requires assistance from an adult so as not to skip the next picture.

If he completes his work box activities ahead of schedule, his personal assistant will offer him a choice of two picture cards representing two leisure activities: listening to music through headphones or looking through a magazine about cars or motorcycles. Dale makes his selection by removing the picture from the assistant's hand and moving to that area of the classroom. He usually chooses to listen to music. When he does elect to browse a magazine, he turns pages from the front of the magazine to the back, sometimes turning several pages at once, and sometimes pointing to named pictures of common objects (e.g., car or motorcycle). He has not been observed calling attention to print or tracking the movement of print across the page.

Unless prompted to do so, Dale does not interact with peers or the other adults (teacher and aide) in the classroom. His spontaneous interactions with peers tend to be negative, as in loudly and physically complaining if a peer chooses his preferred set of headphones before he can. Dale uses some automatic social speech ("Good morning," "Please," "Thank you.") and some carrier sentences when prompted ("I want _____"). He consistently responds to concrete yes/no questions, but does not respond to Wh-questions. When he becomes upset with another student, he often screams, "That red," apparently in reference to the classroom's color-coded behavioral system in which a "red" behavior requires a significant consequence (e.g., removal from the classroom).

Dale has been given a programmable augmentative and alternative communication (AAC) device which has from 2 to 16 spaces. Overlays can be created using pictures, text, or a combination of both along with a recorded spoken message. Currently, Dale's device has an overlay for snack time and leisure time choices which use the nine-space array. Dale rarely uses his device; most of the time it remains either in his backpack or at the back of this work table. When his personal assistant prompts him, he will use the device to answer yes/no questions or request a bathroom break.

Discussion of Dale and the CCSS

Dale is a young man without a functional communication system. Though he has access to a programmable AAC device, he does not know how to use it for interaction or communication during his daily activities. His screaming and acting out behaviors appear to be attempts to communicate his message of frustration or uncertainty. It is possible that these behaviors may reduce in frequency as his functional communication skills increase.

Following the classroom observation, the SLP and special educator meet to discuss Dale's communication learning needs through the lens of the CCSS. An examination of the ninth-grade CCSS confirms their belief that these standards are well outside of Dale's current reach (see Table 5–2). For example, the speaking and listening standard for Grade 9–10 (CCSS.ELA.Literacy.SL.9-10) (NGA & CCSSO, 2010) expects that Dale should "propel" conversations by posing and responding to questions that relate to a current curriculum-based discussion. Moving backward through the standards to earlier grade levels results in the identification of the

Table 5–2. Unpacking the CCSS for Dale

Current Grade-Level Standards	Standards at Preceding Grade Levels	Present Level of Performance	Observed Classroom Behaviors	Interventions to Promote Success
CCSS.ELA–LITERACY.SL.9–10.1.C Propel conversations by posing and responding to questions that relate the current discussion to broader themes or larger ideas; actively incorporate others into the discussion; and clarify, verify, or challenge ideas and conclusions.	**CCSS.ELA–LITERACY.SL.6.1.C** Pose and respond to specific questions with elaboration and detail by making comments that contribute to the topic, text, or issue under discussion. **CCSS.ELA–LITERACY.SL.4.1.C** Pose and respond to specific questions to clarify or follow up on information, and make comments that contribute to the discussion and link to the remarks of others. **CCSS.ELA–LITERACY.SL.K.3** **Ask and answer questions in order to seek help, get information, or clarify something that is not understood.**	Has an AAC device but rarely uses it; when prompted, will use device to respond to yes/no questions; does not request information; initiates rarely and only when prompted; does not make comments; answers concrete yes/no questions about the here and now; does not answer wh– questions; takes two or fewer turns in conversation.	Remains in work area until all work tasks are completed; uses visual schedule to track and predict movement through the day's planned events; becomes physically aggressive toward others and loud when his routine is violated in any way.	**Special Education Teacher and SLP will collaborate to implement the following strategies:** **Visual Supports** (used to clearly define expectations and participation in and out of the classroom) **AAC** functionally embedded into daily activities with opportunities for providing and requesting information **Social Stories** (written from learner's perspective to provide situational cues and contexts for specific instances of initiating and asking [for example, when someone is in his chair]) **Video Modeling** (brief homemade clips showing a teenage boy asking same-aged peers for an object or asking for help) **Peer Training** (to equip a small group of receptive peers to be good communication partners with Dale as he uses his AAC device)

continues

95

Table 5–2. *continued*

Current Grade–Level Standards	Standards at Preceding Grade Levels	Present Level of Performance	Observed Classroom Behaviors	Interventions to Promote Success
<u>CCSS.ELA–LITERACY.L.9–10.1</u> Demonstrate command of the conventions of standard English grammar and usage when writing or speaking: Use various types of phrases (noun, verb, adjectival, adverbial, participial, prepositional, absolute) and clauses (independent, dependent; noun, relative, adverbial) to convey specific meanings and add variety and interest to writing or presentations.	<u>CCSS.ELA–LITERACY.L.5.1.A</u> Explain the function of conjunctions, prepositions, and interjections in general and their function in particular sentences. <u>CCSS.ELA–LITERACY.L.K.1.D</u> **Understand and use question words (interrogatives) (e.g., *who, what, where, when, why, how*).**	Does not ask questions; does not use wh– words	Rarely engages/ interacts with others; if confused or uncertain about a task or expectation, may throw objects, overturn furniture, or scream.	**AAC** (along with adult modeling embedded in functional activities) to demonstrate how to use device to make requests for objects, information, or assistance.)
<u>CCSS.ELA–LITERACY.RH.9–10.5</u> Analyze how a text uses structure to emphasize key points or advance an explanation or analysis.	<u>CCSS.ELA–LITERACY.RF.2.3</u> Know and apply grade–level phonics and word analysis skills in decoding words: Distinguish long and short vowels when reading regularly spelled one–syllable words. <u>CCSS.ELA–LITERACY.RF.K.1</u> **Demonstrate understanding of the organization and basic features of print: Follow words from left to right, top to bottom, and page by page.**	Leafs through magazines about cars or motors; consistently turns pages from the beginning of the magazine to the back; may turn several pages at once; sometimes points to common pictures when named (e.g., car or motorcycle); does not reference or track print.	Tracks longitudinal array of pictures from left to right by moving clothespin from one picture to the next; sometimes needs assistance from personal assistant so as not to skip a picture.	**Interactive Shared Reading** (about topics of interest and simplified text; to model tracking of text *and* to facilitate question asking and answering, facilitated by picture supports for Who? What? Where?)

Note. Standards in bold have been selected as targets by his SLP and teacher.

96

kindergarten standard as the place to begin for Dale. This thread of the standard (CCSS.ELA.LITERACY.SL.K.3) (NGA & CCSSO, 2010) requires that he develop proficiency with asking and answering questions in order to seek help, get information, or clarify something that is not understood. Also see Chapters 7 and 9 for discussion of use of the Dynamic Learning Maps for students with severe disabilities.

A review of the ASHA Evidence Maps for ASD (NCEBPCD, n.d.) describes the use of AAC as a powerful, evidence-based intervention (see also Wegner, 2012). As Dale already possesses a device, he now needs to learn how to use it effectively for functional communication and interaction. His teacher and SLP have decided to embed the use of the AAC device in all of his daily activities while at the same time creating opportunities for the functional use of the device for communication. At the SLP's suggestion, the personal assistant, teacher, and teacher's aide have mapped out Dale's day to identify the times and activities when Dale could initiate an interaction and have created a question-asking routine. For example, when Dale enters the classroom each morning, he will use the AAC device to ask a peer, "How are you?" or "What did you do last night?" When it is work time, he will ask his personal assistant, "Where is my work box?" or "Where is my pencil?" In the cafeteria, he will ask, "What is for lunch?" In addition to providing him with the programmed message, he will need an explicit demonstration in how to use the AAC device to seek and gain information. His support team has agreed to use the strategy of one adult using the AAC device to model the asking of the question to a second adult or another student so that Dale can observe and follow into the interaction with support.

Other evidence-based strategies will also be implemented by Dale's education support team. These strategies will include the consistent and widespread use of both within-activity and between-activity visual schedules to clearly inform Dale of the expectations across his day (Earles-Vollrath, Cook, & Ganz, 2006). For example, a visual support will be introduced which informs Dale of what he must do in the cafeteria to move independently through the line, secure a seat next to a peer, clean up his space, and interact quietly until the bell rings. The SLP has also recommended training a small group of interested peers in how to be good communication partners with Dale (Carter, Sisco, & Chung, 2012) as he uses his AAC device at lunch; the SLP has agreed to take the lead in implementing the peer-training strategy.

As has been previously mentioned, Dale has a favorite set of headphones (the ones with red ear covers) and becomes upset and physically aggressive if someone else selects those headphones first. To provide Dale with information about relevant cues and contexts and alternative behaviors, the SLP will write a Social Story (Hutchins, 2012) with a suggested alternative behavior of offering to trade headphones. His personal assistant has agreed to read the story to Dale each morning when he arrives at school and to take daily data to observe any change in his behavior. Video modeling will also be used to provide Dale with opportunities to view brief video clips of a student engaging in a positive interaction (e.g., asking another for the preferred headphones) (Buggey, 2012). The video clip will be shown at least once daily by his personal assistant. Video clips and the reading of the Social Story will be alternated on a weekly basis to observe if one or the other is more successful in generating the target behavior for Dale.

Dale's support team has also identified a language standard that will dovetail nicely with the identified speaking and listening standard. The ninth-grade language standard (CCSS.ELA.LITERACY.L.9-10b) (NGA & CCSSO, 2010) is clearly not an appropriate target for Dale. This standard expects the development of competency with using a variety of phrases and clauses to demonstrate a command of the conventions of standard English. However, walking backward to earlier grade levels of this strand leads to the kindergarten language standard which is more likely an achievable goal. This standard (CCSS.ELA.LITERACY.L.K.1D) (NGA & CCSSO, 2010) expects competency with understanding and using question words (e.g., who, what, where, when, why, how). Adding the use of visual supports to this strategy is likely to facilitate the comprehension and use of question words (Earles-Vollrath et al., 2006). For example, representing Who? What? Where? on individual picture cards that contain a single picture and word representation will input the type of information sought by each question word (Who? + picture of person; Where? + picture of place; What? + picture of object). It will be important to embed the use of the picture question cards in a variety of activities including shared reading and leisure activities.

The final CCSS that Dale's education support team has identified for his IEP is one related to literacy. Dale needs to develop competencies with written language as well as with spoken. A ninth-grade standard for reading (CCSS.ELA.LITERACY.RH.9-10.5) (NGA & CCSSO, 2010) expects the development of the ability to analyze the use of text structure for emphasizing key points or advancing an analysis or explanation—not an appropriate goal for Dale. However, the kindergarten standard (CCSS.ELA.LITERACY.RF.K.1) (NGA & CCSSO, 2010) is a better match. This standard expects that Dale will demonstrate understanding of the organization and basic features of print: following words from left to right, top to bottom, and page by page. To facilitate the development of this standard, a shared reading intervention will be implemented. High interest stories will be created around topics of interest to Dale (e.g., motorcycles and cars), using simplified language, picture supports, and a modified dialogic reading strategy (Waylon, Martinez, Shannon, Butcher, & Hanline, 2015). A new story will be introduced once each week. Repeated readings throughout the week will provide Dale with an opportunity to develop print awareness and early speech-to-print connections. Adult readers will model left-to-right and top-down tracking of print and turning of single pages. Additionally, the Who? What? Where? question cards will conclude each reading to facilitate recall and question answering. Additional picture supports will be added to the recall activity to support Dale in successfully answering the questions using his AAC device.

The special educator, personal assistant, and SLP have decided to collaborate on these identified interventions. The SLP will take the lead on writing the Social Story, preparing the video clips, and doing the peer training. The teacher aide will create the weekly high interest story with direction from the SLP. The SLP will enter the classroom twice each week to provide needed overlays and to facilitate the use of the AAC device during classroom activities. All members of the team have agreed to collect data for progress monitoring and to meet once every 2 weeks to review data and make needed adjustments to the intervention plan.

CONCLUSIONS

The prevalence of ASD in classrooms across the country is increasing. Children and adolescents with a varying severity of impairments of social interaction and communication and narrow or restricted interests or behaviors are posing significant challenges for regular and special educators, school-based therapists, and SLPs who must meet their unique learning needs under the law. Most states have adopted the Common Core State Standards (CCSS) as the curriculum framework for what *all* students must achieve and demonstrate. Students with ASD will rarely be able to independently meet the expectations of grade-level CCSS. Educators and SLPs will need to march backward through the grade-level expectations to find the standards at prior grade levels that match the learner's current level of performance. Identifying the standard at which the learner can perform successfully and then systematically assisting the learner to gain the missing skills that undergird higher grade–level standards will be essential to helping the learner access the general curriculum and prepare to transition from public school to the community.

REFERENCES

American Psychiatric Association. (2013). *Diagnostic and statistical manual, Fifth edition (DSM-5). Autism spectrum disorder.* Retrieved February 11, 2015, from http://www.dsm5.org/Documents/Autism%20Spectrum%20Disorder%20Fact%20Sheet.pdf

American Speech-Language-Hearing Association. (2006a). *Knowledge and skills needed by speech-language pathologists for diagnosis, assessment, and treatment of autism spectrum disorders across the life span* [Knowledge and skills]. Retrieved from http://www.asha.org/policy

American Speech-Language-Hearing Association. (2006b). *Principles for speech-language pathologists in diagnosis, assessment, and treatment of autism spectrum disorders across the life span* [Technical report]. Retrieved from http://www.asha.org/policy

American Speech-Language-Hearing Association. (2014). *2014 Schools survey. Survey summary report: Number and type of responses, SLPs.* Retrieved from http://www.asha.org

Anzalone, M., & Williamson, G. (2000). Sensory processing and motor performance in autism spectrum disorders. In A. M. Wetherby & B. M. Prizant (Eds.), *Autism spectrum disorders: A transactional developmental perspective* (pp. 143–166). Baltimore, MD: Brookes.

Autism Speaks. (2015). *DSM-5 diagnostic criteria.* Retrieved April 12, 2015, from https://www.autismspeaks.org/what-autism/diagnosis/dsm-5-diagnostic-criteria

Baio, J. (2014). Prevalence of autism spectrum disorder among children aged 8 years: Autism and developmental disabilities monitoring network, 11 sites, United States, 2010. *Morbidity and Mortality Weekly Report, 63*(2), 1–22. Retrieved February 11, 2015, from http://www.cdc.gov/mmwr/pdf/ss/ss6302.pdf

Baron-Cohen, S. (1990). Autism: A specific cognitive disorder of "mind-blindness." *International Review of Psychiatry, 2*(1), 81–90.

Baron-Cohen, S., & Swettenham, J. (1997). Theory of mind in autism: Its relationship to executive function. In D. Cohen & F. Volkmar (Eds.), *Handbook of autism and pervasive developmental disorders* (2nd ed.). Charlottesville, VA: John Wiley and Sons.

Bieber, J. (Producer). (1994). *Learning disabilities and social skills with Richard Lavoie: Last one picked . . . first one picked on.* Washington, DC: Public Broadcasting Service.

Buggey, T. (2012). Video modeling applications for persons with autism. In P. Prelock & R. McCauley (Eds.), *Treatment of autism spectrum disorders: Evidence-based intervention strategies for communication & social interactions* (pp. 345–370). Baltimore, MD: Paul H. Brookes.

Carlson, S. M., & Moses, L. J. (2001). Individual differences in inhibitory control and children's theory of mind. *Child Development, 72,* 1032–1053.

Carter, C., Sisco, L., & Chung, Y. (2012). Peer-mediated support interventions. In P. Prelock & R. McCauley (Eds.), *Treatment of autism spectrum disorders: Evidence-based intervention strategies for communication & social interactions* (pp. 221–254). Baltimore, MD: Paul H. Brookes.

Center on the Developing Child at Harvard University. (2015). *Key concepts: Executive function.* Retrieved March 5, 2015, from http://developingchild.harvard.edu/key_concepts/executive_function

Centers for Disease Control and Prevention (CDC). (2014). *CDC estimates 1 in 68 children has been identified with autism spectrum disorder.* Retrieved March 6, 2015, from http://www.cdc.gov/media/releases/2014/p0327-autism-spectrum-disorder.html

Centers for Disease Control and Prevention (CDC). (2015). *Autism spectrum disorder (ASD): Data and statistics.* Retrieved from http://www.cdc.gov/ncbddd/autism/data.html

Chawarska, K., Klin, A., Paul, R., Macari, S., & Volkmar, F. (2009). A prospective study of toddlers with ASD: short-term diagnostic and cognitive outcomes. *Journal of Child Psychology and Psychiatry, 50*(10), 1235–1245.

Constable, S., Grossi, B., Moniz, A., & Ryan, L. (2013). Meeting the common core state standards for students with autism: The challenge for educators. *Teaching Exceptional Children, 45*(3), 6–13. Retrieved March 6, 2015, from http://www.cdd.unm.edu/autism/handouts/Article%20Constable%20et%20al.%202013.pdf

Dodd, J. (2014). Taking measure. *The ASHA Leader, 19*(9), 56–59.

Earles-Vollrath, T., Cook, K., & Ganz, J. (2006). *How to develop and implement visual supports.* Austin, TX: Pro-Ed.

Frith, U., & Happe. F. (1994). Autism: Beyond "theory of mind." *Cognition, 50,* 115–132.

Frombonne, E. (2003). Epidemiological surveys of autism and other pervasive developmental disorders: An update. *Journal of Autism and Developmental Disorders, 33*(4), 365–382. doi:0162-3257/03/0800-0365/0

Ganz, J., Cook, K., & Earles-Vollrath, T. (2006). *How to write and implement social scripts.* Austin, TX: Pro-Ed.

Goldstein, G., Johnson, C. R., & Minshew, N. J. (2001). Attentional processes in autism. *Journal of Autism and Developmental Disorders, 31*(4), 433–440.

Grafodatskaya, D., Chung, B., Szatmari, P., & Weksberg, R. (2010). Autism spectrum disorders and epigenetics. *Journal of the American Academy of Child & Adolescent Psychiatry, 49*(8), 794–809.

Haager, D., & Vaughn, S. (2013). The Common Core State Standards and reading: Interpretations and Implications for elementary students with learning disabilities. *Learning Disabilities Research and Practice, 28,* 5–16.

Happé, F. (1994). An advanced test of theory of mind: Understanding of story characters' thoughts and feelings by able autistic, mentally handicapped and normal children and adults. *Journal of Autism and Developmental Disorders, 24*(2), 129–154.

Hutchins, T. L. (2012). Social stories. In P. Prelock & R. McCauley (Eds.), *Treatment of Autism spectrum disorders: Evidence-based intervention strategies for communication & social interactions* (pp. 313–370). Baltimore, MD: Paul H. Brookes.

Hutchins, T. L., & Prelock, P. A. (2006). Using social stories and comic strip conversations to promote socially valid outcomes for children with autism. *Seminars in Speech and Language, 27*(1), 47–59.

Johnson, A., Johnston, E., & Weinrich, B. (1984). Assessing pragmatic skills in children's language. *Language, Speech, and Hearing Services in Schools, 15,* 2–9. doi:10.1044/0161-1461.1501.02

Joliffe, T., & Baron-Cohen, S. (2001). A test of central coherence theory: Can adults with high-functioning autism or Asperger syndrome integrate fragments of an object? *Cognitive Neuropsychiatry, 6*(3), 193–216. doi:10.1080/13546800042000124

Lunday, A. M. (1996). A collaborative communication skills program for Job Corps centers. *Topics in Language Disorders, 16*(3), 23–26.

Minshew, N. J., Meyer, J., & Goldstein, G. (2002). Abstract reasoning in autism: A dissociation between concept formation and concept identification. *Neuropsychology, 16*(3), 327–334.

Morgan, J., Brown, N., Hsiao, Y., Howerter, C., Juniel, P., Sedano, L., & Castillo, W. (2014). Unwrapping academic standards to increase the achievement of students with disabilities. *Intervention in School and Clinic, 49*(3), 131–141. doi:10.1177/1053451213496156

Myles, B. (2014). *Making sense of the hidden curriculum.* Retrieved February 11, 2015, from http://www.education.com/reference/article/hidden-curriculum-school-asperger/

Myles, B. S., & Simpson, R. L. (2001). Understanding the hidden curriculum: An essential skill for children and youth with Asperger syndrome. *Intervention in School and Clinic, 36*(5), 279–286.

Myles, B. S., Trautman, M., & Shelvan, R. (2004). *Asperger Syndrome and the hidden curriculum. Shawnee Mission.* Lenexa, KS: Autism Asperger Publishing.

National Autism Center. (n.d.). *What are the symptoms of ASD?* Retrieved February 11, 2015, from http://www.nationalautismcenter.org/autism/

National Center for Evidence-Based Practices in Communication Disorders. (n.d.). *ASHA's evidence maps.* American Speech-Language-Hearing Association. Retrieved from http://www.asha.org

National Governors Association Center for Best Practices, Council of Chief State School Officers. (2010). *Common Core State Standards.* Washington, DC: National Governors Association for Best Practices, Council of Chief State School Officers.

National Institute of Environmental Health Sciences. (2014). *Autism.* Retrieved February 11, 2015, from http://www.niehs.nih.gov/health/topics/conditions/autism/

Ozonoff, S., & McEvoy, R. E. (1994). A longitudinal study of executive function and theory of mind development in autism. *Development and Psychopathology, 6*(3), 415–431.

Ozonoff, S., Pennington, B. F., & Rogers, S. J. (1991). Executive function deficits in high-functioning autistic individuals: Relationship to theory of mind. *Journal of Child Psychology and Psychiatry, 32*(7), 1081–1105.

Tager-Flusberg, H. (n.d.). *Language and understanding minds: Connections in autism.* Retrieved March 4, 2015, from http://www.ucd.ie/artspgs/langimp/TAG2.pdf

Tager-Flusberg, H. (1996). Current theory and research on language and communication in autism. *Journal of Autism and Developmental Disorders, 26*(2), 169–172.

U.S. Department of Education. (2002). *No Child Left Behind Act of 2001.* Retrieved from http://www2.ed.gov/policy/elsec/leg/esea02/index.html

U.S. Department of Education (U.S. DOE). (2004). *The Individuals with Disabilities Education Act.* Retrieved March 7, 2015, from http://idea.ed.gov/explore/view/p/,root,regs,300,A,300%252E8,c

U.S. Department of Education. (2013). *Fast facts: Inclusion of students with disabilities.* [Table 50]. National Center for Education Statistics. Institute of Education Sciences. Retrieved March 31, 2015, from http://nces.ed.gov/fastfacts/display.asp?id=59

Waylon, K., Martinez, J., Shannon, D., Butcher, C., & Hanline, M. (2015). *The impact of reading to engage children with autism in language and learning (RECALL).* Retrieved April 14, 2015, from http://tec.sagepub.com/content/early/2015/01/07/0271121414565515, doi:10.1177/0271121414565515

Waylon, K., Otaiba, S., & Delano, M. (2009). Evidence-based reading instruction for individuals with autism spectrum disorders. *Focus on Autism and Other Developmental Disabilities, 24*(1), 3–16. doi:10.1177/1088357608328515

Wegner, J. (2012). Augmentative and alternative communication strategies: Manual signs, picture communication, and speech-generating devices. In P. Prelock & R. McCauley (Eds.), *Treatment of autism spectrum disorders: Evidence-based intervention strategies for communication & social interactions* (pp. 27–48). Baltimore, MD: Paul H. Brookes.

Winner, M. G. (2007). *Thinking about you thinking about me.* San Jose, CA: Think Social Publishing.

Zein, E., Solis, M., Vaughn, S., & McCulley, L. (2013). Reading comprehension interventions for students with autism spectrum disorders: A synthesis of research. *Journal of Autism and Developmental Disorders, 44,* 1303–1322. doi:10.1007/s10803-013-1989-2

CHAPTER 6

Students Who Are Deaf or Hard of Hearing

Brenda C. Seal

Hearing loss is often cited as our most common birth defect (ASHA, n.d.b; Ross, et al., 2008), yet the U.S. Department of Education (USDE, 2014) has reported it as a low-incidence disability in our nation's schools. The incidence of hearing impairment for 6- to 21-year-olds served under the Individuals with Disabilities Education Improvement Act (IDEA) (2004) has been at 0.1% since 2003. The apparent discrepancy between prevalence of pediatric hearing loss and incidence in the USDE report is largely in the counting; schools generally report hearing loss as a primary disability in those students who have moderate, severe, and profound losses. Mild, moderate, fluctuating, and unilateral hearing losses are much more prevalent than more severe losses (NIDCD, 2006). In addition, schools only report the primary disability to USDE, so hearing loss is not counted for students with another primary disability (Power-deFur, 2011). Further, students with both deafness and blindness are counted in the category of deaf-blindness (see Chapter 7). Regardless, concerns that the incidence

should be 7% or 7.5% (Pape, Kennedy, Kaf, & Zahirsha, 2014) are supported by speech-language pathologists (SLPs), educational audiologists (EAs), and teachers of deaf and hard-of-hearing students (TODHH), particularly those who work in schools with large immigrant enrollments, and those who work in high schools where acquired hearing loss continues to rise (see the box below). At least 12% of high school students (ages 14 and above) have an acquired noise-induced hearing loss (ASHA, n.d.c). Undiagnosed and untreated losses can become more severe over time, with increasingly negative learning consequences.

Prior to the turn of the 21st century, most children with severe and profound hearing losses were identified around 2.5 years old (e.g., Yoshinaga-Itano, 2003). Technological advances have since enabled the testing of newborns. Early hearing detection and intervention (EHDI) programs in the United States have brought remarkable improvements in the educational outcomes of children who are deaf or hard-of-hearing. At the same time, today's improved medical interventions save many infants born with complex medical needs. Hearing loss may be

Referring to children with hearing loss as either "Deaf," "deaf," or "hard-of-hearing" rather than "hearing impaired" follows the World Health Organization's International Classification of Functioning, Disability, and Health (2015) that "hearing impairment" refers to the physical loss.

Referring to individuals as Deaf, with an uppercase "D," suggests a cultural membership in the ASL Deaf community, where Deaf and hard-of-hearing are also used both as adjectives and nouns.

Referring to "children with hearing impairment" as a collective term is more common in school settings and among educators as this is the term used in IDEA. "Hearing impair-

ment," like "hearing loss," is all-inclusive.

"Deaf" generally refers to those who have severe to profound losses, those who have not acquired spoken language, or those who do not use spoken language. "Hard-of-hearing," often without hyphens, refers to those who have access to and use spoken language.

Children-first language calls for phrases like "child with hearing loss" or "children who are deaf or hard-of-hearing" rather than "a deaf child" or a "hard-of-hearing child." Children-first language is prioritized in this chapter, except in those instances where ease-of-reading and Deaf culture preferences dictate.

only one of multiple sensory, motor, and cognitive issues in about 36% of children (Antia, Jones, Reed, & Kreimeyer, 2009; Mitchell & Karchmer, 2004). Children with multiple disabilities are also identified by their school systems as students served under IDEA with the disabilities of severe disabilities, deaf-blindness, or multiple disabilities.

Children born prematurely, and those diagnosed with genetic syndromes, are more likely to have hearing loss than full-term babies and those without syndromes. About 95% of children born with hearing loss are from hearing families, not Deaf families as is commonly assumed (Mitchell & Karchmer, 2004); and at least 50% of babies with hearing loss and hearing parents have genetic etiologies (Smith, Shearer, Hildebrand, & Van Camp, 2014). Most genetic hearing losses involve recessive genes; some recessive etiologies are

progressive, with normal hearing at birth and a gradual or sudden loss of hearing over time.

The American Speech-Language-Hearing Association (ASHA, n.d.b) reported early onset hearing loss in 4 to 11 of every 10,000 children, with at least 3 per 1,000 born with hearing loss. Some babies are identified with a newborn hearing screening but then lost to follow-up. That is, their parents do not follow through with audiological testing, hearing aid fitting, and early intervention by 6 months of age, as recommended by the Joint Committee on Infant Hearing (2007). These children often come from low socioeconomic status (SES) families who fail to understand the hospital's discharge papers and fail to refer for audiological testing. Delays in intervention for these children suggest delays in their readiness for kindergarten at age 5.

CHARACTERISTICS OF STUDENTS WHO ARE DEAF OR HARD-OF-HEARING

About 85% of students with hearing loss are educated in local, regional, and/or charter schools, either fully or partially included with their hearing peers (Shaver, Marschark, Newman, & Marder, 2014). The female–male split is relatively equal, 50.3% female and 49.7% male. The majority are white (60%), followed by Hispanic (17%), and African American (16%). Profoundly deaf students, especially those who attend schools for the deaf, are more likely to use sign language to communicate. Students who attend their local schools may also use sign language with needed accommodations—like sign language interpreters, cued speech transliterators, captioners, and notetakers (Leppo, Cawthon, & Bond, 2013). Profoundly deaf students are also more likely to have cochlear implants than students with mild or moderate losses who usually are fitted with hearing aids for their development of and access to spoken language. The earlier implants and hearing aids are fitted, the better the prognosis is for spoken language acquisition and use.

Variability also characterizes children who use sign and spoken language. Some Deaf parents who have deaf or hard-of-hearing children want them to attend a school for the deaf where American Sign Language (ASL) is the instructional and social language. Other Deaf parents choose to have their deaf children implanted and request bimodal-bilingual communication programming or a focus on spoken English for some of the school day and ASL for other parts of the school day. Similar bilingual choices are common among hearing families who use a spoken language other than English at home, but want their child with hearing loss to be English language learners at school. Students from signing and spoken language homes may also be offered Cued Speech (or Visual Phonics) to support spoken language acquisition and literacy development; some require Augmentative and Alternative Communication choices when neither spoken language nor sign language is effective for communication. Table 6–1 offers a listing of terms and their definitions.

You will read about five students in this chapter—Olivia, Jin, Juan, Dakota, and Shaundra. As individuals, they are as diverse as any five students can be. Collectively, however, they all have a hearing loss that affects "listening" and learning in the core curriculum. We return to them later, but for now, a brief description of each student should personalize some of the different characteristics associated with hearing loss.

Olivia is a 6-year-old kindergartener with recessive genetic (connexin) deafness. She was diagnosed within weeks after referral from the hospital's screening. Her educated hearing family participated in early intervention services at home, learned to insert and troubleshoot her bilateral hearing aids from 3 to 12 months, at which time she received bilateral cochlear implants. They continued services in the natural environment until she was 3, when they transitioned Olivia to the local preschool for children with hearing loss. Both mother and father used signs along with spoken language, like her teachers at the total communication preschool. But as Olivia's spoken language grew, she began to drop signs. She now relies on spoken English to communicate with her family, although signing appears when her implants are off—at bath time and bedtime and when she is misunderstood.

Table 6–1. Communication Terms Associated With Pediatric Hearing Loss

Terms	Definition and Common Usage
Total Communication	Philosophy supporting any and all communication modalities to maximize communication. Most commonly, TC refers to signing and talking, either simultaneously (also known as Simultaneous Communication, SC) or with a predominance of spoken English supported by signing (also known as Sign Supported English and Pidgin Sign English)
Bimodal-Bilingual Communication	Philosophy supporting both sign and spoken language acquisition, but with a distinction away from SC. Most commonly, bimodal-bilingual proponents emphasize spoken language for some of the day in an environment where American Sign Language (ASL) is used
Bilingual-Bicultural Communication	Philosophy supporting ASL as a first language and written English as a second language. Bi-bi is common to schools for the deaf where ASL is the cultural norm.
Auditory Verbal Therapy	An early intervention approach that advocates development and use of audition while de-emphasizing use of vision in learning spoken language. AVT proponents commonly reject any signing, speechreading, or other visual supports for spoken language acquisition. AVT is considered a unisensory approach.
Cued Speech or Cued Language (LaSasso, Crain, & Leybaert, 2010)	A system of handshapes that combine with the visible movements of the mouth to support speechreading. Most commonly, cued speech users rely on spoken language but may need interpreters (known as transliterators because of the literal translation with the addition of cues) for access to new content.
See the Sound Visual Phonics (ICLI, 2011)	A copyright-protected system of visual symbols developed and promoted by the International Communications Learning Institute (2011) that represent the articulatory configuration of phonemes. Most commonly, SLPs and teachers trained in Visual Phonics use the symbols for phonological awareness and speech production training.
Augmentative and Alternative Communication (AAC)	Low- and high-tech technologies that enable communication for individuals without spoken language. Originally, AACs were limited to "hearing" individuals. Today, however, AACs are offered to students whose motor, social, and/or cognitive skills limit spoken and/or sign language acquisition and use.

Jin is an American-born second grader whose family immigrated from South Korea for his father's work. Jin's hearing loss resulted from bacterial meningitis at 30 months of age. He received a cochlear implant within weeks of his diagnosis. His parents reported that they tried a hearing aid on the unimplanted ear for several months after his surgery, but he rejected it. Jin also attended a preschool program for children with hearing loss for 1 year; its Auditory Verbal Therapy program differed from Olivia's preschool communication philosophy. Jin's teachers use spoken

English when communicating with him and his parents; his parents use spoken English with Jin and his younger brother, and Korean with each other and his paternal grandmother who lives with them.

Juan's family came to the United States when he was 2. At 10, he entered the state's deaf school (his older brother entered 3 years earlier); he was in several public school programs before, both in classes for deaf students and in mainstream classes. His parents moved across country several times when he was younger, but they have been settled in their current home for the past 3 years. Juan has two hearing sisters (10 and 14 years old) who use spoken Spanish at home with their parents. Juan and his brother (16 years old) use ASL at the deaf school and with each other. Juan is now 12, working at a fifth-grade level.

Dakota has a profound hearing loss and multiple learning issues stemming from cytomegalovirus (CMV). Many CMV babies have a difficult development, and Dakota was hospitalized for much of his early life. He is currently 15 and in a technical school that hosts special education classes for independent living skills. Dakota has a full-time sign-language interpreter-aide who assists with his mobility. Dakota is in a wheelchair with mixed cerebral palsy. He has about 200 functional signs, along with an iPad for alternative speech communication.

Shaundra is 17 years old and a percussionist in the school band. She loves music more than anything and wants to go to a college with a big marching band. Shaundra's grades have always been in the B to C range, though. After failing the eighth-grade hearing screening, she was diagnosed with a bilateral high-frequency hearing loss. She received hearing aids but only wore them for a few months after receiving them, during her sophomore year. As a junior, Shaundra worries about passing one last test that addresses core curriculum standards.

The characteristics of these five students are also common to thousands of students who do not have hearing loss and to other students described in this book. Juan and Jin share many of the characteristics of English language learners described in Chapter 10. Dakota has many similar characteristics as students with vision impairments in Chapter 7. Shaundra is not identified as a special education student, but she shares many characteristics of secondary students who receive special education. The impact of these mixed characteristics is a contributor to the USDE's report of hearing impairment as a low-incidence disability.

TYPICAL CHALLENGES TO THE CURRICULUM

Anderson and Arnoldi (2011) grouped the multiple challenges students with hearing loss experience in accessing the general education curriculum into three areas: (a) rate or pace of instruction, (b) rigor or complexity of instructional content, and (c) incidental learning or passive absorption of language and content without instruction.

To understand the impact of rate, a reflection on your own learning experiences is helpful. You have probably experienced teachers who talked and wrote on the board, as in a math class; or talked and demonstrated, as in a lab class; or talked and clicked, as in a lecture class. In your current classes, you probably move your eyes from one slide to another and then to your paper or laptop/notebook to enter notes as you "listen" to your teachers. Given 14, 16, 18, or more years to master this dual-sensory learning experience, you are probably quite comfortable with the pace of most instructors and the rate of most instruction.

If you had a hearing loss, your ability to rely on vision and audition simultaneously would be cut—perhaps by as much as half—as you would look to your interpreter, or read the captions and then look at the movie, or watch the teacher's facial movements that enable you to speechread and then look to your interpreter and then to a movie. The fast pace of instruction that relies on simultaneous visual and auditory input is very challenging. Reducing this typical dual-sensory input to one input modality, or even one primary visual modality with some secondary auditory input or some primary auditory input with secondary visual support, is also challenging to the instructor and support personnel who want the student with hearing loss to keep up. Research points to what is often overlooked in a typical day for students with hearing loss who do keep up—they experience considerable fatigue (Hornsby, Werfel, Camarata, & Bess, 2014).

Rigor of content is easily understood by those familiar with the Common Core State Standards (CCSS). Table 6–2 includes sample Speaking and Listening Standards for our five students' grade levels. The premium placed on speaking, listening, reading, and writing in school is a given for hearing students, but how can our five students, especially Juan and Dakota who use sign language instead of spoken language, be held to these same standards? You may assume, as many do, that when speaking and listening are impossible, reading and writing are preserved, the choice alternatives. A reflection on your own learning may again help you understand that an assumed reliance on reading is wrong.

Return to the previous paragraph, and "listen" to yourself read silently. As a hearing person, you most likely read by listening to yourself say the words, phrases, sentences, and paragraphs. If you come to words that you do not know, like these, Берите бумагу и пишите, your reading comes to an immediate halt. Why? Because you have no "auditory code" by which to convert these print symbols into your spoken language. You may try decoding strategies with the few symbols you recognize, like "Mary," but with no help in reading these directions written in Russian that translated mean, "take out paper and write."

Students with hearing loss commonly struggle with reading because they have a limited "auditory code" by which to map meaning to the words they "hear." Reading is most problematic for students with moderate, severe, and profound hearing losses, but also with some who have mild losses. Given the heavy focus of reading to learn, the challenge of learning content from expository textbooks can be next to impossible.

The third category of challenges for students with hearing loss contributes to both the first and second: challenges with incidental learning. Most hearing children enter kindergarten with a brain full of world knowledge, stuff never taught but simply absorbed by overhearing the interactions of others. Listening to parents read to their children fills children with language of stories, and listening to parents talk with each other fills children with arbitrary words and phrases (sometimes unwanted) of adult experiences. Listening

Table 6–2. Selected Speaking and Listening Standards From English-Language Arts CCSS

Sample kindergarten standards for Olivia	Listen to others and take turns discussing kindergarten topics in small and larger groups. Speak audibly, expressing thoughts, feelings, and ideas clearly.
Sample second-grade standards for Jin	Follow the rules for discussions, gain the floor respectfully, listen to others with care, and speak one at a time about a topic. Tell a story or recount an experience with descriptive details and coherent sentences.
Sample fifth-grade standards for Juan	Paraphrase portions of a text read aloud or information presented in diverse media and formats, including visually, quantitatively, and orally. Identify the reasons and evidence a speaker provides to support particular points.
Sample ninth- to tenth-grade standards for Dakota	Propel conversations by posing and responding to questions that relate the current discussion to broader themes or larger ideas; actively incorporate others into the discussion; and clarify, verify, or challenge ideas and conclusions. Evaluate a speaker's point of view, reasoning, and use of evidence and rhetoric, identifying any fallacious reasoning or exaggerated or distorted evidence.
Sample 11th- to 12th-grade standards for Shaundra	Respond thoughtfully to diverse perspectives; synthesize comments, claims, and evidence made on all sides of an issue. Resolve contradictions when possible; and determine what additional information or research is required to deepen an investigation or complete the task.

Note. Adapted from NGA Center & CCSSO (2010), *Common Core State Standards.*

to siblings at play, to social conversations on the bus and in the school hallway, to the commercials from a radio, television, or computer, listening *any*where to *any* auditory message, builds a depository of world language that readies children for school.

Children who have limited experiences with incidental listening generally struggle with both the incidental and intentional listening required for social and academic learning. Their world knowledge depository is small; their vocabularies are small; their figurative expressions are limited; and their social skills are less language-rich than those of their hearing peers. Their listening brains simply do not hold the same incidental "fill" we expect from hearing children. For many children with hearing loss, listening is effortful, used to being adult directed, and very fatiguing.

Table 6–2 has a sampling of the Speaking and Listening CCSS expected for Olivia, Jin, Juan, Dakota, and Shaundra. After reading through the list and thinking about the challenges of rate, rigor, and incidental learning, you might ask why we would hold students with hearing loss to the same standards expected of hearing students. For more than two centuries (yes, deaf education was the first special education in the United States), researchers and educators who specialized in pediatric hearing loss tried to answer this question. Many theories and philosophies have emerged, but no definitive answers. Here we are, individually and collectively, attempting to answer the same question in this book. Hopefully, your experiences with our five cases will help you understand this thinking: How could we *not* hold students with hearing loss to the same standards to which we hold students who hear? We know that what works for one hearing child or child with hearing loss will not always work for another. We attempt to individualize educational programs to meet individual students' current and future needs. We use practices supported by the literature, and we attempt to be effective in communicating about those practices with students and their families, always honoring their expectations and cultural preferences. We value evidence-based practices (see Hoffman, Ireland, Hall-Mills, & Flynn, 2013) that are also standards-based practices.

OLIVIA

Olivia's Individualized Education Program (IEP) was developed in June. It is now mid-September and she has been in school just 3 weeks.

What are relevant standards for Olivia? Olivia's parents and other IEP committee members agreed in their sum-

mer meeting that all CCSS intended for the hearing kindergarteners are appropriate for Olivia. They also agreed that the following standards may require additional support because of Olivia's hearing loss:

Comprehension and Collaboration:

■ CCSS.ELA-LITERACY.SL.K.1 and subskills 1.A and 1.B: Participate in collaborative conversations with diverse partners about kindergarten topics and texts with peers and adults in small and larger groups.
■ CCSS.ELA-LITERACY.SL.K.2: Confirm understanding of a text read-aloud or information presented orally or through other media by asking and answering questions about key details and requesting clarification if something is not understood.
■ CCSS.ELA-LITERACY.SL.K.3: Ask and answer questions in order to seek help, get information, or clarify something that is not understood.

Presentation of Knowledge and Ideas:

■ CCSS.ELA-LITERACY.SL.K.4: Describe familiar people, places, things, and events and, with prompting and support, provide additional detail.
■ CCSS.ELA-LITERACY.SL.K.6: Speak audibly and express thoughts, feelings, and ideas clearly.

Vocabulary Acquisition and Use:

■ CCSS.ELA-LITERACY.L.K.4 and Subskills 4A and B: Determine or clarify the meaning of unknown and multiple-meaning words and phrases based on kindergarten reading and content.

- CCSS.ELA-LITERACY.L.K.6: Use words and phrases acquired through conversations, reading and being read to, and responding to texts.

What language and communication skills are required for Olivia's success with these standards? Olivia must demonstrate intelligible spoken language represented by (near) age-appropriate vocabulary, syntax, morphology, phonology, and pragmatics. In addition, she must have conversational competence in asking and answering questions, and taking conversational turns about different topics with different partners. Both of these skills require an ever-growing vocabulary, including emerging site word reading, and an awareness of conversational breakdowns and willingness to ask for repairs when she is not understanding or is not understood.

What are Olivia's current skills and needs? Olivia's IEP offers several standardized test scores. All scores fall within average performance for her age and hearing peer group, although auditory comprehension and expressive vocabulary are a few points from the cutoff level for one standard deviation (s.d.) below average, as shown in Table 6–3.

In addition to the standardized tests, the SLP and classroom teacher systematically documented Olivia's speech intelligibility, academic readiness, and communication behaviors during the first 2 weeks of school. A 2-min audio recording of Olivia's spontaneous spoken language during an individual speech session was offered to two unfamiliar and two familiar listeners who rated her spoken language intelligibility at an average of 4.75 (of 5). This rating is compatible with her Goldman-Fristoe Test of Articulation–2 scores, although single-word articulation test results do not always predict spontaneous spoken language intelligibility (see Ertmer, 2011; Seal, 2014). She received mixed scores in the "pass" and "at risk" range on academics, attention,

Table 6–3. Olivia's Present Level of Academic Achievement and Functional Performance

Standardized Tests	Standard Scores
Preschool Language Scales, 4th Edition (Zimmerman, Steiner, & Pond, 2002):	Total Score: 90 Expressive Communication: 92 Auditory Comprehension: 88
Expressive Vocabulary Test–2 (Williams, 2007)	87
Goldman-Fristoe Test of Articulation–2 (Goldman & Fristoe, 2000)	105
Observational Scales	Results (Pass, At Risk)
Screening Instrument for Targeting Educational Risk (*SIFTER*, Anderson & Matkin, 1996)	Expressive Communication: 14 (Pass) (At risk at 13 points)
	Socially Appropriate Behaviors: 11 (At Risk) (At risk at 11 points)

communication, class participation, and social behavior categories of the *Preschool Screening Instrument for Targeting Educational Risk (Preschool SIFTER;* Anderson & Arnoldi, 2011; designed for 3-year-olds through kindergarten). These scores are also shown in Table 6–3. The two questions below, both highly relevant to the CCSS, received low scores:

- Q 9. How proficient is the student at telling a story or relating happenings from home when compared to classmates?
- Q 10. How often does the student volunteer information to class discussions or in answer to teacher questions?

What are Olivia's instructional goals and accommodations for the year? Olivia's IEP lists these accommodations:

1. Routine Ling 6-Sound Test and cochlear implant check by classroom teacher and/or SLP.
2. Teacher use of a lapel microphone compatible with Olivia's personal FM to reduce signal-to-noise ratio during instructional time.
3. Teacher transfer of FM microphone to others as needed (e.g., SLP for pull-out work, Librarian) and acoustic treatment of classroom to reduce noise.

The IEP identifies SLP services to include 20 min of individual and/or small group SLP weekly (commonly divided as 10 and 10) and 20 min of classroom communication support twice weekly to work on these goals:

1. Olivia will use intelligible spoken language to interact with peers and teachers in at least 70% of docu-

mented interactions. Note that this will be measured routinely during in-class SLP support and measured quarterly with expressive communication checklists (e.g., *Observation of Social Interaction—Preschool and Kindergarten,* Anderson, 2011).

2. Olivia will ask and answer questions appropriately and maintain conversations with peers and adults in at least 80% of documented interactions. This will be documented routinely during in-class SLP support and during pull-out SLP sessions and documented quarterly for progress reports and parent–teacher conferences.
3. Olivia will indicate a need for/attempt to repair when she fails to understand others or is not understood by others in at least 80% of prompted opportunities. Documented routinely during in-class SLP support and during pull-out SLP sessions. Documented quarterly for progress reports and parent–teacher conferences. Note that the SLP routinely records baseline and prognostic criterion levels for IEP goals. The focus on standards-based goals does not eliminate the need to collect data and document progress, but the focus in this chapter is on the standards and the goals, not on the SLP's data collection.

Olivia's SLP recommended these, which were added at the next IEP team meeting:

4. Olivia will indicate when either of her two implants fails and request assistance from the teacher or SLP in restoring function in at least 80% of prompted opportunities following difficulty on the Ling 6-Sound Test.
5. Olivia will interact with at least one new classmate weekly (either to ini-

tiate or in response to an initiation), 80% of the time with supportive prompts during the SLP's in-class and small group work.

6. Olivia will use new vocabulary from classroom instruction in individual and small-group sessions with the SLP with 90% accuracy when prompted.

What are the classroom activities and responsibilities? As of the third week of school, Olivia's SLP and classroom teacher agreed that several daily activities and routines were important to the goals. Table 6–4 lists these.

What interventions will promote Olivia's success with these goals? In addition to the activities and routines common to most kindergarten classes, Olivia's SLP and classroom teacher agreed on these intervention routines for themselves:

1. Address all children by name and encourage Olivia (and others) to *"ask _____,"* or *"tell _____ he dropped his hat; it's time for calendar; you need help with clean-up,"* etc.

2. Make transition announcements and directions (e.g., *"It's story time, please*

put away your . . . ") from a consistent spot in the classroom and ensure Olivia's attention before making the announcement or giving directions.

3. Follow spoken directions and transition announcements with written details (e.g., *Wash up and Line up, Page 2 in _____)*

4. Use "raise your hand if you hear me" prompts to gain Olivia's (and others') attention.

5. Require "raise your hand" and other rules for asking and answering questions.

6. Instruct all children about hearing, listening, and noise.

7. Use pause time (e.g., an intentional self-count to 5) to encourage Olivia (and others) to respond to a topic, to ask and answer questions, to encourage conversation turns.

8. Collaborate—plan, instruct, assess, discuss, document, and work together for Olivia's (and others') best learning.

Summary: Olivia's performance at this early point in the school year reveals several speaking and listening needs that may be exacerbated by the personality

Table 6–4. Kindergarten Activities and Routines That Align With Olivia's Goals

Activity/Routine	SLP and Teacher Shared Responsibilities
Unstructured time during morning arrival Ling 6-Sound Test, CI and FM check	Accommodations 1 and 2
Structured "floor" time for calendar, weather, greetings, and day's plans	Accommodations 1, 2, and 3
Structured language arts time	Accommodations 1, 2, and 3
Structured story time	Accommodations 1, 2, and 3
Unstructured "centers" time	IEP Goals 1, 2, and 3
Structured speech time (in/outside class)	IEP Goals 1, 2, and 3

traits her parents offered. They described her as a shy child, an introvert, an observer, and a follower. These descriptions can also characterize a child who does not have optimal access to the social and academic language in an active kindergarten. Multiple studies have pointed to an important relationship between communication competence and social interactions that predict friendships and school performance (see Batten, Oakes, & Alexander, 2013, for a systematic review).

Olivia's SLP and classroom teacher have already joined their observational and instructional forces to assess Olivia's interactions and needs. Together, they are prepared to nurture Olivia's improved interactions, to build her communication competence to communicate as effectively as all other students. The SLP has worked with profoundly deaf children before and shares her experiences with the classroom teacher who does not have the same background. The classroom teacher brings her knowledge of and experiences with the CCSS and the curriculum to her collaboration with the SLP, raising their combined skills and expectations for Olivia's learning.

JIN

Jin's IEP was developed the previous April when he was in first grade. It is now March and he is fully included in the second grade with reading support from the reading specialist, communication support from the SLP, and academic support from TODHH. At this point in the year, the classroom teacher has joined these other professionals to revisit some of the core standards as they prepare for the next IEP meeting a month from now.

What are the relevant standards for Jin? Jin's parents and the IEP committee agreed that all grade-level CCSS were appropriate for Jin, but that some (listed below) could be more difficult for him because of his hearing loss.

Comprehension and Collaboration:

- CCSS.ELA-Literacy.SL.2.1 and Subskills 2.1a through c: Participate in collaborative conversations with diverse partners about *Grade 2 topics and texts* with peers and adults in small and larger groups.
- CCSS.ELA-Literacy.SL.2.2: Recount or describe key ideas or details from a text read-aloud or information presented orally or through other media.
- CCSS.ELA-Literacy.SL.2.3: Ask and answer questions about what a speaker says in order to clarify comprehension, gather additional information, or deepen understanding of a topic or issue.

Presentation of Knowledge and Ideas:

- CCSS.ELA-Literacy.SL.2.4: Tell a story or recount an experience with appropriate facts and relevant, descriptive details, speaking audibly in coherent sentences.
- CCSS.ELA-Literacy.SL.2.5: Create audio recordings of stories or poems; add drawings or other visual displays to stories or recounts of experiences when appropriate to clarify ideas, thoughts, and feelings.
- CCSS.ELA-Literacy.SL.2.6: Produce complete sentences when

appropriate to task and situation in order to provide requested detail or clarification.

Knowledge of Language:

■ CCSS.ELA-Literacy.L.2.3 and Subskill 2.3.a: Use knowledge of language and its conventions when writing, speaking, reading, or listening.

Vocabulary Acquisition and Use:

■ CCSS.ELA-Literacy.L.2.4 and Subskills 2.4 a through e: Determine or clarify the meaning of unknown and multiple-meaning words and phrases based on Grade 2 reading and content, choosing flexibly from an array of strategies.
■ CCSS.ELA-Literacy.L.2.5 and Subskills 2.5 a and b: Demonstrate understanding of word relationships and nuances in word meanings.
■ CCSS.ELA-Literacy.L.2.6: Use words and phrases acquired through conversations, reading and being read to, and responding to texts, including using adjectives and adverbs to describe.

An area of concern that developed since the last IEP involves Jin's comparative strengths in math computations relative to challenges with math problems that are "language heavy" and "symbol heavy" (Alt, Arizmendi, & Beal, 2014).

From the Standards for Mathematical Practice (NGA & CCSSO, 2010): In Grade 2, instructional time should focus on four critical areas: (1) extending understanding of base-ten notation; (2) building fluency with addition and subtraction; (3) using standard units of measure; and (4) describing and analyzing shapes . . . Students should develop, discuss, and use efficient, accurate, and generalizable methods to . . . compute in base ten. . . . Students should investigate, describe, and reason about decomposing and combining shapes to make other shapes. . . . In addition, students should (1) Make sense of problems and persevere in solving them; (2) Reason abstractly and quantitatively; (3) Construct viable arguments and critique the reasoning of others; and (4) Look for and express regularity in repeated reasoning.

What language and communication skills are required for success with these standards? Jin's SLP has identified these three areas of competence to present at the IEP meeting:

■ Communication competence. The American Speech-Language-Hearing Association (ASHA) and the Council of Education of the Deaf (CED) described communication competence for children who are deaf and hard-of-hearing "as the ability to understand and use one or more languages effectively in a variety of sociocultural contexts" (2004). They further described the facilitation of communication competence as a "collaboration" of understanding and respect among SLPs and teachers of children who are DHH to "stimulate [their] interpersonal communication skills and literacy."
■ Emerging literacy. Children's awareness of, interaction with, and application of spoken language skills to print (reading and writing) occurs developmentally from birth. Children with hearing loss

are expected to go through the same period as their hearing peers during which spoken language, reading, and writing skills emerge as complementary and mutually reinforced skills in literate learning environments (Williams, 2004).

■ Emerging mathematical literacy. Much like emerging literacy skills, emerging mathematical literacy occurs developmentally in both hearing children and those with hearing loss. The acquisition of mathematical constructs benefits from and feeds to simultaneous cognitive development that benefits and feeds to language acquisition

that feeds to and benefits from the acquisition of math constructs. The interaction of all three is expected in a healthy learning environment (Geist, 2008).

What are Jin's current skills and needs? In reviewing Jin's current IEP and preparing for the upcoming IEP meeting, the school psychologist and TODHH have administered several tests from the *Woodcock Johnson III Tests of Achievement* (Woodcock, McGrew, & Mather, 2007). Jin's performance was splintered, with a mixture of higher than average, average, and below-average scores, as shown on Table 6–5. The SLP and TODHH also

Table 6–5. Jin's Present Level of Academic Achievement and Functional Performance: Standardized Tests

Tests	Standard Scores
Woodcock-Johnson III Achievement Tests	
Math:	
Calculation (computations):	120*
Math Fluency (rapid math facts):	124*
Applied Problems (reading comprehension):	75**
Quantitative Concepts (vocabulary, concepts, reasoning)	90
Woodcock-Johnson III Achievement Tests	
Reading:	
Sound Awareness (phonemic awareness):	100
Alphabetic Principle (letter-word identification):	90
Word Attack:	90
Spelling:	80
Reading Fluency:	77**
Reading Vocabulary:	72**
Picture Vocabulary:	90
Passage Comprehension:	85

Note. * = 1 standard deviation **above** average. ** = 1 standard deviation **below** average.

collaborated with the reading specialist and classroom teacher to complete the *Activities for Listening and Learning (ALL)* (Anderson & Arnoldi, 2011), identifying several listening, communication, and learning strengths and needs for Jin's April IEP meeting. These are also listed in Table 6–6.

What are Jin's instructional goals and accommodations for the year? Jin's IEP offers two accommodations:

- Routine Ling 6-Sound Test and cochlear implant check by TODHH and/or SLP, and transitioning to independence in Jin's reporting difficulty/failure.
- Teacher use of a lapel microphone compatible with Jin's personal FM to reduce signal-to-noise ratio during instructional time, and transitioning to Jin's responsibility for transfer of FM mic to others as needed (SLP, TODHH, Librarian, etc.).

His services include 20 min of individual SLP services, 20 min small group SLP work, and 30 min of SLP classroom support weekly. He also receives language services from the TODHH two mornings per week in Jin's classroom and two mornings per week of pull-out work, for a total of 3 hours weekly; and pre-, parallel-, and postinstructional services from the reading specialist 40 min weekly to work on literacy skills (Table 6–7). Jin's current IEP goals include these:

1. Jin will assume responsibility for his listening needs by informing others when his implant is not functioning, when noise levels are too high, and/or when he does not understand or misunderstands, as measured with *Progress Observations* from the Florida

Cochlear Implant Work Group (2005; in Anderson & Arnoldi, 2011).

2. Jin will demonstrate gains in conversational competence from a Stage 2 to a Stage 3 as measured on *Tracking Development of Conversational Competence* (Stone, 1988; in Anderson & Arnoldi, 2011) by
   □ initiating conversations with idiomatic expressions;
   □ extending conversations with multiple turns with teachers and peers;
   □ requesting clarification with polite forms; and
   □ producing narratives with more than one episode, resolution, and with time and causal connectors.

3. Jin will improve phonological awareness skills to 80% accuracy as measured with SLP monthly assessments of word attack skills, sight-word reading, and spelling conventions; and with improved reading vocabulary and reading fluency as measured by the teacher in weekly oral reading assignments.

4. Jin will improve literacy skills to 80% accuracy as measured with SLP monthly assessments of comprehension of contextual passages and with increased independence in reading weekly library books, as measured by the reading teacher's monthly assessments.

5. Jin will improve math literacy skills, as measured with SLP monthly assessments in talking through language-heavy and symbol-heavy math problems.

What classroom activities and responsibilities facilitate these goals? At this seventh month of the school year, Jin's educational team members agreed that

Table 6–6. Jin's Present Level of Academic Achievement and Functional Performance: Relative Strengths and Needs

Activities for Listening and Learning (ALL, Caleffe-Schenck, 1980, 2010)		
Listening	**Listening Strength**	**Listening Need**
Auditory Association	Functions and uses for objects	Logical relationships
	Goes together	Associations from description
	Same-different	Associations from functions
	Absurdities	Multiple uses of words
		Analogies
Auditory Discrimination	Sounds and words	Figure-ground
Auditory Memory	Letter and number sequences	Songs, rhymes
	Sentences	Oral directions
	Story events	Repeat/retell stories
	Sequencing words (months, days)	Create sentences with sequencing words
Auditory Closure	Word identification	Phonological awareness
	Phrase completion	Similes
		Sentences with varied possibilities
Communication	**Communication Strength**	**Communication Need**
	Question and answer	Conversing
	Experience book	Discussing
	Past experiences	Changing topics
	Polite requests	Decision making
		Encouraging/clarifying
		Revising/clarifying
		Humor: Word combinations and humor discussions
Reading	**Learning Strength**	**Learning Need**
	Environmental	Pleasure reading
	Oral reading	Literature
	Categories	Vocabulary
	Abbreviations	Definitions
	Component parts	Antonyms
	Synonyms	Homonyms

their collaboration has been important to the second-grade activities and routines, listed in Table 6–7. They also agreed that the progress Jin has made on several goals is important to his success in the third grade (see Table 6–7).

What interventions have promoted Jin's success? The SLP, TODHH, reading specialist, and classroom teachers agree that these collaborative practices have contributed to Jin's growth in second grade and should be continued in third grade:

1. Consistency in encouraging all students to follow the classroom communication rules (e.g., raise your hand and wait to be acknowledged).
2. Instruction in classroom noise, hearing, and hearing loss: The fall unit on hearing, hearing loss, and classroom noise (SLP, TODHH, and classroom teacher) included Sound Level Meter measurements (with iPad apps) at different times and places that were then integrated into math work "story problems."

Table 6–7. Activities, Corresponding Goals, and Professional Responsibilities

Activities	SLP, TODHH, Reading Specialist, and Teacher's Shared Responsibilities
Arrival, Breakfast, RR, and CI Check, Goal 1	Ling 6-Sound Test, CI and FM check
Unit on Hearing and Noise	3-week unit for all second graders
Language Arts: S & L	"Show and Tell" time
IEP Goals 1 and 2	Small group work with SLP, individual work with SLP, individual work with TODHH
Language Arts: Reading and Writing Goals 1, 2, 3	Story mapping; "My Funny Bone" Unit: Humor; individual work with reading specialist and with SLP; telling and retelling stories; writing stories; defining words; figurative language
Math Measures: Goal 5	Word problems; "explain what you did"
Social Sciences and Drama Goals 1, 2, 3, 4, and 5	Historical character roles: Columbus Day, Thanksgiving, Martin Luther King Day, Lincoln, Saint Patrick, and others

3. Collaboration for all new unit start-ups and completions to integrate core standards in Jin's communication goals, literacy goals, and mathematic work.

4. Scaffolding and latticing (Morgan et al., 2013) Jin's more advanced skills and knowledge (e.g., in computations) to support new spoken language and improved literacy.

Summary: Jin's performance on the second-grade CCSS has revealed many strengths at this point in the school year, particularly in math calculations and concepts, that contrast with several needs, as in language arts. His teachers have observed and documented his competitive need to be first in the class to finish math work and an overt frustration when he has to redo written language assignments. Recent testing and observational recording should facilitate the IEP conference as the team suggests new and continued goals for the rest of this year and for third grade. The SLP remains optimistic about Jin's learning, but she and the classroom teacher are also prepared to suggest to his parents the potential benefits of summer work to facilitate his readiness for more challenging third-grade standards.

JUAN

Juan is in a fifth-grade group at the state school for the deaf. He resides in the dormitory during the week, sharing a room with his older brother, and returns home by bus (2-hour ride) on weekends. With the winter holiday break and midterm approaching, Juan's SLP has revisited their work this year and prepared a packet of homework for Juan to complete with his family. This "home" work addresses several CCSS.

What are the relevant standards for this fifth-grader? Teachers at Juan's school (and at many schools for the deaf) have worked with their state departments and boards of education to adopt (and adapt) the CCSS school-wide. Much of the adaptation in schools for the deaf has involved the use of ASL. All of Juan's teachers instruct in ASL and in written English. Some use spoken English with their ASL, and some students use spoken English with and without ASL. Regardless, ASL and written English do not share an "auditory" code. Typically, teachers at schools for the deaf teach their ASL students to convert literal English text into more meaningful ASL. Similarly, they teach their students to convert ASL into meaningful and accurate written English. This "bilingual" interpretation and translation is successful with some students, but generally fails to take half of their students beyond a fourth-grade reading level (Traxler, 2000).

Juan's SLP collaborates weekly with his language arts (LA) teacher, and together they have identified the literacy standards below for additional attention:

Text Types and Purposes:

- CCSS.ELA-Literacy.W.5.1 and subskills a through d: Write opinion pieces on topics or texts, supporting a point of view with reasons and information.
- CCSS.ELA-Literacy.W.5.2 and subskills a through e: Write informative/explanatory texts to examine a topic and convey ideas and information clearly.
- CCSS.ELA-Literacy.W.5.3 and subskills a through e: Write narratives to develop real or imagined experiences or events

using effective technique, descriptive details, and clear event sequences.

Production and Distribution of Writing:

- CCSS.ELA-Literacy.W.5.4: Produce clear and coherent writing in which the development and organization are appropriate to task, purpose, and audience.
- CCSS.ELA-Literacy.W.5.5: With guidance and support from peers and adults, develop and strengthen writing as needed by planning, revising, editing, rewriting, or trying a new approach.
- CCSS.ELA-Literacy.W.5.6: With some guidance and support from adults, use technology, including the Internet, to produce and publish writing as well as to interact and collaborate with others; demonstrate sufficient command of keyboarding skills to type a minimum of two pages in a single sitting.

Research to Build and Present Knowledge:

- CCSS.ELA-Literacy.W.5.7: Conduct short research projects that use several sources to build knowledge through investigation of different aspects of a topic.
- CCSS.ELA-Literacy.W.5.8: Recall relevant information from experiences or gather relevant information from print and digital sources; summarize or paraphrase information in notes and finished work, and provide a list of sources.

Range of Writing:

- CCSS.ELA-Literacy.W.5.10: Write routinely over extended time frames (time for research, reflection, and revision) and shorter time frames (a single sitting or a day or two) for a range of discipline-specific tasks, purposes, and audiences.

What language and communication skills are required for success with these standards? What are Juan's current skills and needs? Juan's teachers have acknowledged many times that Juan is acquiring ASL quickly, after entering the school just 2 years ago. Some of his teachers think his quick ASL acclimation occurred because his older brother had already been using ASL with Juan prior to his enrollment. Juan's parents reported that he was introduced to signing when he was 4 years old at a Head-Start program. Regardless, Juan's stakeholders agree that his ASL has "taken off" in just the past year.

Juan's fifth-grade IEP, developed and signed by his parents in early September, reveals several standardized test scores from the previous May and June, as shown in Table 6–8. These standardized test scores suggest that Juan's language learning is lower than his potential, or that what "has been" learned is not representative of what "can be" learned (Hasson & Joffe, 2007; Kapantzoglou, Restrepo, & Thompson, 2012). Consequently, Juan's SLP relied on her previous experiences with international deaf students to engage Juan in several "dynamic assessment" activities (Mann, Pena, & Morgan, 2014). Her plans to try dynamic assessment did not materialize, however, until an incident occurred in which he picked up her cell phone (from her office desk) and signed MY BROTHER NUMBER (suggesting that he knew his brother's cell phone number). By convention, ASL signs are "glossed" or transcribed into written English with

Table 6–8. Juan's Present Level of Academic Achievement and Functional Performance: Standardized Test Scores

Standardized Tests	Standard Scores/Levels/Percentiles
Weschler Intelligence Scale for Children-IV (2003)	
Nonverbal IQ:	112
Vocabulary:	85 (using ASL signs)
English Language Assessment (ELA)	
Reading:	Limited English Proficient, Level 2
Writing:	Limited English Proficient, Level 2
Oral Written and Language Scales-II (OWLS) (Carrow-Woolfolk, 1996)	Written Expression Scale: 80 (using ASL signs, picture prompts, and gestures
Carolina Picture Vocabulary Test (Layton & Holmes, 1985)	80th percentile score (using signs)

uppercase letters. With that experience, the SLP later designed and documented these three simple assessments, shown in Table 6–9.

What are Juan's speech-language goals and experiences? Juan receives daily work with the SLP (20 min per session) in individual and classroom sessions, with a focus on dual-language support (seeBunta & Douglas, 2013) and written language for communication. The SLP has been working on these IEP goals identified at the school opening: (1) Juan will improve written English with increased semantic and grammatical accuracy, from an average of 60% at the end of the previous school year to an average of 90% at the end of this school year, as measured with monthly teacher and SLP documentation; and (2) use technology to communicate with others, with SLP guidance in e-mailing, texting, and using the videophone, and with increasing independence by school-year's end. Since the dynamic assessment, the SLP has focused on these procedures in her pull-out session:

1. Drafting electronic messages (as in simulating an e-mail and/or text message) to his brother, sisters, and parents.
2. Referring to an Internet translation program to convert written English e-mail and text messages to Spanish for his parents.
3. Creating a portfolio of sample narratives, opinion pieces, personal scripts, conversations, and biographical stories of events/experiences, crossing ASL, written English, and translated Spanish, in both video format (with and without captions) and in written format (typed and handwritten).
4. Adhering to rules for communicating across social media, including texting protocols, e-mail protocols, translation protocols, Video Relay protocols, and captioning protocols to apply written text to his ASL samples.

What classroom activities and responsibilities facilitate these goals? Juan's SLP works with his language arts

Table 6–9. Dynamic Assessment Activities and Juan's Results

Activity	Step 1	Step 2	Step 3	Outcome
Calling brother	SLP made call as Juan offered the number from memory, SLP left a text message: *Juan is learning how to text you.*	Juan took cell phone, entered number, but signed DON'T KNOW	SLP signed HI BROTHER, And waited as Juan hit H-I and E-D-U-A-R-D-O	SLP encouraged MORE, and Juan typed S-P-E-E-C-H P-H-O-N-E B-Y
E-mailing LA teacher	SLP e-mailed teacher with: "Juan wants to email you." She hit Send and signed to Juan YOUR TURN	Juan typed LA in Subject line and signed DON'T KNOW NAME	SLP wrote the teacher's e-mail address on the board and observed Juan type it correctly from the board	Juan tabbed to message, following SLP's point and typed: H-I M-i-s-s L-u-c-y M-e e-m-a-i-l. B-y
Cell phone movie	SLP recorded Juan signing his name and age	Juan signed DON'T KNOW	SLP saved video and e-mailed to the Internet	Juan watched video and signed FOR MOM DAD SISTERS.

(LA) teacher weekly to collaborate with her unit plans that are also approved weekly by the school's middle school supervisor. The SLP works in her office where a dedicated laptop and Internet connection allow Juan's ASL to be video-recorded (through a webcam) and saved. This recording procedure is common to SLPs who collect and analyze ASL communication samples. Juan translates his ASL messages and narratives from the recordings into written English. Written English choices are discussed, corrected, and rewritten over the week's sessions, and Juan e-mails a final edited copy of his weekly writing assignments to his LA teacher each Friday. Juan's LA teacher copies, reviews, marks, and sends Juan's writing samples home each weekend, usually as e-mail attachments. Juan's LA teacher and SLP also plan homework assignments for extended breaks, including these for the upcoming 2-week winter break:

1. Juan should expect and participate in one scheduled video relay call and a follow-up e-mail from his SLP (agreed to in writing by his parents).
2. Juan should expect and respond to one scheduled text message from his classroom teacher (also agreed to by his parents).
3. Juan should request from his parents the written Spanish words to match a selection of 30 English words associated with Christmas; he will return the new Spanish vocabulary to his teacher (in his own handwriting) and SLP.

What interventions will promote Juan's success? The goals and activities described above are designed to support

Juan's success as an ASL, English, and Spanish learner. They address vocabulary from classroom instructional activities, including his textbooks (Dolman, 2013), and transfer the meaningful use of new words and phrases across Juan's multiple modalities and languages. They also engage Juan in his family's home language, Spanish, in functional ways that should lead to increasing independence for social media and telecommunication exchanges in Spanish.

Summary: In spite of Juan's late identification of hearing loss, lack of early intervention, and prior experiences with amplification; in spite of prior multiple school programs and inadequate foundation in a solid language base; perhaps because of Juan's supportive older brother's experiences with ASL at the deaf school; and probably because of Juan's high nonverbal intelligence and motivation to learn languages along with the SLP's sensitivity to Juan's bilingual communication needs (ASHA, 2004b) and with insights from dynamic assessment, Juan's teachers have reported to the SLP that his written English and classroom grades are improving. Juan reported in a recent e-mail to the SLP, "Thank you for working with me. Speech is fun."

"Speech" as a collective name for SLP services tends to misrepresent the broad scope of practice that belongs to speech-language-hearing services. Some SLPs who specialize with the population of deaf and hard-of-hearing individuals describe their scope of practice as including intervention with "spoken language, sign language, and written language." Juan's SLP is one of those. She also knows her scope of practice includes working with multiple technologies to ensure and facilitate Juan's most effective communication.

DAKOTA

Dakota entered a residential rehabilitation center in January where SLPs, occupational therapists (OTs), and other staff members specialize in transition assessments and planning. Dakota is still enrolled in his regional technical school where he has been in a class for students with multiple disabilities and complex communication needs with the same three to four other students for the past 2.5 years. Prior to that, he was at the middle school with some of these same few students. Part of the 6-week evaluation at the center involves Dakota's trials with different augmentative and alternative communication (AAC) devices, across different activities of daily living (ADLs), different simulated classroom experiences, and across different simulated jobs. The center provides sign language interpreters who are nationally certified and experienced in these evaluation procedures.

What CCSS standards are relevant for Dakota? Identifying appropriate standards for Dakota and other students with complex communication needs (CCNs) can be conflicting for SLPs who want to hold their students to the highest possible standards, yet promote realistic expectations for them, their families, their teachers, and peers. The itinerant SLP who works with secondary students in Dakota's school system has visited the rehab center several times during his stay there, to observe and to participate as an informant for and communication partner in some of the assessments. Her experiences after 4 weeks have encouraged her to revisit the CCSS, including the following:

Comprehension and Collaboration:

- CCSS.ELA-LITERACY.SL.9-10.1: Initiate and participate effectively in a range of collaborative discussions (one-on-one, in groups, and teacher-led) with diverse partners on Grades 9–10 topics, texts, and issues, building on others' ideas and expressing their own clearly and persuasively.
- CCSS.ELA-LITERACY.SL.9-10.1.B: Work with peers to set rules for collegial discussions and decision making (e.g., informal consensus, taking votes on key issues, presentation of alternate views), clear goals and deadlines, and individual roles as needed.
- CCSS.ELA-LITERACY.SL.9-10.1.D: Respond thoughtfully to diverse perspectives, summarize points of agreement and disagreement, and, when warranted, qualify or justify their own views and understanding and make new connections in light of the evidence and reasoning presented.

Presentation of Knowledge and Ideas:

- CCSS.ELA-Literacy.SL.9-10.4: Present information, findings, and supporting evidence clearly, concisely, and logically such that listeners can follow the line of reasoning and the organization, development, substance, and style are appropriate to purpose, audience, and task.
- CCSS.ELA-Literacy.SL.9-10.5: Make strategic use of digital media (e.g., textual, graphical, audio, visual, and interactive elements) in presentations to enhance understanding of findings, reasoning, and evidence and to add interest.
- CCSS.ELA-Literacy.SL.9-10.6: Adapt speech to a variety of contexts and tasks, demonstrating command of formal English when indicated or appropriate.

See also Chapters 7 and 9 for discussion of use of the Dynamic Learning Maps for students with more severe disabilities.

The SLP has also begun drafting new goals to bring to the next IEP meeting, to align with these standards in anticipation of the postevaluation IEP conference with Dakota's IEP team. At this point, she is proposing these new standards-based goals:

1. Dakota will initiate discussion and respond to diverse communication partners (one-on-one, in groups, and with teachers) about relevant *Grades 9–10 topics* (e.g., new vocabulary from health class, math work, etc.) using one or more of his AAC apps (e.g., Scene Speak), supportive gestures and/or signs, and his interpreter.
2. Dakota will work with classmates to create a list of rules for discussions that lead to decision making (e.g., *Majority rules in choosing next month's field trip; one person communicates at a time*, etc.) with flexibility in moving from one communication choice to another.
3. Dakota will respond to other classmates' points of agreement and disagreement thoughtfully (e.g., *I agree with _____; Sorry, I disagree with _____*, etc.), through multiple communication choices.
4. Dakota will present information clearly so that communication partners can

follow, or, when they do not follow, present the same information through alternative approaches to enable understanding.

5. Dakota will use textual, graphical, audio, visual, and interactive media to enhance understanding.
6. Dakota will adapt communication to a variety of contexts and tasks.

What language and communication skills are required for his success with these standards? What are Dakota's current skills and needs? Flexibility in communication has been identified as an asset for secondary students who are deaf or hard-of-hearing, even a predictor for getting into and graduating from college (Convertino, Marschark, Sapere, Sarchet, & Zupan, 2009). At 15, Dakota's communication experiences in school have been relatively restricted, particularly to just a few communication partners in his small class placements. The SLP has also observed Dakota's signs to be limited: (a) in their "phonology"—with only Level 1 handshapes and movements (Seal, Nussbaum, Belzner, Scott, & Waddy-Smith, 2011), (b) in their "symbolic complexity"—with a predominance of iconic signs, and (c) in their use—primarily with his interpreter. She suspects that his comprehension of ASL is more advanced than his expressive skills demonstrate, and she has come to realize from the weeks at the rehab center, where Dakota has experienced multiple communication partners who do not use signing and multiple interpreters skilled in ASL, that flexibility across modalities and across communication partners is important (Sweigert, 2012).

Flexibility in communication also requires functional access to multiple communication choices. Selecting the most appropriate AAC choices and most appropriate accommodations for Dakota's access to the CCSS returns us to his evaluation. Although Dakota's evaluation is still ongoing, the SLP has learned of several results through her visits. She compiled a list of the preliminary results that had been shared with her thus far; they are documented in Table 6–10.

How might these skills, needs, and recommendations be addressed? What classroom activities, instructor responsibilities, and interventions will promote success? Dakota's SLP knows that she must carefully plan with Dakota, his grandmother, current IEP stakeholders, teachers at the technical center, special education director, and other support staff members—occupational therapist (OT), physical therapist (PT), audiologist (AUD), and interpreter—to translate the rehabilitation center's evaluation findings and recommendations. She hopes to

- follow through with an audiological workup (including hearing aid fittings, CI consult, and intensive auditory rehabilitation [AR]) to reduce barriers to auditory access;
- reconsider the current self-contained placement with more opportunities to explore his personal interests (graphic arts and health services) and reduce barriers to the CCSS;
- include a speech-generating device in his AR program to reduce barriers associated with a restricted pool of communication partners and expand communication with hearing peers (see AAC devices for face-to-face communication, NIDCD, 2011);
- explore a summer program at the state's deaf school to address barriers associated with his limited ASL exposure and use;

Table 6–10. Preliminary Results From the Rehab Center's Comprehensive Evaluation of Dakota

Vestibular evaluation:	Not completed by the vestibular team (AUD, OT and PT), but obvious balance and mobility restrictions that led to his being wheelchair bound
Vision evaluation:	Current fitted glasses sufficient in natural and artificial light for letter recognition, color discrimination, sight reading (Font at 14), small picture (line drawings) identification, visual tracking across horizontal and vertical planes. Peripheral vision restricted to 50° R&L of midline.
	Recommendation for annual eye examinations (and new lenses to replace his heavily scratched lenses).
Cognitive evaluation:	Not completed but nonverbal IQ measures (with no time constraints) test cognitive skills at the low end of average or within 1 standard deviation below average
AAC-Interaction evaluations:	Not completed but measures to date reveal:
Motor skills (upper limbs):	right-hand dominance, low-motor tone/ataxia, but sufficient strength and range of motion to pick up, carry, hold, and use AAC devices of 1 to 2 pounds (e.g., his current iPad)
Symbolic skills:	Currently decodes/encodes with a mixture of picture symbols, including visual display pictures, pictures of signs, and printed English
	Recommendation for expanded apps on his personal iPad and exploration of a speech-generating device to expand communication to hearing
Interest inventory: *Pictorial Inventory of Careers* (2013): Personal interests	Health service careers at 98th percentile and communication/graphics art at 95th percentile
Accommodations assessment:	Limited auditory access to spoken language
Barriers to communication:	Limited access to multiple speakers, signers, and interpreters
	Limited mobility—restricted to wheelchair
	Recommendations to increase access to different communication partners, including multiple sign language users and different interpreters, to explore amplification and auditory habilitation

- request multiple interpreters from the school's interpreting coordinator to address barriers associated with a single long-term interpreter-aide; and

- revise Dakota's IEP to address the CCSS with attention to transition goals.

Summary: Dakota's history resembles that of many students who present with a diagnosis of multiple disabilities and complex communication needs. There is no single approach to meeting their communication and learning needs. Sadly, however, SLPs have traditionally compartmentalized their interventions in small classes of similar students and with discrete periods of training and practice, rather than expanding intervention across multiple learning experiences with multiple modalities, multiple partners, and multiple contexts (Kamhi, 2014). Today's SLPs are more likely to be trained in more varied interventions than SLPs graduating decades ago. The more confident the SLP in working in multiple environments with multiple interventions, the more likely he or she will be confident in advocating for the same for his or her students. That confidence feeds successful collaborations.

Dakota is also not unlike many students whose signing experiences are restricted to a single interpreter over several years. Even though a single interpreter may be appropriate for some students and is common in smaller school systems where the availability of qualified interpreters is limited (Seal, 2004), skill in working with different interpreters is important for adult independence. That skill can only be promoted when students get to work with different interpreters. The same desire for flexibility in AAC approaches applies to signers and interpreters. Sadly, school systems have traditionally hired less-accomplished, less-credentialed interpreters and interpreter-aides for students whose language facility is less accomplished, less complex. This practice is rarely discussed as a "restriction," but in the same way that a self-contained special education classroom is restrictive for many students, a single interpreter-aide over consecutive years can be restrictive to communication growth.

Finally, it is not uncommon for auditory (re)habilitation, and all other SLP interventions, to be decreased, rather than increased, in adolescence. Scott (2014) explained that the percentage of children served under IDEA with speech-language impairments drops from about 49% at 6 years of age to only 4% by age 15. Because auditory habilitation includes speech-language-hearing services, chances are rather strong that attention to Dakota's spoken language needs have probably been reduced for some time. His SLP found in his central office files that he had inconsistent use of a single analog hearing aid in kindergarten and first grade, but no amplification from that year on. She knows that years without auditory stimulation are counterindicative of learning to use and benefit from hearing aids or cochlear implants. She also knows that if Dakota were born today with the same CMV diagnosis and multiple needs, he would have been a ready candidate for hearing aids and implants. Dakota's SLP hopes that trial hearing aids will encourage Dakota and his grandmother to pursue implants, not as a fix to his complex communication needs, but as another avenue for increased access to communication partners and improved access to the CCSS.

SHAUNDRA

Shaundra does not have an IEP and has made it clear she does not want to be "treated like a special ed student." Documentation of her high-frequency hearing loss revealed normal hearing in the low frequencies with a drop to 35 dB from

4000 to 8000 Hz in the right ear and to 45 dB from 4000 to 8000 Hz in the left ear (Figure 6–1). As a result, the educational audiologist recommended a 504 meeting to revise her 504 plan.

What are relevant standards for this high school junior? All CCSS identified for Grades 11 and 12 are appropriate for Shaundra. And Shaundra's 504 plan includes several needs and accommodations that are important to her access of the CCSS. Table 6–11 shows her 504 plan.

What are Shaundra's strengths and needs? Shaundra's strengths and primary interests lie in music. She is in the school's marching band, concert band, jazz band, and pep band (for basketball games). Shaundra loves the drums, but she is first chair for xylophone and cymbals, two other percussion instruments. Shaundra's goals are to attend college and play in the school's marching band. She wants a degree in music, but she is not sure if she can even get into college with her grades (she maintains a B average, with occasional Cs in required courses—earth science, world history, and health—but As in all music courses). She is not enrolled in AP classes, and she has not yet passed all mandatory CCSS testing for graduation.

What are the classroom activities and responsibilities? All classroom and music room activities must be available or accessible to Shaundra. Responsibilities for this access can easily fall through the cracks. Some states have educational audiologists (EAs) who serve many roles, including identifying, tracking, trouble-shooting, and maintaining students' amplification needs. EAs are not likely to monitor older students' use of amplification, simply because they expect older students to be independent users of their hearing aids, cochlear implants, and FMs. Shaundra's EA was involved in her original audio-logical workup a year ago, assisting with appointments that led to diagnosis of the hearing disability and hearing aid fitting and her hearing aid use for 30 days. Beyond the annual hearing conservation program (and an invitation for Shaundra to be the "poster" student this year on the "turn down the volume" campaign), and beyond her constant advocacy for noise-safe learning environments, Shaundra's school's EA has had little interaction with and no responsibility for what has become Shaundra's infrequent hearing aid use in the 11th grade.

So to whom would Shaundra's needs fall when she reports she is not wearing her hearing aids or using the earplugs, when she is at risk of continued exposure to loud noise that will worsen her current loss, and when her dream of going to college is growing more fragile? Responsibility belongs to the school's "general education" staff and administrators, not the "special education" staff and administrators (Office for Civil Rights, U.S. Dept. of Education, 2010). Many students with disabilities have a 504 team that includes the individual, parents, teachers, and a school administrator. Most schools have a 504 representative who reports to a 504 coordinator who is responsible for 504 programs district-wide. The responsibility of the 504 team members is to ensure that students' rights and needs are being met without discrimination. Shaundra has a right to the same educational opportunities that her peers without hearing loss are afforded. She has a right to optimal seating in her classrooms and to a personal FM system for optimal access to her teachers' voices. Shaundra also has earned the right to play cymbals, drums, and other percussion instruments in music, even though the music environment exposes her to high decibels and may be contributing to

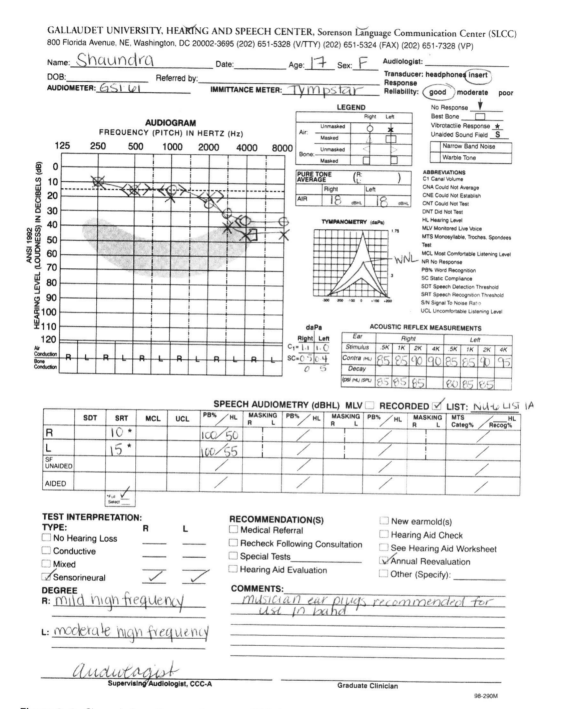

Figure 6–1. Shaundra's audiogram. Courtesy of Kristin Roush, PhD, CCC-A, Gallaudet University Hearing and Speech Center.

Table 6–11. Shaundra's 504 Plan

Specific need	Optimal visual and auditory access to instruction, including instruction for the CCSS and instruction for music and other required and elective courses
Accommodations	Bilateral personal amplification (behind-the-ear hearing aids) with a personal FM system booted to the hearing aids to assure auditory access; preferential seating in classroom and music room for visual access; musician's earplugs to reduce exposure to damaging intensities
Special materials or training needed	Who, how, and when? Assistance from the educational audiologist to adjust to hearing aids for 30 school days following the hearing aid fittings
Criteria for evaluating success	Satisfactory use of hearing aids, FM, musician's earplugs, and appointed classroom seating

her hearing disability. Shaundra also has a right to protect her vulnerable hearing in this environment. Ironically, she must choose to comply with these accommodations for her rights.

What interventions will promote her success? Fortunately, Shaundra's general education teachers and administrators (her 504 team) had observed an improvement in Shaundra's attention and performance last spring when she moved to the front of class and when they used the FM mic that made their voices clearer for her hearing aids. Their positive report at the end of her sophomore year led Shaundra's parents to higher expectations for her junior year and increased hopes that college would be a possibility after all. At this October meeting, Shaundra admitted that she does not want to use the accommodations. Her 504 team recommended referral to the educational audiologist and speech-language pathologist.

Here's where special services become important for Shaundra. She needs auditory rehabilitation (AR). The term is synonymous with *aural* and *audiologi-cal rehabilitation*, all three referring to an interactive approach to maximize hearing for communication. (Auditory habilitation is appropriate for someone who has always had a hearing loss, like Dakota, while auditory *re*habilitation is appropriate for Shaundra who is losing her hearing.) AR falls under the scope of practice of both audiologists and speech-language pathologists. Both professions are responsible for interventions that "minimize the impact of hearing loss on educational, social, vocational, psychological well-being and quality of life" (ASHA, 2001). Audiologists generally take on AR diagnostic and amplification interventions, while SLPs usually handle communication interventions. In the best of worlds, the two professionals work together to plan, administer, and document their interventions and outcomes to improve Shaundra's use of, protection of, and advocacy for optimal audition.

SLPs and EAs working with general educators are concerned with a student's compliance response to the teachers' expectations. What would those expectations be? Boothroyd (2007) defined AR as the reduction of hearing-loss deficits, but unlike the ASHA's 2001 definition, he added efforts to reduce deficits of "function, activity, and participation" to his definition. He also stressed "instruction" for those whose experiences result in selective or complete nonuse of their hearing aids.

We cannot be sure that Shaundra's positive experiences with her hearing aids last spring ended in summer when she "only wore them when they went out, never at home" where she says she wears her iPod all the time. Shaundra's iPod-instead-of-hearing-aids-summer probably set her back, not only in having to start over with the hearing aids for school this fall, but also in having to relearn the differences in hearing with and without amplification. Her experiences without hearing aids may have deluded her into a false perception that she does just as well without them as she does with them.

The SLP's and EA's AR program would instruct Shaundra in the nature of her hearing loss, the physical consequences of more noise exposure, and the positive outcomes she can expect if she takes charge of her hearing loss needs. The AR program offered by the SLP and EA should also motivate Shaundra to receive help, and here's where returning to the education standards is important. Shaundra's state requires passage on a standards-based exam for graduation. Shaundra has passed all tests but one, the History/Social Studies exam. The standards for History/SS follow.

Key Ideas and Details:

- CCSS.ELA-LITERACY.RH.11-12.1: Cite specific textual evidence to support analysis of primary and secondary sources, connecting insights gained from specific details to an understanding of the text as a whole.
- CCSS.ELA-LITERACY.RH.11-12.2: Determine the central ideas or information of a primary or secondary source; provide an accurate summary that makes clear the relationships among the key details and ideas.
- CCSS.ELA-LITERACY.RH.11-12.3: Evaluate various explanations for actions or events, and determine which explanation best accords with textual evidence, acknowledging where the text leaves matters uncertain.

Craft and Structure:

- CCSS.ELA-LITERACY.RH.11-12.4: Determine the meaning of words and phrases as they are used in a text, including analyzing how an author uses and refines the meaning of a key term over the course of a text (e.g., how Madison defines faction in Federalist No. 10).

Integration of Knowledge and Ideas:

- CCSS.ELA-LITERACY.RH.11-12.7: Integrate and evaluate multiple sources of information presented in diverse formats and media (e.g., visually, quantitatively, as well as in words) in order to address a question or solve a problem.
- CCSS.ELA-LITERACY.RH.11-12.9: Integrate information from diverse sources, both primary and secondary, into a coherent understanding of an idea or event,

noting discrepancies among sources.

What interventions will promote her success on the state's test? The SLP and EA can address Shaundra's auditory access needs and support her goal to pass the state test in history by working with her general educators. Addressing language from her textbooks and lectures, and persuading her with motivating interventions like these that follow, could make an important contribution to her future:

- instruction in iTunes, iPhone, iPad, and iPod apps compatible with Shaundra's hearing aid programs, with individual sessions (during study hall) with the SLP and EA;
- a collection of audio recordings of students' and teachers' oral readings from the 11th-grade American history textbook, chemistry textbook, and English composition books for independent "listening training" on Shaundra's personal iPad during study hall;
- a collection of musical works prepared by Shaundra's orchestra teacher with challenging listening assignments attached to the scores and iPad recordings, to be completed and submitted for additional points on her midterm exam;
- practice questions for the "History/ Social Studies" CCSS exam are audio-recorded on Shaundra's iPad and iPhone for independent study, and new questions are to be recorded once mastery (at 90%) is reached;
- encouragement from the band teacher for Shaundra to wear her

musician's plugs and a video recording of her performance with them, to use in her instructional program with the SLP and EA demonstrating the benefits of ear protection; and

- an online assignment for Shaundra to investigate five of her favorite professional musicians' use of ear protection with a presentation to her class on what she finds.

Summary: Shaundra's hearing loss is likely to worsen over her life span. Without immediate and convincing intervention at this important age, her future dreams and aspirations risk failure. With carefully tailored instruction about her hearing loss and needs, with guided practice using material from her classes that address the CCSS and engage her in listening with amplification and across different apps to challenging assignments that address her high-stakes goal, and with supportive collaboration from her now expanded 504 team, we can expect Shaundra's AR program to be successful. Successful AR for this 16-year-old will also predict success for amplification and hearing protection for the rest of her life.

CONCLUDING THOUGHTS

Hearing loss is pervasive across our schools. Its impact on learning is also pervasive. The five students presented in this chapter are diverse in their hearing loss etiologies, interventions, communication profiles, learning strengths, and needs. Their speech-language pathologists and educational audiologists have translated professional knowledge and skills in speech-language-hearing to meaningful interventions that should maximize their students' learning. The common thread across each case has been collaboration with teachers who instruct in the CCSS. Collaboration requires a competence in one's scope of practice and a confidence in sharing that scope of practice in ways that enable others to share with reciprocal competence and confidence. The challenge to work with students like Olivia, Jin, Juan, Dakota, and Shaundra, and to grow competence and confidence in pediatric AR, can also be yours.

REFERENCES

Alt, M., Arizmendi, G. D., & Beal, C. R. (2014). The relationship between mathematics and language: Academic implications for children with specific language impairment and English Language Learners. *Language, Hearing, and Speech Services in Schools, 45,* 220–233.

American Speech-Language-Hearing Association. (n.d.a). *Facts about pediatric hearing loss.* Retrieved from http://www.asha.org/aud/Facts-about-Pediatric-Hearing-Loss/

American Speech-Language-Hearing Association. (n.d.b). *The prevalence and incidence of hearing loss in children.* Retrieved from http://www.asha.org/public/hearing/Prevalence-and-Incidence-of-Hearing-Loss-in-Children/

American Speech-Language-Hearing Association. (n.d.c). *Hearing loss (ages 5+).* ASHA Practice Portal. Retrieved from http://www.asha.org/PRPSpecificTopic.aspx?folderid=8589935335&section=Incidence_and_Prevalence

American Speech-Language-Hearing Association. (2001). *Knowledge and skills required for the practice of audiologic/aural rehabilitation* [Knowledge and skills]. Retrieved from http://www.asha.org/policy

American Speech-Language-Hearing Association. (2004a). *Roles of speech-language pathologists and teachers of children who are deaf and hard of hearing in the development of communicative and linguistic competence* [Position statement]. Retrieved from http://www.asha.org/policy

American Speech-Language-Hearing Association. (2004b). *Knowledge and skills needed by speech-language pathologists and audiologists to provide culturally and linguistically appropriate services.* ASHA Supplement 24. Retrieved from http://www.asha.org/policy

Anderson, K. L., & Arnoldi, K. A. (2011). *Building skills for success in the fast-paced classroom: Optimizing achievement for students with hearing loss.* Hillsboro, OR: Butte Publications.

Antia, S., Jones, P., Reed, S., & Kreimeyer, K. (2009). Academic status and progress of deaf and hard-of-hearing students in general education classrooms. *Journal of Deaf Studies and Deaf Education, 14,* 293–311.

Batten, G., Oakes, P. M., & Alexander, T. (2014). Factors associated with social interactions between deaf children and their hearing peers: A systematic literature review. *Journal of Deaf Studies and Deaf Education, 19,* 285–302.

Boothroyd, A. (2007). Adult aural rehabilitation: What is it and does it work? *Trends in Amplificaiton, 11,* 63–81.

Bunta, F., & Douglas, M. (2013). The effects of dual-language support on the language skills of bilingual children with hearing loss who use listening devices relative to their hearing peers. *Language, Speech, and Hearing Services in Schools, 44,* 281–290.

Carrow-Woolfolk, E. (1995). *Oral and Written Language Skills (OWLS).* Circle Pines, MN: American Guidance Service.

Convertino, C. M., Marschark, M., Sapere, P., Sarchet, T., & Zupan, M. (2009). Predicting academic success among deaf college students. *Journal of Deaf Studies and Deaf Education, 14*(3), 324–343.

Dolman, D. (2013, July–August). The common core standards: Why they matter to teachers and parents of children with hearing loss. Alexander Graham Bell Association for the Deaf and Hard of Hearing: *Volta Voices.* Retrieved from http://www.listeningandspokenlanguage.org/CommonCoreStandards.aspx

Ertmer, D. J. (2011). Assessing speech intelligibility in children with hearing loss: Toward revitalizing a valuable clinical tool. *Language, Speech, and Hearing Services in the Schools, 42,* 52–58.

Florida Cochlear Implant Work Group. (2005). Progress observations. In K. Anderson & K. Arnoldi (Eds.), (2011), *Building skills for success in the fast-paced classroom: Optimizing achievement for students with hearing loss.* Hillsboro, OR: Butte Publications.

Geist, E. (2008). *Children are born mathematicians: Supporting mathematical development, birth to age 8.* Boston, MA: Pearson Education.

Goldman, R., & Fristoe, M. (2000). *Goldman-Fristoe Test of Articulation–2.* Boston, MA: Pearson.

Hasson, N., & Joffe, V. (2007). The case for Dynamic Assessment in speech and language therapy. *Child Language Teaching and Therapy, 23*(1), 9–25.

Hoffman, L. M., Ireland, M., Hall-Mills, S., & Flynn, P. (2013). Evidence-based speech-language pathology practices in schools: Findings from a national survey. *Language, Speech, and Hearing Services in Schools, 44,* 266–280.

Hornsby, B. W. Y., Werfel, K., Camarata, S., & Bess, F. H. (2014). Subjective fatigue in children with hearing loss: Some preliminary findings. *American Journal of Audiology, 23,* 129–134.

Individuals With Disabilities Education Act, 20 U.S.C. § 1400 (2004).

International Communication Learning Institute (ICLI). (2011). *See the Sound Visual Phonics.* Retrieved from http://seethesound.org/visual_phonics.html

Joint Committee on the American Speech-Language-Hearing Association and the Council on Education of the Deaf. (2004). The roles of speech-language pathologists and teachers of children who are deaf and hard of hearing in the development of communicative and linguistic competence: Technical report. *ASHA Supplement,* 24. doi:10.1044/policy. TR2004-00256

Joint Committee on Infant Hearing. (2007). Year 2007 position statement: Principles and guidelines for early hearing detection and intervention programs. *Pediatrics, 120,* 898–921.

Kamhi, A. (2014). Clinical Forum: Improving clinical practices for children with language and learning disorders. *Language, Speech, and Hearing Services in Schools, 45,* 92–103.

Kapantzoglou, M., Restrepo, M., & Thompson, M. (2012). Dynamic assessment of word learning skills: identifying language impairment in bilingual children. *Language, Speech, and Hearing Services in Schools, 43,* 81–96.

LaSasso, C., Crain, K. L., & Leybaert, J. (2010). *Cued speech and cued language for deaf and hard of hearing children.* San Diego, CA: Plural.

Layton, T. L., & Holmes, D. W. (1985). *Carolina Picture Vocabulary Test.* Austin, TX: Pro-Ed.

Leppo, R. H. T., Cawthon, S. W., & Bond, M. P. (2013). Including deaf and hard-of-hearing students with co-occurring disabilities in the accommodations discussion. *Journal of Deaf Studies and Deaf Education, 19,* 189–202.

Mann, W., Pena, E. D., & Morgan, G. (2014). Exploring the use of dynamic language assessment with deaf children, who use American Sign Language: Two case studies. *Journal of Communication Disorders, 52,* 16–30. doi:10.1016/j.jcomdis.2014.05.002

Mitchell, R., & Karchmer, M. A. (2004). Chasing the mythical ten percent: Parental hearing status of deaf and hard of hearing students in the United States. *Sign Language Studies, 4,* 138–163.

Morgan, J. J., Brown, N. B., Hsiao, Y.-J., Howerter, C., Juniel, P., Sedano, L., & Castillio, W. L. (2013). Unwrapping academic standards to increase the achievement of students with disabilities. *Intervention in School and Clinic, 49*(3), 131–141. doi:10.1177/1053451213496156.

National Governors Association Center for Best Practices, Council of Chief State School Officers. (2010). *Common Core State Standards.* Washington, DC: Author. Retrieved from http://www.corestandards.org/the-standards

National Institutes on Deafness and Other Communication Disorders (NIDCD). (2006). *Statistical report: Prevalence of hearing loss in U.S. children, 2005. Epidemiology & Biostatistics Program.* Bethesda, MD: National Institutes of Health. Retrieved from http://www.nidcd.nih.gov/funding/programs/hb/outcomes/Pages/report.aspx

National Institutes on Deafness and Other Communication Disorders (NIDCD). (2011). *Assistive devices for people with Hearing, Voice, Speech, or Language Disorders,* Retrieved from http://www.nidcd.nih.gov/health/hearing/pages/assistive-devices.aspx

Pape, L., Kennedy, K., Kaf, W., & Zahirsha, Z. (2014). Immigration within the United States: Prevalence of childhood hearing loss revisited. *American Journal of Audiology, 23,* 238–241.

Pictorial Inventory of Careers. (2013). *Work interest assessment.* Jacksonville, FL: PIC Pathfinder. Retrieved from http://www.talentassessment.com/pages/PIC

Power-deFur, L. (2011). Special education eligibility: When is a speech-language impairment also a disability? *ASHA Leader, 16,* 12–15.

Ross, D., Holstrum, W. J., Gaffney, M., Green, D., Oyler, R., & Gravel, J. (2008). Hearing screening and diagnostic evaluation of children with uniolateral and mild bilateral hearing loss. *Trends in Amplification, 12*(1), 27.

Scott, C. M. (2014). Clinical forum: One size does not fit all: Improving clinical practice in older children and adolescents with language and learning disorders. *Language, Speech, and Hearing Services in Schools, 45,* 145–152.

Seal, B. C. (2004). *Best practices in educational interpreting.* Boston, MA: Pearson.

Seal, B. C. (2014). Speech development for children with hearing impairment: Ling revisited. In R. H. Hull (Ed.), *Aural rehabilitation: Serving children and adults.* San Diego, CA: Singular.

Seal, B. C., Nussbaum, D. B., Belzner, K. A., Scott, S., & Waddy-Smith, B (2011). Consonant and sign phoneme acquisition in signing children following cochlear implantation. *Cochlear Implants International, 12,* 34–43.

Section 504 of the Rehabilitation Act of 1973, Pub. L. No. 93-112, 87 Stat. 394 (Sept. 26, 1973), codified at 29 U.S.C. § 701.

Shaver, D. M., Marschark, M., Newman, L., & Marder, C. (2014). Who is where? Characteristics of deaf and hard-of-hearing students in regular and special schools. *Journal of Deaf Studies and Deaf Education, 19,* 203–219.

Smith, R. J. H., Shearer, A. E., Hildebrand, M. S., & Van Camp, G. (2014). Deafness and hereditary hearing loss overview. In R. A. Pagon (Ed.), *GeneReviews.* Retrieved from http://www.ncbi.nlm.nih.gov/books/NBK1116/

Stone, P. (1988*). Blueprint for developing conversational competency: A planning/instruction model with detailed scenarios.* In K. Anderson & K. Arnoldi, (2011), *Building skills for success in the fast-paced classroom: Optimizing achievement for students with hearing loss.* Hillsboro, OR: Butte Publications.

Sweigert, P. D. (2012). Understanding the importance of the partner in communication development of individuals with sensory and multiple disabilities. *Perspectives on Augmentative and Alternative Communication, 12,* 167–173.

Traxler, C. B. (2000). The Stanford Achievement Test, 9th edition: National norming and performance standards for deaf and hard-of-hearing children. *Journal of Deaf Studies and Deaf Education, 5,* 337–348.

U.S. Department of Education (2014). *Thirty-sixth annual report to Congress on the implementation of the Individuals with Disability Education Act.* Washington, DC: Office of Special Education and Rehabilitation Services and Office of Special Education Programs. Retrieved from http://www2.ed.gov/about/reports/annual/osep/2014/parts-b-c/36th-idea-arc.pdf

U.S. Department of Education's Office of Civil Rights. (2010). *Guidelines for educators and administrators for implementing Section 504 of the Rehabilitation Act of 1973: Subpart D.* Washington, DC: U.S. Department of Education. Retrieved from https://doe.sd.gov/oess/documents/sped_section504_Guidelines.pdf

Wechsler, D. (2003). *Wechsler Intelligence Scale for Children* (4th ed.). San Antonio, TX: Psychological Corporation.

Williams, C. (2004). Emergent literacy of deaf children. *Journal of Deaf Studies and Deaf Education, 9,* 352–365.

Williams, K. T. (2007). *Expressive Vocabulary Test (EVT)-2.* San Antonio, TX: Pearson.

Woodcock, R. W., McGrew, K. S., & Mather, N. (2001, 2007). *The Woodcock-Johnson III Tests of Achievement (WJ III ACH).* Rolling Meadows, IL: Riverside.

World Health Organization. (2015). *International Classification of Functioning, Disability and Health.* Retrieved from http://www.who.int/classifications/icf/icf_more/en/

Yoshinaga-Itano, C. (2003). Screening to early identification and intervention: Discovering predictors to successful outcomes for children with significant hearing loss. *Journal of Deaf Studies and Deaf Education, 8,* 11–30.

Zimmerman, I. L., Steiner, V., & Pond, R. E. (2002). *Preschool Language Scale, Fourth edition (PLS-4) English edition.* San Antonio, TX: Pearson.

CHAPTER 7

Students With Visual Impairment or Deaf-Blindness

Julie Durando

How often do students use their vision during the typical school day? To answer this, think of all the visual supports that are available in the typical classroom to support student achievement in Common Core State Standards (CCSS). Some standards have visual components; take for example,

- CCSS.ELA-LITERACY.RL.5.7: Analyze how visual and multimedia elements contribute to the meaning, tone, or beauty of a text (e.g., graphic novel, multimedia presentation of fiction, folktale, myth, poem).

As a speech-language pathologist (SLP), you commonly rely on a student's use of vision when providing services for modeling articulation or social skills, augmentative communication systems, picture communication, picture schedules, or when conducting assessments. Of course, visual supports used in interventions and communication systems will only be useful if the child can see them as intended. So what do you do when the child does not see them? How can you tell when the child is missing out on visual information? What do you do when the child has both vision and hearing loss?

Fortunately, teachers of students with visual impairments (TVIs) specialize in strategies and skills to maximize a student's access to the communication, materials, and activities in the educational environment. The role of a TVI on the educational team includes supporting the other team members in consistently implementing these skills and strategies throughout the student's educational program. SLPs should be familiar with some basic characteristics of students with visual impairments and deaf-blindness and be able to recognize the basic behaviors that indicate a child is missing visual information. This knowledge will help to identify situations that require the support of the TVI and better prepare for implementation of the recommendations. This chapter describes types of visual impairments and the implications on CCSS that an SLP should consider when providing services to a student with visual impairments, including those with deaf-blindness or multiple disabilities.

CHARACTERISTICS OF CHILDREN WITH VISUAL IMPAIRMENTS OR DEAF-BLINDNESS

Although estimates vary, sighted children receive about 80% of what they learn through their vision, and as much as 40% of our brain is devoted to the vision process (American Optometric Association, 2014; Titiro, 2008). The benefits of visual information in understanding spoken words, both in and out of context, have been demonstrated by research (Helfer, 1997). Children with visual impairments require thoughtfully planned accommodations to access this same information for cognitive, language, and social development that children with normal sight and hearing access incidentally. Simply enlarging text or pictures does not benefit every child with a visual impairment. Giving a miniature object, such as a toy bus, does not provide a child who is totally blind with the same information that a picture of a bus provides to a child with sight. The type of accommodation that is helpful to a student with blindness or visual impairments depends on a number of factors including the sensory information available to the child and the concepts the child has already developed.

Types of Visual Impairment

Many of us take the complexity of sight for granted. The following text box is a simplified version of the basic steps involved in looking at this book.

The muscles attached to the eye aim the eyes at the words on the page. Light enters the eyes through the clear window of the cornea. The pupil constricts or dilates to allow in just the right amount of light. Little muscles attached to the pliable lens contract or relax to focus the light on the back of the eye where it is gathered by rod and cone receptors on the retina. The retina sends the information through the optic nerve to the occipital lobe of the brain where it is processed. The brain then determines what information is important (the text on the page) and what can be ignored (the background of the page and any imperfections or smudges on the paper). The brain also compares the visual information to what it has already learned to make meaning of the text.

Visual impairment may result from damage to the structures involved in any one or several of these steps. This section will review the characteristics and implications of the basic types of visual impairments. However, it is important to realize the implications are unique for each student, and collaboration with the teacher for students with visual impairments will be necessary to provide individualized accommodations.

Total Blindness

Total blindness, also noted in medical reports as "No Light Perception (NLP)" is the absence of any sight. Approximately 10% of children identified with visual impairments are reported to have total blindness (Hatton, Ivy, & Boyer, 2013). Individuals without light perception rely on their other senses to gather information about the world around them. Total blindness can impact a child's willingness or unwillingness to explore the environment, how the child interacts socially, and concept development. Early intervention can help parents recognize unique behaviors, such as a baby engaging with them by quieting when the parent talks. This understanding can help foster the bonding that usually occurs with eye contact and imitation.

Children with visual impairments may walk later because they do not have visual incentives to move forward or because they do not feel safe or have the balance to try to stand. Some blind children walk with a wide gait, placing their feet more than shoulder width apart. Orientation and mobility specialists are trained to work with children with visual impairments to safely, and gracefully, move through their environment (Koenig & Holbrook, 2000b). This includes teaching a child how to use a cane, or in the case of a toddler or young child, how to use a pre-cane, which may or may not provide some support similar to that of a push-toy typically used by a toddler just starting to walk (Skellenger, 1999). Helping a child to feel safe and confident that there are no obstacles in his or her immediate space encourages exploration of the environment and promotes concept development. In the school setting, a child who is blind may need time to tactually explore a room the first few times he or she enters it to feel comfortable with where the tables and chairs are or what produces noises, such as an air vent or printer. If working with a child in a new environment other than the classroom, it may be useful to consult with the child's orientation and mobility specialist for suggestions or assistance in orienting the student to the new setting.

Contrary to popular beliefs, people with total blindness do not have innate super-hearing or touch senses. These senses must be developed through meaningful learning opportunities. The plasticity of the brain does allow the parts of the brain usually used for visual processing and memories to be reassigned to tactile or auditory information. For example, activation of the primary visual cortex has been found not just when a person who is blind reads braille, but also when a person with sight spends an extensive time blindfolded. This reorganization in the brain is reduced when a person who is blind spends several weeks without reading braille and when the person who is sighted no longer wears the blindfold; however, it regenerates once braille reading or wearing a blindfold resumes and, thus, demonstrates that these skills require frequent practice and experience to be developed and maintained (Hannan, 2006).

Materials for a child with total blindness most often need to be tactual. Once again, consulting with the student's TVI to determine the exact specifications is important. Knowing the age the child became blind can also help to determine if the child might have acquired visual concepts. A child who lost sight after a car accident at the age of 6 will have very different visual concepts from a child who was blind from birth. Using real or whole objects is preferable to using pictures adapted with raised lines (e.g., tracing the drawing in glue to make the lines raised), because the pictures rely on visual characteristics not available without vision, especially with large objects, such as a bus or house. Providing the brailled word while exploring the real object can be more meaningful.

Light Perception and Projection

An individual with light perception can only perceive the presence or absence of light. Light projection is the ability to perceive the direction of the light source (Cassin & Solomon, 1990). This information can be useful in orienting to the environment. For example, if a classroom has windows down the back wall, the child may use the light source to determine which direction he or she is facing. From an educational standpoint, a child with only light perception requires most of the same educational considerations as a child with total blindness.

Acuity

Acuity loss refers to how clearly one sees. Acuity is measured at 20 feet with best possible correction (wearing glasses or contacts) and is reported as a fraction that compares to a person with normal vision. For instance, 20/20 would be interpreted as the individual seeing clearly at 20 feet what a person with normal vision sees clearly at 20 feet. Legal blindness due to an acuity loss is defined as the individual seeing clearly at 20 feet what a person with normal vision sees clearly at 200 feet in his or her better eye wearing corrective glasses or contacts (Koestler, 1976). In an educational setting, an acuity of 20/70 or worse with correction is generally considered to have a significant impact and requires accommodations and/or special education services (Hatton et al., 2013). Acuity loss can affect near vision, which is used in reading, differently from distance vision, which is used to watch a teacher model a skill or to read information from a whiteboard in the front of a classroom.

A child with acuity loss may squint or hold items very close to his or her face. A challenge when working with a child who has acuity loss is that it can be dif-

ficult to determine what level of detail the child can see. When trying to determine what a child can see, avoid asking the question, "Can you see this?" Children will likely answer "yes" either to please you or because they see something in the spot you are indicating and do not realize there are details they are missing. Instead, ask him or her to describe what he or she sees. For example, can he or she make out the letters on the whiteboard fast enough to keep up with instruction? Can he or she see the details in a picture that will help them read the emotions on faces to understand the context? Can he or she see the details on a picture to be used for communication? Pay attention to the speed and ease of the child's answer. If it is a strain, accommodations will need to be made to ensure he or she can benefit from the instruction without causing headaches and fatigue. The child's TVI can provide guidance and recommendations for implementing strategies and presenting materials or devices.

Field Loss

Field of vision is everything a person can see without moving his or her eyes or shifting gaze (Riordan-Eva & Cunningham, 2008). Field loss does not affect acuity; however, an individual could have both a field loss and an acuity loss at the same time. Field loss can result in tunnel vision, holes or blind spots in the vision, or hemianopsia, the loss of vision on one half of the visual field, which is sometimes due to a brain injury or stroke. A person is considered legally blind if his or her visual field in the better eye is 20 degrees or less (Koestler, 1976). An individual with a field loss may hold his or her head at an unusual angle when walking or reading.

It may appear that the person is looking above or to the side of you as he or she is talking to you. This should not be confused with avoiding eye contact or ignoring you, rather, the individual is using his or her best vision to look at you. The student's TVI can help recommend how to best present information to the student. In general,

- Allow the student to adjust head position or position materials according to his or her preference.
- Do not enlarge materials. A field loss reduces how much can be seen at one time, requiring the student to scan to a page systematically, remembering what was already viewed and mentally combining it to understand the bigger picture or sentence. Enlargement exaggerates this challenge and makes viewing materials more laborious.

Did you know you have a blind spot?

Everyone has a blind spot where your optic nerve leaves the retina. The brain naturally fills in this spot so we do not notice it. Try this: On a blank sheet of paper, make a dot; then, 4 inches to the right make an X. Cover your left eye. Hold the paper about 6 inches from your nose with the dot straight in front of your right eye. You should see the X in your peripheral vision, but maintain your focus on the dot. Slowly move the paper away from your face, staring at the dot and keeping it straight in front of your right eye. At some point, the X will fall into your blind spot and seem to disappear. Notice how there does not seem to be a hole in the paper.

Ocular Movement

After 6 months of age, the eyes should move smoothly together. The term *strabismus* refers to when the eyes are not in alignment. One or both eyes may drift in any direction away from the focus. Strabismus can be lessened or corrected with better outcomes if it is treated before the age of 2 years. If untreated, the discrepancy between the eyes can cause a loss of acuity in one eye. *Nystagmus* is used to describe the condition when eyes do not move smoothly, but instead, seem to have a jerky movement or rhythmic oscillations (Riordan-Eva & Hoyt, 2008). Most often, nystagmus occurs along with another condition. It sometimes gets worse or more evident with visual fatigue, such as after the child has been reading for 20 min. Consult with the student's TVI for optimal positioning of materials and recommendations for frequency of visual breaks to prevent fatigue and discomfort.

Causes of Visual Impairments and Blindness

Blindness and visual impairments may be caused by a variety of factors, including congenital abnormalities, congenital illness or exposures, injury to the brain or eye, or muscle imbalances. The effect of these factors on an individual's vision may vary from person to person and impact vision in different ways.

Hatton and her colleagues (2013) conducted a review of referral data from a national registry between 2005 and 2011 that included data from more than 5,000 children, between birth and 3 years of age, in 28 states across the country. In this review, the leading causes of visual impairments and blindness reported were

- *Cortical visual impairment (CVI)* was the most commonly diagnosed visual impairment accounting for 24.9% (Hatton et al., 2013). This type of visual impairment is caused by perinatal hypoxia, prematurity, or hydrocephalus resulting in damage to the part of the brain that processes the visual information sent from the eye (Khetpal & Donahue, 2007). CVI can be challenging to diagnose because it is not apparent during an eye exam in the same way an ocular disease or abnormality would be, such as cataracts. In the case of a child with additional disabilities, the child's vision may be considered less important than other challenges despite the importance of vision's role in development (Dutton & Bax, 2010). Children with CVI may have varying degrees of functional vision that may be affected by other qualities, such as background noise and visual clutter in the sensory environment. Research has found that many children can improve their use of functional vision when given appropriate accommodations (Khetpal & Donahue, 2007; Lantzy & Lantzy, 2010).
- *Retinopathy of prematurity (ROP)* was the second most commonly diagnosed visual impairment at 11.8% of reported cases, a decreased rate compared to previous years (Hatton et al., 2013). ROP occurs in children born very early (before 30 weeks' gestational age) and at a very low birth weight (less than 1,500 g) when the delicate retina

are still developing. Although current laser treatments and careful monitoring are improving outcomes for many children, the risk of damage to the retina and retinal detachment can result in poor acuity, blind spots, field loss, and even total blindness (Chang & Capone, 2014).

- *Optic nerve hypoplasia (ONH)* is characterized by underdevelopment of the nerve that transmits visual information from the eye to the brain. ONH increased slightly since the previous study to 11.4% of all reported cases (Hatton et al., 2013). ONH may occur sporadically or as the result of prenatal exposure to alcohol, lysergic-acid-diethylamide (LSD), phencyclidine (PCP), cytomegalovirus (CMV), or maternal diabetes (Wright, 2003). In most cases, it occurs in both eyes and may occur along with endocrine abnormalities and central nervous system malformations.

The remaining categories were structural disorders (7.9%), retinal disorders (5.5%), and albinism (4.5%), described in case study one. Approximately two-thirds of the children registered were found to have additional disabilities or developmental delays.

Causes of Deaf–Blindness

The leading causes of deaf-blindness relate to heredity, extreme prematurity, pre- and postnatal complications, and infectious diseases (Killoran, 2007). Three of the more common etiologies are as follows:

- The CHARGE syndrome acronym is based on the major characteristics of the disorder: coloboma (a cleft in the eye that may cause field loss), heart defect, atresia choanae (narrowing of one or both nasal passages), delays or abnormalities in growth and development, genital abnormality, and ear abnormality. Note that the "r" in CHARGE stood for an outdated term; however, the acronym has not been changed. Individuals with CHARGE syndrome have distinctive facial characteristics, including asymmetric features and a square shape and varying degrees of medical complications, cognitive function, and sensory implications. In addition to the senses of vision and hearing, this syndrome can affect the sense of smell and balance (National Library of Medicine, 2008).

- Usher syndrome is a genetic condition that impacts vision and hearing differently, depending on which of the three types of the syndrome an individual has. The three types of Usher syndrome are divided into subtypes that are beyond the scope of this text. The vision loss associated with Usher syndrome is caused by retinitis pigmentosa (RP) which begins as difficulty seeing at night and then, slowly peripheral vision is reduced by blind spots, eventually leading to tunnel vision. Acuity can sometimes be reduced, especially if cataracts develop (National Library of Medicine, 2007).
  - Type I typically causes an individual to be born deaf or lose most hearing by the age of one, to have difficulties with balance, and to experience vision loss beginning in childhood.
  - Type II typically causes an individual to have mild to severe hearing loss from birth and vision loss that begins in adolescence or adulthood.
  - Individuals with Type III are born with typical vision and hearing, then begin progressively losing hearing in late childhood. Retinitis pigmentosa begins late in childhood or during adolescence (National Library of Medicine, 2007).

- Congenital cytomegalovirus (CMV) infection can cause sensorineural hearing loss, vision loss, cognitive disabilities, seizures, and other abnormalities (Swanson & Schleiss, 2013). Hearing loss may be unilateral or bilateral and progressive. Specific causes of vision loss associated with CMV include cataracts, micropthalmia (small eyes), optic atrophy, and optic disk malformation (Thomas & Graham, 2008).

CHILDREN WITH ADDITIONAL DISABILITIES

Children may have a wide range of functional vision and hearing as well as additional disabilities. Children with multiple disabilities are more likely to have sensory impairments (Beange, Lennox, & Parmenter, 1999). Unfortunately, screenings by researchers found more than half of the sensory impairments in individuals with multiple and/or intellectual disabilities were unidentified (Fellinger, Holzinger, Dirmhirn, van Dijk, & Goldberg, 2009; Hild, Hay, Baumann, Montgomery, Euler, & Neumann, 2008). The impact of sensory loss may be even greater in individuals who have intellectual disabilities (Beange et al., 1999). Therefore, if the behaviors described that indicate poor acuity, field loss, or other visual impairments are recognized in a child not currently identified to have a visual impairment, the educational team should consider the need for referral. Once the team understands what sensory information a student perceives, they can collaborate by designing accommodations and interventions to maximize the student's access to sensory information and to optimize the development of concepts, communication, and emotional security.

AUTISM AND VISUAL IMPAIRMENTS

Individuals with blindness and visual impairments sometimes exhibit stereotypical behaviors that could be associated with autism, such as rocking or flapping hand movements. These behaviors may serve to provide a sense of regulation for the individual (van Dijk, Klomberg, & Nelson, 1997). They may also add to the difficulty of accurately determining if a student with visual impairments also has autism (Fink & Borchert, 2011; Williams, Fink, Zamora, & Borchert, 2014). Although research is ongoing in this area, preliminary findings note that some characteristics are common to both children with severe visual impairments as well as individuals with autism, including interpreting repetitive or stereotypic hand movements, noise sensitivity, limited facial expressions, the absence of pointing, and difficulty with imaginary play and establishing friendships. However, these characteristics should be inter-

preted cautiously, as they were not found to be clinically significant in diagnosing autism in children with severe visual impairments (Williams et al., 2014). Children with visual impairments have also been found to have deficits in pragmatics, similar to those found in children with autism (Tadic, Pring, & Dale, 2010). Areas of deficits that have been found to be more reliable to identify autism in blind children include responding appropriately to shared enjoyment, offering comfort, and directing the attention of others (Williams et al., 2014). Behaviors such as not making eye contact or reacting to interaction by quieting or stilling should not be confused as disengagement (Peltokorpi & Huttunen, 2008). Focusing on nonvisual interventions and strategies, such as responding more to a child's gestures and using tactile contact to establish joint attention, can better help a child with visual impairment to expand communicative and social development (Peltokorpi & Huttunen, 2008; van Dijk et al., 1997).

Stereotypic Behaviors

Some children who are blind, particularly those with more severe visual impairment, may engage in behaviors, such as body rocking, repetitive head movements, or eye poking or pressing. Sometimes, these behaviors decrease as a child matures, obtains more advanced motor development, or learns other ways to obtain an equivalent stimulation. The behaviors may be more intense or persistent in children with multiple disabilities (Molloy & Rowe, 2011).

CHILDREN WITH COMBINED VISION AND HEARING LOSS

The combined effect of vision and hearing loss has a much greater impact than simply adding a loss to an existing vision loss or hearing loss (Arnold, 1998; Miles, 2008). Consider that you are in a noisy, crowded restaurant and you are speaking to a friend holding a menu blocking her face. You might ask her to put the menu down to help you "hear" her better. Most likely, you do not consciously read lips; however, the visual information is still useful. The same is true for students in a classroom. If a student with hearing loss is sitting too far away from the teacher to gain useful visual information, he or she will have greater difficulty learning from the instruction. Similarly, if a teacher is pointing out to the class a country on the globe, a child who is blind can listen to the description and follow along on a tactual globe or map. In both of these examples, the student is using his or her remaining senses to access the content in the classroom. These examples also assume that the child has the language needed to understand the words being presented.

Much of what a child learns is learned incidentally, meaning that the child learns it without someone specifically identifying the information. For example, a child sees his or her parent dialing a telephone, holding it to his or her ear and speaking into it. The child will pick up the phone and imitate the actions he or she observed the parent doing earlier. A blind child does not see the parent pick up the telephone and does not see the parent dial. However, he or she may hear the parent talking or the phone ringing and inquire about it. If the child has deaf-blindness, he or she may not have any awareness of the phone or the conversation. Even a child with some vision may see the parent walk across the room but not see enough detail to see that she picked up the phone. The absence of incidental information reduces opportunities for concept, language, and literacy development. A child who is blind needs to be brought close to objects in order to explore them tactually. A child with visual impairment would need to be close enough to see the object clearly and may still need to be able to explore tactually. One challenge with this need, especially in a busy classroom setting, is that it takes much longer for a child with blindness or visual impairments to gain the same amount of information that his sighted peers gain very quickly from looking at instructional materials. This requires the teacher to plan ahead and possibly provide the student with his or her own set of materials to explore as the teacher explains the lesson.

EDUCATIONAL SERVICES

The Individuals with Disabilities Education Improvement Act (IDEA; 2004) defines visual impairment, including blindness, as "impairment in vision that, even with correction, adversely affects a child's educational performance. The term includes both partial sight and blindness (34 CFR §300.8(c)(13))." In most states, children are eligible for services and accommodations under the category of visual impairments if they have been determined to have one of the following: acuity of 20/70 or worse with correction; a visual field of 20 degrees or less; or a functional loss of vision determined to impact learning (Hatton et al., 2013).

If the child with visual impairment is also deaf or hard of hearing, he or she would be more appropriately eligible under the category of deaf-blindness. The title of this category can cause people to presume that in order to qualify a student would not have usable vision or hearing. However, deaf-blindness is defined in IDEA as "concomitant hearing and visual impairments, the combination of which causes such severe communication and other developmental and educational needs that they cannot be accommodated in special education programs solely for children with deafness or children with blindness" (IDEA, 34 CFR § 300.8(c)(2), 2004). In other words, if the student's vision is not sufficient to gain what is not heard and the child does not hear well enough to catch what is not seen, he or she is considered to have deaf-blindness.

It is difficult to accurately determine the number of students currently receiving services as students with blindness and visual impairment, because students who receive services under more than two categories may not be reported with vision impairment as the primary disability. The Federal Quota Census Data indicates that 60,393 students were registered to be eligible to receive adapted materials from the American Printing House for the Blind (APH), including braille, auditory, and tactile products (2014). These materials are typically ordered by the teacher for students with visual impairments.

Teachers of Students With Vision Impairment

Teachers of students with vision impairment are trained at the undergraduate or graduate level to assess the educational needs related to visual impairment, adapt materials, and teach compensatory skills (which are also referred to in the field as the expanded core curriculum). Note the role of TVIs should not be confused with a vision therapist. Vision therapists are trained and certified to work in clinical, not educational, settings (Koenig & Holbrook, 2000b). During the initial eligibility process and at triannual reviews, the teacher of students with visual impairments will conduct a functional vision assessment (FVA) and a learning media assessment (LMA) to determine how the student uses his or her senses and the best ways to provide materials and instruction to a student. These assessments then guide the instruction and services provided to the student.

Functional Vision

Functional vision refers to the useful vision an individual can use during daily activities. More than 90% of individuals with visual impairments have enough residual vision to perceive light and 82% can perceive objects (Hatton et al., 2013). "Perception" means the individual has enough visual information to know that an object is at an approximate location. One should not assume that a student can identify the object or visually discriminate any details of the object, based solely on the fact that he or she looks toward or reaches for the object. The FVA is conducted by reviewing the student's medical eye report, observing the student in a variety of educational settings, and directly assessing visual skills. The purpose is to determine what factors in the educational environment help or hinder the child's use of vision. These factors include types of lighting, visual clutter, contrast, print size, the use of optical devices, fatigue, seating, and many others. The TVI then prepares a report of the assessment results describing recommendations for the educational team to address each of these factors (Koenig et al., 2000).

Learning Media

Learning media include standard print, large print, braille, auditory books and materials, tactile graphics, digital media, and other forms of adapted materials. A LMA is conducted by the TVI through both observation, discussion with other team members, and direct assessment. This assessment considers the student's learning in regard to all senses to determine the preferred sensory channels (Koenig et al., 2000). Ultimately, the assessment aims to identify the most efficient and effective primary and secondary media forms for the student to use.

DISCUSSION OF PRINCIPLES OF INSTRUCTION FOR THIS POPULATION

Ensuring that children with visual impairments and deaf-blindness receive a quality education hinges on providing them with the same information available to their peers. This can take a significant amount of time and planning. Consider this in the context of a science lesson exploring the parts of a flower. The lesson might begin with planting the seeds, watering it each day, waiting, and then watching it grow. The importance of language and vocabulary are obvious in this scenario. If the child already knows the basic vocabulary terms involved in the lesson, the teacher

can use some visual descriptions as he or she puts the seed into the dirt and has another child pour the water on it. However, if the child is not familiar with the concepts associated with seed, soil, water, and plant, then it will be meaningless for the child to just hear them described.

Concepts must be developed by meaningful hands-on experiences. For example, in advance of the actual planting of the seed, working on the concept of soil could involve going outside and digging small samples from the schoolyard. By allowing the child to feel the difference between the dirt the grass is growing in, the dirt of the baseball diamond, the potting soil, and sand, the student can compare and contrast the different types of dirt. The lesson can be tied in with literature by having the students select from the samples which type of dirt would be similar to the setting in each story. A science experiment could be conducted by adding a set amount of water to each sample and observing which dries out the fastest. These activities allow the child to gain a greater understanding of the difference between the dirt in the schoolyard and the soil used for potted plants than a more rote explanation would provide. Many of these differences can be obtained with a fast glance. For a child with visual impairment, richer experiences are needed to understand the concept of the words we use every day (Koenig & Holbrook, 2000a).

In the primary grades, teachers may hold up big books and point to the words on the page as they read. Teachers often write key words on the board during lessons. It is important that children with visual impairments also have an opportunity to "see" these words. Having a teacher speak what he or she is writing on the board does not give the child with visual impairments an equivalent experience. The child with visual impairments would need his or her own print copy modified to meet the visual needs for size, contrast, or complexity; a braille copy; or a tactile form that may include tactile symbols or object symbols.

SLPs and general educators should review the materials selected for a session to see if there are any concerns about the size, contrast, or complexity to meet the recommendations provided in the functional vision assessment by the TVI. If using objects, be sure they are not miniatures, and realize that tactile drawings are extremely abstract and will not be meaningful for a student who has never seen the image being represented. Use real, full-size objects or parts of the object, if large. Many pictures and symbols are based on visual characteristics that are not distinguishable enough to be meaningful to an individual with visual impairments in the natural environment. These details may be too small, such as the facial characteristics used to make a smiley face or frowning face. Or, the characteristics may be based on the shape of an object too large to be gathered by touch, such as the commonly used shape of a house.

Some educators hold the misconception that children with visual impairments and multiple disabilities do not need or benefit from braille, tangible symbols, or even large print until they demonstrate readiness skills and knowledge of language. Research has found this to be wrong, even for the children with the most severe additional disabilities and most significant developmental delays. In fact, a study investigating the acquisition of tangible symbol recognition in children with multiple disabilities and visual impairment found that student skill levels in the areas of play, intention-

ality, symbolism, and language did not predict achievement. What did contribute to achievement was the consistent use of meaningful symbols within daily routines (Trief, Cascella, & Bruce, 2013).

> ## IMPLEMENTING THE CCSS FOR STUDENTS WITH VISUAL IMPAIRMENTS AND DEAF-BLINDNESS

The following case studies illustrate how educators might approach helping a variety of students with visual impairments and deaf-blindness to achieve success in meeting various CCSS.

Case Study One: Lavon

Lavon is a 10-year-old boy who is in a general education fifth-grade classroom. He was born with albinism, a genetic condition that caused him to have far less pigment in his skin, hair, and eyes than his family members. He has light skin, curly platinum blond hair, and light blue eyes. Lavon needs to protect his skin and eyes from the sun due to the lack of pigment. He often prefers to wear dark tinted glasses, both inside and outside, to protect his sensitive eyes from light.

Lavon's Individualized Education Program (IEP) team includes Lavon and his parents, his general education teacher, a SLP, a teacher TVI, an orientation and mobility instructor, and a school administrator. According to the FVA conducted by his teacher TVI, Lavon has acuity loss, light sensitivity, and occasionally nystagmus. Lavon's visual acuity is 20/400 with his glasses on; therefore, he qualifies as legally blind and is eligible to receive materials available on quota funds from the American Printing House for the Blind. Although he does not have a field loss, his best vision for detail, or focal point, is slightly off center due to abnormalities in his retina. This causes him to have a tendency to tilt his head a bit when he looks at things. He needs visual demonstrations to be presented within 2 feet and can use a video magnifier to view pictures or graphics. He also sits in the front row of his classroom.

Lavon can spot large objects and people from 8 feet away; however, he does not see them clearly enough to recognize or identify them until they are within 2 feet. Lavon can walk independently. He uses his cane to help him detect uneven surfaces, compensate for his poor depth perception, and avoid other potential dangers when not in familiar areas, like his home or classroom. He is able to navigate independently around his school and to the park, which is a block from his home. His older brother or a friend will tag along with him in the neighborhood. He practices locating crosswalks and street crossing techniques with his orientation and mobility instructor for 30 minutes each week. When traveling unfamiliar routes, Lavon will use a sighted guide technique of taking the arm of another person and walking one step behind. His teachers and classmates received training at the beginning of the year to ensure they understood the basic guidelines of being a sighted guide, such as always allowing Lavon to take their arm or wrist if they are much taller, as opposed to taking his hand; pausing before going up or down stairs; and not walking away from him unless he is in contact with a wall, railing, or other stable object (American Foundation for the Blind, n.d.).

Lavon has been fascinated with trains since riding one during a summer camp after second grade. Each month, he borrows a different braille book about trains from National Library Service for the Blind and Physically Handicapped (NLS) and reads it cover to cover. He can also read large print; however, it must be at least a 36-point font and his eyes fatigue quickly, which is evident by their rapid involuntary movements (nystagmus). He prefers using braille for reading books and will use a screen reader to access the Internet and computer programs needed to complete his homework.

Lavon uses an electronic braille note taker to complete his classwork. The braille note taker has a refreshable braille display and memory similar to that of a small computer. He can store all of his textbooks and assignments on it. This type of device has been found to increase a student's engagement in writing and improve student writing skills (Kamei-Hannan & Lawson, 2012). He types directly into the note taker at his seat and then connects the note taker to the classroom computer to e-mail the information to his teacher. She grades it and returns the file to him so that he can read her comments on the device or computer. The documents can be printed on a regular printer or a braille printer, as well. All of his textbooks are ordered in braille, well in advance of the upcoming school year. His teacher gives digital copies of any printed material that will be used in class, including worksheets and tests, to his teacher of students with visual impairments so the material can be brailled in time for him to use with his class.

Lavon loves math and can complete most arithmetic, using his abacus (his equivalent of paper and pencil), faster than his peers can complete it using paper and pencil. His proficiency with the abacus became especially important last year as the curriculum covered multiplication of two-digit numbers, more than he could compute mentally. His goals focused on learning to use tactile graphics as an accommodation for standards involving two-dimensional figures, such as

- CCSS.MATH.CONTENT.4.G.A.2: Classify two-dimensional figures based on the presence or absence of parallel or perpendicular lines, or the presence or absence of angles of a specified size. Recognize right triangles as a category, and identify right triangles.
- CCSS.MATH.CONTENT.4.G.A.3: Recognize a line of symmetry for a two-dimensional figure as a line across the figure, such that the figure can be folded along the line into matching parts. Identify line-symmetric figures, and draw lines of symmetry.

Lavon reads just slightly below his grade level. The deficit is mainly in understanding figurative language or stories based on fantasy or imagination. For example, last year when his class was studying mythology to address CCSS.ELA-LITERACY.RL.4.4 (see below), Lavon was confused by use of the word "harp" as it related to the story of King Phineus.

- CCSS.ELA-LITERACY.RL.4.4: Determine the meaning of words and phrases as they are used in a text, including those that allude to significant characters found in mythology (e.g., Herculean).

Lavon struggled to understand the word "harp" beyond the musical instrument that he had learned about in music. He also had difficulty with CCSS.ELA-

LITERACY.SL.4.1 (see below) and thus had trouble following pragmatic rules and assuming some roles during class and small group discussion, because he missed the subtle visual cues used by his classmates to indicate they are finished talking, wish to have a turn, or have different levels of agreement with what has been said.

- CCSS.ELA-LITERACY.SL.4.1: Engage effectively in a range of collaborative discussions (one on one, in groups, and teacher led) with diverse partners on Grade 4 topics and texts, building on others' ideas and expressing their own clearly.

Lavon receives speech-language services to address his vocabulary needs with figurative language, as well as to address pragmatic deficits. His pragmatic deficits of gauging responses of others, adjusting language, not interrupting, or continuing to talk when another person is wanting a turn are most noticeable in special areas and reading group. His SLP sees him weekly during his reading class and in a small group setting to work on pragmatics. During the small group sessions, his SLP provides additional supports, developed in collaboration with the teacher of students with visual impairments, to focus on the subtle social cues and actions during dialogue with his peers that he is, otherwise, unable to gain incidentally. He also does not incidentally gain information about what his peers are doing to understand the social norms; this must be specifically taught (Silberman, 2000). Occasionally, his TVI will join the class during small reading group discussion to monitor his progress and identify additional strategies that may help achievement. His goals work on understanding metaphors, interrupting, and continuing to talk without giving another person a turn in the conversation, all of which address the following standards:

- CCSS.ELA-LITERACY.SL.5.1: Engage effectively in a range of collaborative discussions (one on one, in groups, and teacher led) with diverse partners on Grade 5 topics and texts, building on others' ideas and expressing their own clearly.
- CCSS.ELA-LITERACY.RL.5.4: Determine the meanings of words and phrases as they are used in a text, including figurative language such as metaphors and similes.
- CCSS.ELA-LITERACY.RL.5.7: Analyze how visual and multimedia elements contribute to the meaning, tone, or beauty of a text (e.g., graphic novel, multimedia presentation of fiction, folktale, myth, poem).

Case Study Two: Tina

Tina is 6 years old with curly blond hair and a huge smile. She has quadriplegic cerebral palsy and cortical visual impairment. She uses a wheelchair. She seems to prefer exploring objects and materials with her left hand; however, her movements are not yet refined enough to use for indicating choices. She will often use facial expressions to respond to "yes" and "no" questions with familiar people. Her speech services focus on programming her augmentative communication device for the vocabulary. Her SLP and her classroom teacher collaboratively select vocabulary for upcoming teaching units,

as well as functional vocabulary words, to request help and socialize with peers.

Tina's goals also focus on feeding and swallowing. The teacher for students with visual impairments consults with the SLP on this goal quarterly to embed strategies to give visual and tactile cues to Tina during meals. For example, since she has difficulty processing visual information in noisy environments, such as the cafeteria, it is important to provide tactile information about where the spoon is and when it is coming toward her. Although her range of motion is limited, the hand-under-hand strategy is modified to allow her to rest her hand on the arm or elbow of the person feeding her. She can then feel when more food is being scooped onto the spoon and when it is approaching her mouth. Sometimes, she will look toward the spoon. Since this technique was implemented, she has seemed to be more relaxed during mealtimes and has not been startled when the spoon was touched to her mouth. She is also introduced to the items on her plate by being given the opportunity to smell a spoonful of each food as the person feeding her tells her the name of the food.

In her most recent functional vision assessment, her TVI determined she is using her vision under specific circumstances. She notices a person approaching when the person is about 10 feet away. Most objects must be within 3 feet of her for her to notice them. The TVI noted that in settings controlled to reduce background noise and light, Tina is visually attending to simple objects of one or two colors placed against a black background on the tray of her wheelchair. Most times the object must be presented and held in her upper left visual field for 30–60 seconds to allow for her visual latency, which is the time it takes her to process the visual information. She may look away from the object initially, but her gaze will return if the object is held in the same location and she is not distracted by verbal prompts or movements. At first, many of those working with Tina had a difficult time resisting the temptation to move the object when she shifts her gaze. With practice, it became natural to recognize that she is processing the information and needs the object to be in the same place when she is ready to look at it again.

Tina is less distracted by overhead lights but still needs to be facing away from brightly lit windows that attract her gaze. At this point, Tina is not able to visually process two-dimensional items, such as pictures, print, or photographs. She does visually attend to the digital display on an electronic tablet; however, it is unclear how much detail she is seeing. Listening skills are Tina's strength. She listens carefully to the social interactions of others. Her facial expressions indicate that she follows conversations and understands most directions. Her vocabulary is somewhat limited by her experiences and by challenges related to her physical and visual impairments. She often needs extensive explanations of new vocabulary words from a person familiar with her current conceptual knowledge and vocabulary.

Tina's IEP has a strong emphasis on expressive communication. In kindergarten, her "yes" and "no" responses were used most often to assess her understanding. Toward the end of the previous school year, her limited response options became increasingly problematic in demonstrating her understanding in all subjects. For example, in mathematics, she was not able to demonstrate that she could independently count from 1 to 100 (CCSS.MATH. CONTENT.K.CC.A.1).

Her visual impairment has had an impact on her progress, as well. For example, in language arts, she was not able to see the illustrations in the books the class read. This impeded her progress toward

- CCSS.ELA-LITERACY.RL.K.7: With prompting and support, describe the relationship between illustrations and the story in which they appear (e.g., what moment in a story an illustration depicts).

She is beginning to learn to use a two-step auditory scanning device for expressive communication. Setting up the device required extensive collaboration between her parents, her SLP, her physical therapist, her classroom teacher, and her TVI. This team determined that for math she would have the numbers 1–10 included, and the device could also be programmed with some common phrases appropriate for conversations with peers about familiar stories.

Tina's goals are guided and assessed using Dynamic Learning Maps. Her team uses the system to work toward her achievement of the standards using essential elements (Dynamic Learning Maps Consortium, 2013). For example, to focus on

- CCSS.ELA-LITERACY.SL.1.1.B: Build on others' talk in conversations by responding to the comments of others through multiple exchanges.

The team focuses on the essential elements of

- EE.SL.1.1: Participate in conversations with adults.

□ Engage in multiple-turn exchanges with supportive adult.

□ Build on comments or topics imitated by an adult.

□ Use one or two words to ask questions related to personally relevant topics.

The Dynamic Learning Maps also help guide the team in including whole objects in repeated readings and her personal experiences. The objects are helpful in addressing her visual needs for three-dimensional materials, as well as her conceptual development. The objects are first presented to her visually. Her teacher tells her what the object is and then gives her time to visually process it without saying anything else, which would distract her. Once she looks at the object, Tina will indicate she is ready to explore the object by moving her hand slightly toward it. The teacher gives her the object to hold and explore. If physical assistance is needed to help her hold it or to explore details, the hand-under-hand technique is used (see box: Under, Not Over).

Case Study Three: Andre

Andre is 9 years old and is fully included in the third grade at the elementary school in his neighborhood. Due to extensive medical procedures, he was delayed in entering school. Many of his classmates have known Andre since kindergarten and do not seem to notice the unique facial features that are unique to children with CHARGE syndrome. The malformation of his ear causes difficulties with his balance, and although he walks independently within his home and classroom, he uses a wheelchair for longer distances,

such as going to the cafeteria or bus. He loves to explore his environment when he can stand close enough to a wall, furniture, or an adult for extra support. When wearing his bone-anchored hearing aid (BAHA), he hears speech at close range in environments with low levels of background noise. In the classroom, he uses an FM system to improve the signal-to-noise ratio. He learned sign language during the time he had a tracheostomy. Even though it was removed when he was 4 years old, he still uses sign language for expressive communication.

He sits in a regular student desk and chair, provided that his feet comfortably rest on the ground. Due to his challenges with balance, a slight wobble in a chair or desk becomes a major distraction. If his desk or chair wobbles, he tires more easily as he shifts his focus off the lesson and onto stabilizing his body. His physical therapist consults with his teacher to ensure that his desk and chair are providing adequate stability. After activities requiring balance or high levels of sensory processing, Andre requires a break for 5–10 minutes in a supported and relaxed position. He prefers to rest lying in a bean bag chair in a quiet corner of the classroom.

Andre's coloboma caused a field loss in his upper right field. His functional vision report indicates that he sees well enough to detect large objects from about 10 feet away. However, to identify and clearly see the object he needs to be within 1–2 feet. Sign language needs to be presented to him from within 2 feet and against a solid background with good contrast. Since sign language is his primary means of expressive communication, it is critical for his instruction to include sign language so that he can continue to expand his expressive vocabulary.

Under, Not Over

The technique of providing hand-over-hand guidance is discouraged with children who are blind or deaf-blind for several reasons. First, hand-over-hand guidance limits the information the child can obtain by shifting the child's attention from the fingertips of his or her own hands to the back of the hands where the adult's hands are making contact. Second, controlling a child's hands can increase passivity and reduce his or her willingness to explore independently (Miles, 2003). To get a better sense of this for yourself, try asking a coworker to help you write a sentence using hand-over-hand while you are blindfolded. Can you determine the sentence you "helped" to write? Does the thought of attempting this activity make you too uncomfortable or tacitly defensive to even try it?

Instead of controlling a child's hand, it is preferable to use a technique referred to as hand-under-hand. Just as it sounds, the adult's hands are provided underneath the child's hands. This allows the child to focus his or her attention on the object explored or the actions of the adult. Hand-under-hand can be used in place of visual modeling or pointing. The adult should expect this technique to take longer than it does to use hand-over-hand, especially if the child is new to using it. A child skilled at this technique will slide his or her hands freely from the adult's hands to the object to gain more information about the bigger picture. This should be encouraged, and the adult may need to pause to allow time for this type of exploration. If the child can hear and understand speech, a verbal prompt such as, "follow my hands," can be used to cue him or her that you have something to show or demonstrate. If the child requires a tactile cue, gently place your hand next to the side of or slightly underneath his or her hand and patiently wait for the child to accept your invitation. The time needed to use this technique will likely decrease with practice.

The hand-under-hand technique is also very useful during feeding times. Inviting the child to follow your hands provides valuable information about approach of the spoon or fork toward his or her mouth. If the child has physical challenges that make it difficult to follow your hands, allowing the child to rest a hand on the elbow of your arm will still provide valuable information and likely improve the child's sense of safety and participation during mealtimes.

Throughout all of his daily activities, his intervener, an individual with specialized training in strategies and communication for children with deaf-blindness, signs to him what is said by the teacher, his classmates, or anyone else in the immediate environment who is communicating with him. The intervener is supported by all of the team members and under the direction of the teacher. Most importantly, the intervener communicates to Andre the information about what is going on around him that his classmates gain from their vision and hearing. For example, when entering the classroom in the morning, his intervener explains who is in the room and what activities are occurring. If an unusual noise or event occurs, the intervener gives Andre relevant information to understand the disturbance and feel safe to continue learning in the environment.

Andre's IEP team includes his parents, general education teacher, SLP, TVI, teacher of the deaf and hard of hearing, audiologist, physical therapist, occupational therapist, an intervener, and a school administrator. The complexity of Andre's needs often requires the perspectives and expertise from each of his team members. To achieve this, the entire team meets every quarter to collaboratively plan and problem-solve challenges presented by the standards that will be addressed in the upcoming quarter. The teacher will share a list of new vocabulary terms, and the teacher of the deaf and hard of hearing will review the signs for these terms. His parents will share any experiences Andre may have had that relate to the new vocabulary terms. His TVI and occupational therapist(s) will identify any challenges with seeing or producing the signs. All members work together to decide on any modifications that need to be made, and they are noted in his personalized communication dictionary.

Andre's team continues to collaboratively remediate his skills in phonological awareness, decoding, and relating images to text. Andre's IEP goals last year addressed the following standards:

- CCSS.ELA-LITERACY.RF.2.3: Know and apply grade-level phonics and word analysis skills in decoding words.
- CCSS.ELA-LITERACY.RI.2.7: Explain how specific images (e.g.,

a diagram showing how a machine works) contribute to and clarify a text.
- CCSS.ELA-LITERACY.L.2.4: Determine or clarify the meaning of unknown and multiple-meaning words and phrases based on Grade 2 reading and content, choosing flexibly from an array of strategies.

His goals in third grade continue to address phonological awareness, decoding, and relating images to text. The standards addressed in these goals include

- CCSS.ELA-LITERACY.RF.3.3: Know and apply grade-level phonics and word analysis skills in decoding words.
- CCSS.ELA-LITERACY.RI.3.7: Use information gained from illustrations (e.g., maps, photographs) and the words in a text to demonstrate understanding of the text (e.g., where, when, why, and how key events occur).
- CCSS.ELA-LITERACY.L.3.4: Determine or clarify the meaning of unknown and multiple-meaning word and phrases based on Grade 3 reading and content, choosing flexibly from a range of strategies.

His teacher of students who are deaf or hard-of-hearing works with him twice weekly on phonological awareness using auditory cues (Narr, 2006). His teacher for students with visual impairments works with him to use optical devices as needed to examine the illustrations in his large-print textbooks. Since it takes him longer than his peers take to look at the pictures, he will spend time looking at them in advance. Often, the new vocabulary is reviewed at this time, if it is part of the illustrations. His intervener continues to support his communication by signing what his TVI says to him. All three have learned to adjust to the slow pace that is required for Andre to shift his visual attention between his intervener's signing to the illustration in the book. Even though he is still a little behind his peers, his assessments indicate that he is catching up.

CONCLUDING THOUGHTS

Students with visual impairments or deaf-blindness, including those with additional disabilities, require highly individualized accommodations in order to ensure they can access all of the communication, learning, and social opportunities in their school settings. Teachers of students with visual impairments and orientation and mobility specialists have specialized training in the strategies and skills to contribute to the educational team. Collaboration of all team members is especially important in creating meaningful individualized education programs that ensure these students have the opportunity to achieve the Common Core State Standards. Familiarity with the basic types of visual impairments and behaviors that indicate a student is having visual difficulties can help SLPs better recognize and meet the needs of their students.

REFERENCES

American Foundation for the Blind. (n.d.) *Being a sighted guide*. Retrieved November 8, 2014, from http://www.afb.org/info/friends-and-family/etiquette/being-a-sighted-guide/235

American Optometric Association. (2014). *School-aged vision: 6 to 18 years of age*. Retrieved from http://www.aoa.org/patients-and-public/good-vision-throughout-life/childrens-vision/school-aged-vision-6-to-18-years-of-age?sso=y

American Printing House for the Blind. (2014). *Annual Report 2014: Distribution of eligible students based on the Federal Quota Census of January 7, 2013*. Retrieved November 1, 2014, from http://www.aph.org/federal-quota/dist14.html

Arnold, K. D. (1998). Deaf-blindness. In L. Phelps (Ed.), *Health-related disorders in children and adolescents: A guidebook for understanding and educating* (pp. 224–232). Washington, DC: American Psychological Association. doi:10.1037/10300-032

Beange, H., Lennox, N., & Parmenter, T. R. (1999). Health targets for people with an intellectual disability. *Journal of Intellectual & Developmental Disability, 24*, 283–297.

Cassin, B., & Solomon, S. A. B. (1990). *Dictionary of eye terminology* (2nd ed.). Gainesville, FL: Triad Publishing.

Chang, E., & Capone, A. (2014). Retinopathy of prematurity (ROP). In P. J. Kertes & T. M. Johnson (Eds.), *Evidence-based eye care* (pp. 301–319). Philadelphia, PA: Lippincott Williams & Wilkins.

Dutton, G. N., & Bax, M. (2010). Introduction. In G. N. Dutton & M. Bax (Eds.), *Visual impairment in children due to damage to the brain*. London, UK: MacKeith Press.

Dynamic Learning Maps Consortium. (2013). *Dynamic Learning Maps essential elements for English language arts*. Lawrence, KS: University of Kansas. Retrieved from http://dynamiclearningmaps.org/content/essential-elements

Fellinger, J., Holzinger, D., Dirmhirn, A., van Dijk, J., & Goldberg, D. (2009). Failure to detect deaf-blindness in a population of people with intellectual disability. *Journal of Intellectual Disability Research, 53*(10), 874–881. doi:10.1111/j.1365-2788.2009.01205.x

Fink, C., & Borchert, M. (2011). Optic nerve hypoplasia and autism: Common features of spectrum diseases. *Journal of Visual Impairment & Blindness, 105*(6), 334–338.

Hannan, C. K. (2006). Review of research: Neuroscience and the impact of brain plasticity on braille reading. *Journal of Visual Impairment & Blindness, 100*(7), 397–413.

Hatton, D. D., Ivy, S. E., & Boyer, C. (2013). Severe visual impairments in infants and toddlers in the United States. *Journal of Visual Impairment & Blindness, 107*(5), 325–336.

Helfer, K. S. (1997). Auditory and auditory-visual perception of clear and conversational speech. *Journal of Speech, Language and Hearing Research, 40*(2), 432–443.

Hild, U., Hey, C., Baumann, U., Montgomery, J., Euler, H. A., & Neumann, K. (2008). High prevalence of hearing disorders at the Special Olympics indicate need to screen persons with intellectual disability. *Journal of Intellectual Disability Research, 52*(6), 520–528. doi:10.1111/j.1365-2788.2008.01059.x

Individuals with Disabilities Education Act, 20 U.S.C. §1400 (2004).

Kamei-Hannan, C., & Lawson, H. (2012). Impact of a braille-note on writing: Evaluating the process, quality, and attitudes of three students who are visually impaired. *Journal of Special Education Technology, 27*, 1–14.

Khetpal, V., & Donahue, S. P. (2007). Cortical visual impairment: Etiology, associated findings, and prognosis in a tertiary care setting. *American Association for Pediatric Ophthalmology and Strabismus, 11*(3), 235–239.

Killoran, J. (2007). *The National Deaf-Blind Child Count: 1998–2005 in review.* Monmouth, OR: National Technical Assistance Consortium for Children and Young Adults Who Are Deaf-Blind (NTAC), Teaching Research Institute, Western Oregon University. Retrieved September 20, 2014, from http://nationaldb.org/NCDBProducts.php?prodID=57

Koenig, A. J., & Holbrook, M. C. (2000a). Planning instruction in unique skills. In M. C. Holbrook & A. J. Koenig (Eds.), *Foundations of education: Volume I. History and theory of teaching children and youth with visual impairments* (2nd ed., pp. 196–220). New York, NY: AFB Press.

Koenig, A. J., & Holbrook, M. C. (2000b). Professional practice. In M. C. Holbrook & A. J. Koenig (Eds.), *Foundations of education: Volume I. History and theory of teaching children and youth with visual impairments* (2nd ed., pp. 260–276). New York, NY: AFB Press.

Koenig, A. J., Holbrook, M. C., Corn, A. L., DePriest, L. B., Erin, J. N., & Presley, I. (2000). Specialized assessments for students with visual impairments. In M. C. Holbrook & A. J. Koenig (Eds.), *Foundations of education: Volume 2. Instructional strategies for teaching children and youths with visual impairments* (2nd ed., pp. 103–172). New York, NY: AFB Press.

Koestler, F. (1976). *The unseen minority: A social history of blindness in the United States.* New York, NY: David McKay.

Lantzy, C., & Lantzy, A. (2010). Outcomes and opportunities: A study of children with cortical visual impairment. *Journal of Visual Impairment & Blindness, 104*(10), 649–653.

Miles, B. (2003). Talking the language of the hands. *DB-LINK.* Monmouth: OR: The National Information Clearinghouse On Children Who Are Deaf-Blind.

Miles, B. (2008). Overview of deaf-blindness. *DB-LINK.* Monmouth, OR: The National Information Clearinghouse On Children Who Are Deaf-Blind.

Molloy, A., & Rowe, F. J. (2011). Manneristic behaviors of visually impaired children. *Strabismus (09273972), 19*(3), 77–84. doi:10.3109/09273972.2011.600417

Narr, R. A. F. (2006). Teaching phonological awareness with deaf and hard-of-hearing students. *Teaching Exceptional Children, 38*(4), 53–58.

National Library of Medicine. (2007). Usher syndrome. In *Genetics home reference.* Retrieved November 1, 2014, from http://ghr.nlm.nih.gov/condition/usher-syndrome

National Library of Medicine. (2008). CHARGE syndrome. In *Genetics home reference.* Retrieved from http://ghr.nlm.nih.gov/condition/charge-syndrome

Peltokorpi, S., & Huttunen, K. (2008). Communication in the early stage of language development in children with CHARGE syndrome. *British Journal of Visual Impairment, 26*(1), 24–49.

Riordan-Eva, P., & Cunningham, E. T., Jr. (2008). Glossary. In P. Riordan-Eva & E. T. Cunningham, Jr. (Eds.), *Vaughan & Asbury's general ophthalmology* (17th ed., pp. 432–436). New York, NY: McGraw-Hill Medical.

Riordan-Eva, P., & Hoyt, W. (2008) Neuro-ophthalmology. In P. Riordan-Eva & E. T. Cunningham, Jr. (Eds,), *Vaughan & Asbury's general ophthalmology* (17th ed., pp. 259–304). New York, NY: McGraw-Hill Medical.

Silberman, R. K. (2000). Children and youth with visual impairments and other exceptionalities. In M. C. Holbrook & A. J. Koenig (Eds.), *Foundations of education: Volume I. History and theory of teaching children and youth with visual impairments* (pp. 186–190). New York, NY: AFB Press.

Skellenger, A. C. (1999). Trends in the use of alternative mobility devices. *Journal of Visual Impairment & Blindness, 93*(8), 516–521.

Swanson, E. C., & Schleiss, M., R. (2013). Congenital cytomegalovirus infection: New prospects for prevention and therapy. *Pediatric Clinics of North America, 60*(2), 335–349.

Tadic, V., Pring, L., & Dale, N. (2010). Are language and social communication intact in children with congenital visual impairment at school age? *Journal of Child Psychology and Psychiatry, 51*(6), 696–705. doi:10.1111/j.1469-7610.2009.02200.x

Thomas, D., & Graham, E. M. (2008). Ocular disorders associated with systemic diseases. In P. Riordan-Eva & E. T. Cunningham, Jr. (Eds.), *Vaughan & Asbury's general ophthalmology* (17th ed., pp. 305–359). New York, NY: McGraw-Hill Medical.

Titiro, A. (2008). *Improving services to children with mild and moderate vision impairment in New Zealand.* Wellington, New Zealand: JR McKenzie Trust.

Trief, E., Cascella, P. W., & Bruce, S. M. (2013). A field study of a standardized tangible symbol system for learners who are visually impaired and have multiple disabilities. *Journal of Visual Impairment & Blindness, 107*(3), 180–191.

van Dijk, J. P. M., Klomberg, M. J. M., & Nelson, C. (1997). Strategies in deaf-blind education based on neurological principles. *Bulletin D'Audioponologie.* Retrieved from http://www.acfos.org/publication/ourarticles/pdf/acfos1/intro_vandijk.pdf

Williams, M. E., Fink, C., Zamora, I., & Borchert, M. (2014). Autism assessment in children with optic nerve hypoplasia and other vision impairments. *Developmental Medicine & Child Neurology, 56*(1), 66–72. doi:10.1111/dmcn.12264

Wright, K. W. (2003). *Pediatric ophthalmology for primary care* (pp. 84–86). Elk Grove, IL: American Academy of Pediatrics.

CHAPTER 8

Students With Specific Learning Disabilities

Sharon H. deFur and Lori Korinek

INTRODUCTION

"Bright, but struggling significantly with . . . ," "really good at . . . , but has trouble with these simpler tasks," "can stay focused at length when he's doing . . . , but when he's (e.g., reading, writing, problem solving), he has such difficulty completing his work"—these phrases represent typical observations about students with specific learning disabilities (SLD). This category of exceptionality under the Individuals with Disabilities Education Improvement Act (IDEA) includes a heterogeneous group of disorders with an almost unlimited number of combinations of characteristics (IDEA, 2004). These students also present varying arrays of strengths and talents. No one profile captures the "typical" student with SLD. However, students with SLD all share the hallmark characteristic of unexpected academic underachievement due to presumed neurological differences. Students with SLD possess average to above-average intelligence, yet do not learn and achieve at the same rate as their typical counterparts in spite of instruction.

CHARACTERISTICS OF STUDENTS WITH SLD

IDEA defines SLD as

A disorder in one or more of the basic psychological processes involved in understanding or in using language, spoken or written, which disorder may manifest itself in the imperfect ability to listen, think, speak, read, write, spell, or do mathematical calculations, including conditions such as perceptual disabilities, brain injury, minimal brain dysfunction, dyslexia, and developmental aphasia. Specific learning disability does not include a learning problem that arises primarily as the result of visual, hearing, or motor disabilities, of intellectual disability, of emotional disturbance, or of environmental, cultural, or economic disadvantage. (IDEA 20 U.S.C. § 1401 [2004], 34 C.F.R. § 300.8[c][10])

Although professional organizations such as the National Joint Committee on

Learning Disabilities, the Learning Disabilities Association, or the Interagency Committee on LD have proposed alternate definitions of SLD, the IDEA definition governs identification of, and service delivery to, students with SLD in public schools in the United States. Common elements in all of the definitions include the presumption of a central nervous system dysfunction, uneven growth patterns and processing deficits, and difficulties in academics. Most definitions also acknowledge the lifelong nature of SLD and the possible coexistence of SLD with other conditions such as attention deficit-hyperactivity disorder (ADHD), social-emotional difficulties (SEDs), and speech-language impairments (SLIs). To meet the criteria for SLD under IDEA, the observed difficulties cannot primarily be due to these other disabilities, or to external factors such as poor instruction, cultural differences, or poverty.

Processing Difficulties

Psychological processing refers to the way the brain interprets and responds to sensory information. Students with SLD frequently have visual or auditory perceptual difficulties (not acuity or hearing issues), where their brains have difficulty making sense of and responding to what they see and hear in an efficient and effective manner (Lerner & Johns, 2009). Processing speed—the length of time it takes for a student to take in, comprehend, interpret, and act upon information received—is also an issue (Calhoun & Mayes, 2005). Common visual processing tasks include accurately recognizing and distinguishing among shapes, letters, and numbers; identifying patterns; and copying from the board or text. Auditory processing tasks involve accurately recognizing and distinguishing among sounds and interpreting spoken words which impacts phonological processing, a critical component of reading (National Reading Panel, 2000). Perceptual processes affect how students read words, align numbers on a page, follow directions, communicate, and interact with others; these are essential for success in all academic subjects (Friend, 2014b).

Students with SLD often exhibit challenges with cognitive processes including attention and memory. Difficulties with selective attention (attending to the most important stimuli, such as the passage before them or the teacher's instruction, while ignoring distractions) and sustained attention (attending long enough to complete tasks in an acceptable manner) are common difficulties among students with SLD (Friend, 2014b). They may "miss the point" or miss critical elements of explanations, instructions, or readings, and often have trouble completing tasks and assignments as a result.

Students with SLD often struggle with retaining and recalling information. Memory difficulties may involve short-term, long-term, or working memory (Hallahan, Lloyd, Kauffman, Weiss, & Martinez, 2005; Vaughn, Wanzek, Murray, & Roberts, 2012). Short-term memory allows students to hold information in mind for a very brief period and is used for tasks such as recording a word or number that is heard, or remembering what they have just read long enough to put it into writing. Long-term memory involves storage of information on a more permanent basis so the information can be retrieved and used in future tasks. Working memory allows students to temporarily store and process information in order to complete tasks at hand, often retrieving information from short- and long-term memory to do so. Working memory has been compared to a "mental workstation" where visual, auditory, and written information is temporarily stored and maintained while the task is being accomplished. Working memory deficits make routine academic tasks such as completing multistep directions, writing essays, solving math problems, and taking relevant notes during lectures difficult for students with SLD. When working memory is overloaded, students struggle to process new information as well as to retrieve previous learning. Students with working memory difficulties may appear to be inattentive because they are struggling to follow directions or begin tasks. Working memory also enables students to compare current actions with a standard or to past performance, so it plays an important role in self-regulation (Martinussen & Major, 2011; Reid, Trout, & Schartz, 2005).

Metacognitive difficulties are also characteristic of many students with SLD. They struggle with information processing on the level of "thinking about their thinking" and have trouble making connections between new and known information; applying learning in novel situations; and selecting, using, and monitoring strategies to approach academic tasks in an efficient and effective manner. Their repertoire of learning strategies is often limited and not well suited to the academic demands they face. They may try to apply the same few strategies that they know to all tasks with limited success, or simply give up on complex tasks because they do not have the strategies to successfully negotiate complex demands (Bulgren, Graner, & Deshler, 2013; Hallahan et al., 2005; Lienemann & Reid, 2006).

Executive Functioning

Closely related to metacognition is executive functioning which refers to the brain's cognitive management system reflected in students' ability to orchestrate their planning, focus, actions, effort, emotions, and memory to accomplish tasks (Barkley, 2006; Brown, 2009; Guare, Dawson, & Guare, 2013; Meltzer, 2010). While students may demonstrate success on isolated tasks, more complex demands (e.g., reading fluently with comprehension, composing a term paper, or completing a multistep project) that require several components working in concert often present major challenges.

Executive function and self-regulation problems result in difficulties often associated with ADHD including impulsivity, distractibility, and hyperactivity. There is considerable overlap between SLD and ADHD, with significant numbers of students showing behaviors associated with both conditions (Mayes, Calhoun, & Crowell, 2000). Students who struggle with executive function deficits have difficulties prioritizing, planning, completing, and evaluating tasks as well as regulating their emotions, motivation, and effort to bring assignments to fruition. Organization, time management, materials management, flexibility, and problem solving pose major challenges for many students with SLD who have executive function deficits (Barkley, 2006; Brown, 2009).

Related to self-regulation is attribution—one's beliefs about the causes of academic failure and success. Students with SLD often attribute their successes to luck or other unstable external factors, and attribute failure to their lack of intelligence or other personal characteristics, failing to see the connection between personal effort and outcomes (Hallahan et al., 2005; Swanson & Deshler, 2003; Vaughn et al., 2012). Faulty attribution may impact motivation and effort toward school-related tasks, which teachers may interpret as laziness, defiance, or disinterest on the student's part.

The combination of characteristics associated with SLD makes generalization and transfer of learning from known to novel tasks and situations highly challenging for most students with SLD (Cortiella & Horowitz, 2014; Friend, 2014b; Haager & Vaughn, 2013). For example, students may not recognize words learned in isolation when they encounter them in text. They do not automatically see the connections between prior and new learning, or between skills learned in one discipline or context as applicable to other disciplines or content. Generalization of learning to new tasks and situations must be deliberately planned and supported, connections between prior and current learning highlighted, and learning strategies explicitly taught rather than left to chance if students with SLD are to succeed in the curriculum (Cortiella & Horowitz, 2014; Deshler & Schumaker, 2006; Haager & Vaughn, 2013).

Academic Characteristics

Students with SLD often come to school unprepared for academic learning. They may lack the language skills, school-related background knowledge and experiences, or interactional skills that make them ready to learn grade-level content. Some, though, fall behind because initial instruction is not matched to their learning needs or is insufficient to ensure adequate progress. Learning difficulties may manifest in a variety of areas and disciplines.

Language

As noted in the IDEA (2004) definition, the underlying processing problems characteristic of SLD have a negative impact on students' academic performance. Many consider SLD to be primarily a language problem, since language skills undergird all other academic areas. Both receptive language (listening and reading) and expressive language (speaking and writing) may be problematic for students with SLD. They often struggle with correctly perceiving and manipulating basic sound units associated with letters and words (phonology) and with understanding and using basic units of meaning such as base or root words, prefixes, suffixes, and word endings that indicate plurals, possessives, inflections, and tenses (morphology). Word order, grammar, and the mechanics of language (syntax) pose problems for most students with SLD in their reading and writing. They demonstrate difficulty with word meanings and relationships (semantics) that are critical to understanding and using multiple meanings of words and figurative language; these in turn have a major impact on vocabulary development (Bryant, Goodwin, Bryant, & Higgins, 2003; Jitendra, Edwards, Sacks, & Jacobsen, 2004). Students with SLD tend to be highly "concrete" in their thinking, and have more difficulty grasping abstract terms and ideas. Pragmatics or social use of language also challenges many students with SLD. Skills such as turn-taking, asking and answering questions, and giving the right kind and amount of information have a major impact on student learning as well on the development of relationships with teachers and peers, so important to achievement and motivation. All of these language difficulties impact students' attainment of reading, writing, mathematics, and content-specific skills.

Reading

One of the most common subtypes of SLD is dyslexia, a disorder in reading characterized by difficulties with decoding, word recognition, fluency, spelling, vocabulary, and comprehension. These difficulties typically result from a deficit in the phonological component of language involving discrimination and use of sounds in words. These difficulties are often unexpected in relation to other cognitive abilities and the provision of effective classroom instruction (Cortiella & Horowitz, 2014). Wei, Blackorby, and Schiller (2011) found that students with learning disabilities performed below grade level on word reading, fluency, and comprehension. Newman et al. (2011) reported that close to half of students with SLD were more than three grade levels behind their typical peers in reading and math.

The National Reading Panel (NRP) (2000) identified five major components of reading, and students with SLD may struggle with each component to varying degrees. Phonemic awareness refers to the knowledge that spoken words can be broken into smaller segments of sound (phonemes). Phonics relates to students' ability to recognize and associate letters with particular sounds, to blend sounds together to form syllables and words, and to "sound out" new words. These skills, along with vocabulary skills, are often referred to as word recognition skills that allow students to decode new words. In addition to difficulties in word recognition, students with SLD may struggle with fluency, the ability to read words with effective speed, accuracy, and expression as well as may struggle with comprehension or understanding of what has been read. On a more positive note, students' listening comprehension often exceeds their reading comprehension (Deshler & Schumaker, 2006), so technology and other accommodations offer promising means of ensuring that students understand the content of subjects even if they have difficulties independently reading content area texts.

Mathematics

Other academic skill deficits demonstrated by students with SLD include difficulties grasping mathematical concepts, reasoning, and solving problems, sometimes referred to as dyscalculia. On average, secondary students with LD are more than 3 years behind their enrolled grade level in math (Cortiella & Horowitz, 2014). Skill areas that often present difficulties include counting and magnitude, comparing numbers, conceptual understanding and retrieval of basic number combinations, place value, and problem solving (Jayanthi, Gersten, & Baker, 2008; Mancini & Gagnon, n.d.; Powell, Fuchs, & Fuchs, 2013). Difficulties in visual and spatial perception, attention, memory, language, and reading described earlier in this chapter affect mathematical achievement as well as achievement in other content areas. Mastery of content-specific vocabulary, higher-level text analysis, comprehension, and subject-specific writing may be hindered due to the underlying characteristics of SLD.

Writing

Writing also proves highly challenging for many students with SLD. Dysgraphia refers to writing deficits such as letter formation and writing within a confined space. Even more serious are composition deficits. Students with SLD exhibit lower levels of performance than typical peers on almost every aspect of writing assessed including quality, ideation, organization, vocabulary, sentence fluency, spelling, grammar, handwriting, and genre elements. Writing conventions (e.g., spelling, grammar, handwriting, usage) and ideation are especially problematic. Students with SLD tend to be less knowledgeable, less positive, less confident, and less motivated about writing compared with their peers. Most writing instruction for students with SLD occurs in general education classrooms, and, notably little instruction takes place beyond third grade (Gillespie & Graham, 2014; Graham & Harris; 2013).

Emotional and Behavioral Characteristics

In addition to academic challenges, many students with SLD demonstrate emotional and behavioral difficulties. After repeated school failures and disappointments, it is not unusual for students with SLD to display lack of motivation or effort when faced with challenging tasks, feelings of hopelessness, disengagement, low self-esteem, and negative affect (e.g., irritability, shame, and nervousness) (Bulgren et al., 2013; Sideridis, 2003). Newman et al. (2011) found that one third of SLD youths are suspended or expelled from school at some point in their school careers. In some districts they are two to three times as likely as their nondisabled peers to be subject to disciplinary actions. Among all students with disabilities, those with SLD experience dropout rates second only to students with emotional disabilities (Cortiella & Horowitz, 2014).

CHALLENGES OF IMPLEMENTING CCSS FOR STUDENTS WITH SLD

Given the characteristics of children and youth with SLD, the probability of being challenged by any one of the CCSS is arguable. The majority of students with SLD have reading disabilities; thus, they will be challenged in achieving the summative CCSS Reading Standard (CCSS. ELA-Literacy.CCRA.R.10) of being able to read and comprehend informational texts at grade-level complexity independently and proficiently. Students with SLD in reading often are described as having difficulty with many of the foundational reading skills specified in the CCSS. For example, the CCSS English Language Arts foundational skills standards include those listed in the box.

By the end of fifth grade students will be able to: use combined knowledge of all letter-sound correspondences, syllabication patterns, and morphology (e.g., roots and affixes) to read accurately unfamiliar multisyllabic words in context and out of context; read with sufficient accuracy and fluency to support comprehension; read grade-level text with purpose and understanding; read grade-level prose and poetry orally with accuracy, appropriate rate, and expression on successive readings; and use context to confirm or self-correct word recognition and understanding, rereading as necessary. (National Governors Association Center for Best Practices [NGA] & Council of Chief State School Officers [CCSSO], 2010b)

Many of these objectives are interdependent and developmental, so failure to become proficient with foundational skills often impacts demonstration of higher-level reading skills. On the other hand, Individualized Education Programs (IEPs) for students with SLD often mistakenly focus only on developmental reading skills without simultaneously examining how to develop the critical thinking and comprehension skills essential to the CCSS.

As spelling and writing are closely linked to reading skills, foundational deficits in reading are almost always accompanied by difficulties in writing. Furthermore, many students with SLD also have fine motor difficulties, so the actual physical act of writing often interferes with idea generation and knowledge expression. The CCSS anchor standards for writing state that students must devote significant time and effort to writing, producing numerous pieces over short and extended time frames throughout the year. They are expected to write routinely during shorter time frames (a single sitting or a day or two) and over extended time frames (allowing time for research, reflection, and revision) for a range of tasks, purposes, and audiences (NGA & CCSSO, 2010b).

Fewer students have SLD in only mathematics, but those who do, as well as those who have reading, writing, or attention difficulties, will be challenged by the mathematical practices that undergird the CCSS expectations. These practices were derived from the National Council of Teachers of Mathematics (NCTM) process standards in mathematics, including problem solving, reasoning and proof, communication, representation, and connections. Many students with SLD will experience challenges in these strands of mathematic competence identified by the

Mathematics Learning Study Committee of the National Research Council (Kilpatrick, Swafford, & Findell, 2001) National Research Council that the CCSS used as a basis in developing the Mathematics Standards. These strands include those as stated in the following box.

- Conceptual understanding—comprehension of mathematical concepts, operations, and relations
- Procedural fluency—skill in carrying out procedures flexibly, accurately, efficiently, and appropriately
- Strategic competence—ability to formulate, represent, and solve mathematical problems
- Adaptive reasoning—capacity for logical thought, reflection, explanation, and justification
- Productive disposition—habitual inclination to see mathematics as sensible, useful, and worthwhile, coupled with a belief in diligence and one's own efficacy

(Kilpatrick et al., 2001, p. 116)

One challenge in the implementation of CCSS for students with SLD is the documented lack of content knowledge and familiarity with standards by special educators and related service providers who might be supporting students with SLD in the general curriculum (Leko & Brownell, 2009). Likewise, general educators in co-teaching settings, particularly at the secondary level, often express concern that their special educator co-teachers do not have content expertise; thus, general educators often are reluctant to share lesson planning, delivery, and assessment with their partners. In an era of standards-based education and IEPs, special educators and related service providers may need to assume more responsibility for developing their own knowledge base of the standards.

By law, students with SLD are entitled to reasonable and appropriate accommodations to enable them access to the general curriculum (IDEA, 2004), including the CCSS. The challenge exists in ensuring that accommodations are both reasonable and appropriate for the student and their teachers while maintaining the content area standard. At the same time, high-stakes accountability expectations may result in increased requests for accommodations. The CCSS focus on preparing all students to be college and career ready; for students with SLD, this means that the accommodations identified need to be ones that provide a differential boost for those students, are recognized by the students as critical to their success so they will use them throughout life, and are eventually transferable to college and careers. Overaccommodating (requiring accommodations not needed for improved academic, behavioral, or social outcomes) has the potential to interfere with setting ambitious academic goals for students who have the ability to be successful in both college and careers. Including extensive accommodations in the IEPs for students in inclusive classrooms serving multiple students with IEPs creates a situation where the many accommodations may be, realistically, impossible to implement; consequently, students with SLD may actually miss out on critical accommodations. A focus on providing a long list of accommodations in the IEP may also detract from making the explicit and direct instruction that students need to achieve high standards a priority. Providing necessary and appropriate accommodations while delivering effective instruction aligned with the standards is the ultimate goal.

Overcoming the challenges to learning presented by characteristics of SLD may seem daunting to both students and teachers. Despite the challenges, with collaboration among professionals, careful planning, and specially designed instruction informed by frequent progress monitoring, students with SLD can be successful in meeting higher standards. The following sections explain and illustrate guiding principles for effective instruction of students with SLD.

GUIDING PRINCIPLES FOR TEACHING STUDENTS WITH SLD

Many students with SLD come to school lacking pre-academic skills and basic vocabulary, acquire them more slowly, and need more intensive instruction from the beginning of their school careers. According to the CCSS, "Application to Students with Disabilities" document (NGA & CCSSO, 2010a), in order for students with disabilities to succeed in meeting the conceptual and procedural knowledge and skills outlined in the CCSS, instruction must incorporate supports and accommodations that include an IEP with annual goals designed to facilitate attainment of grade-level standards; supports and related services to accommodate their unique needs and allow access to the general education curriculum; teachers and instructional support personnel prepared and qualified to deliver high-quality, evidence-based, and individualized instruction; and instructional supports for learning based on the principles of Universal Design for Learning (UDL) which foster engagement by presenting information in multiple ways and allowing for diverse avenues of action and expression (National Center on Universal Design for Learning, n.d.). These broad instructional supports are generally promoted by the Center on Instruction and the National Center on Intensive Intervention that outline more specific guidelines for helping students with disabilities access and succeed in the curriculum framed by the CCSS. The following sections detail the principles for effectively meeting the needs of students with SLD in the CCSS curriculum.

Effective Instruction for Students With SLD

In addition to focusing on what to teach as outlined in the CCSS, educators must examine how they teach and deliver instruction in order to be successful with students with SLD. Given the characteristics of these students and the expectations for higher-level learning, students with SLD will need high-quality explicit, systematic, and intensive instruction informed by assessment and the use of evidence-based practices in order to meet the standards (Gareis & Grant, 2008; Gersten et al., 2009; Murray, Coleman, Vaughn, Wanzek, & Roberts, 2012; Stecker, Fuchs, & Fuchs, 2008).

Explicit Instruction

Explicit instruction involves "overtly teaching the steps or processes needed to understand a construct, apply a strategy, and/or complete a task" (Vaughn et al., 2012, p. 17). It entails setting specific learning objectives; providing clear, detailed explanations of concepts and skills with step-by-step models or demonstrations

of what is expected; and providing sufficient guided practice with feedback prior to independent practice. Feedback should clarify what students have done correctly and how to change what needs to be improved. Instruction and pacing are guided by data from pre-assessments and frequent progress monitoring to ensure that needed skills are being addressed, and that students are making adequate and efficient progress on foundational and grade-level skills (Gersten, et al., 2009; Jitendra et al., 2004; Swanson & Deshler, 2003; Vaughn et al., 2012).

Since students with SLD lag behind their peers in foundational skills, they require explicit instruction in these skills while simultaneously exposing them to grade-level content and expectations. For example, for most students with SLD, teachers will need to incorporate foundational reading skills such as phonemic awareness, decoding, and fluency into lessons with a broader literacy focus (Haager & Vaughn, 2013). Educators should not focus on just one skill at a time, but rather work on several foundational skills simultaneously using accessible materials related to grade-level subject matter.

Systematic Instruction

Systematic instruction involves breaking complex tasks into smaller steps and instruction into simpler, more manageable segments or "chunks." For example, a complex math problem may be broken down into steps or processes; a writing passage may be edited for different aspects (spelling, grammar, word choice, etc.) on different passes. Systematic instruction also involves careful sequencing of learning chunks from easier to more difficult (e.g., phonics instruction proceeds from smaller to larger units and easier to more difficult sounds and word types), and providing temporary supports to control the level of difficulty throughout the learning process. Ideally, teachers teach each chunk to mastery before combining the entire process (Vaughn et al., 2012).

Intensive Intervention

Since students with SLD are typically performing below grade-level expectations, they need more intensive intervention to close the achievement gap and to prevent students from falling further behind. To provide an intensive instructional program, educators must consider whether instruction is responsive to students' individual characteristics and processing difficulties, whether instruction is being sufficiently differentiated, whether the time devoted to instruction is adequate, and whether the learning environment provides sufficient engagement, opportunities to respond, and alignment with students' needs (Vaughn et al., 2012). Intensive intervention is individualized and often involves different content and pedagogy, with more frequent and precise progress monitoring than is used with typical peers. Intensive instruction is not a single approach, manual, or preset program, but an ongoing process of data-based individualization (DBI) that systematically uses data to determine when and how to provide more intensity. Assessment data are used to identify needed skills; progress monitoring data guide adaptations to interventions and measurement of their impact on student achievement to help ensure adequate progress (Hunt & Little, 2014; Stecker, Fuchs, & Fuchs, 2008).

Gersten et al. described intensive reading instruction as focusing on a small, targeted set of foundational skills, slow-

ing the pacing of lessons, scheduling multiple and extended sessions daily, including opportunities for extensive practice and feedback, and using frequent and precise progress monitoring data to individualize the intervention and teach to mastery (Gersten et al., 2009). Fuchs, Powell, and Zumeta (2014) described intensive math instruction as involving smaller steps, precise and repeated language, student explanations, teacher modeling, use of manipulatives, worked examples and think-alouds, repeated practice, error correction, fading support, teaching to fluency, and then moving on to the next skills.

Organizing and planning intensive intervention may involve changing the dosage of time, changing the learning environment to promote greater attention and engagement, combining cognitive processing strategies with academic learning, and modifying delivery of instruction (Vaughn et al., 2012). Timing strategies used to intensify instruction may include "double dipping"—breaking a long intervention block into two shorter periods, one in the morning and the other in the afternoon. Intensity may also be increased by scheduling additional or supplemental instructional time (e.g., duration or number of sessions daily, weekly, or after school). Smaller group instruction and increased opportunities for individual responding with immediate and specific feedback also increase intensity (Gersten et al., 2009; Hunt & Little, 2014). Using entry or exit routines for students to quickly, consistently, and efficiently practice skills (e.g., letters, math facts, oral reading) alone or with a partner is another technique for increasing intensity. Incorporating these routines may also reduce the time that students spend waiting and increase their academic engagement, especially important for students with SLD. Reinforcement (e.g., specific verbal praise, points toward a reward) helps to promote on-task behavior during activities and allows teachers to manage a larger number of students. Careful attention to making efficient transitions between classroom activities and maximizing instructional time during the school day (Stevenson, 2014) are also important in securing the additional teaching and learning time that will be needed in order for students with SLD to succeed in meeting the CCSS.

Any supplemental instruction that takes place beyond the elementary grades should be guided by the K–5 CCSS reading foundational skills in English/Language Arts and the domains of the K–5 mathematics standards to ensure that students have acquired the developmental prerequisites for middle and high school. This supplemental instruction must be based on assessment data and include regular cumulative reviews to ensure that students eventually develop critical tool skills required to meet higher-level expectations. The CCSS foundational skills in English Language Arts include working knowledge of concepts of print, alphabetic and phonological principles, and basic conventions of writing in English. The mathematical domains for math include counting and cardinality, operations and algebraic thinking, number and operations in Base 10, number and operations focusing on fractions, measurement and data, and geometry. While still mastering the foundational skills, older students with SLD must be exposed to grade-level content and skills in an accessible manner to prevent their falling farther behind in their education and to make them college and career ready. For example, content vocabulary, informational text from science and social stud-ies, or word problems from grade-level mathematics may be used to expose students to critical concepts, ideas, and skills that they will encounter in grade-level instruction, while working on mastery of foundational reading and math skills. Small group instruction may also be used to pre-teach essential vocabulary and concepts so that students are more prepared to benefit from whole class instruction in grade-level material.

Making the Curriculum Accessible

Even though effective instruction for students with SLD should be routinely and consistently explicit, systematic, and sufficiently intense, these students often require additional supports tailored to their individual characteristics to access and succeed in the CCSS curriculum.

Scaffolding

Scaffolding refers to the provision of additional temporary supports and techniques that control the difficulty of tasks early in the learning process. These supports are gradually reduced or faded as the student becomes more skilled and independent. Scaffolds may take many forms including outlines, rubrics, exemplars of completed projects, templates, graphics, guiding questions, hints or verbal prompts, highlighted text, study guides, documents, think-alouds, peer tutoring, coaching, simpler texts, or any number of other supports. Scaffolds can reduce the frustration, negativity, and discouragement students experience when attempting difficult tasks independently. Universally designed instruction that affords different representations of content, methods of engagement, and forms of expression, along with use of instructional technology for all students often reduce (but do not eliminate) the need for individual scaffolds. Students with SLD typically require more scaffolding than their peers for longer periods of time, but the overall goal is to gradually remove the extra supports and to develop more independent learners.

Accommodations

In addition to scaffolds for particular tasks, accommodations tailored to students' individual needs must be considered to reduce the impact of their disabilities on classroom performance (Thompson, Morse, Sharpe, & Hall, 2005). These supports are intended to provide students access to grade-level or course curriculum and assessments, without altering the curriculum. Examples of potential accommodations include adaptations in the way content is presented (e.g., read-aloud, large print); setting (e.g., small group, preferential seating); timing (e.g., frequent breaks, extended time, time of day); response modes (e.g., verbal rather than written responses, scribe); or other reasonable accommodations. Assistive technology (e.g., spell check, keyboards, text-to-speech, dictation software) may also be an important part of student accommodations.

The IEP team, of which the student and parents are a part, decides which accommodations are appropriate for instruction and assessment. Accommodations must be used on a regular basis in the classroom so that the student is familiar with their use to optimize learning and performance. Concerted efforts to directly teach students strategies that will make them more independent learners over time and less dependent upon accommodations are critical to their prepara-

tion for college and careers. As noted in the challenges section of this chapter, the IEP team needs to carefully consider the ramifications when selecting accommodations. Modifying (i.e., making significant changes to) the curriculum for students with SLD serves to lower expectations and should be avoided for students who have the intellectual capacity to achieve college and career readiness standards.

Strategy Instruction

Explicitly teaching students strategies or techniques, principles, and rules that guide them to complete tasks independently has been found effective in addressing weaknesses evidenced by students with SLD (Bulgren et al., 2013; Friend & Bursuck, 2011; Meltzer, Katzir-Cohen, Miller, Reddy, & Roditi, 2004; Scruggs, Mastropieri, Berkeley, & Graetz, 2010). The University of Kansas Center for Research on Learning has decades of research supporting the efficacy of its content enhancement and learning strategies for acquiring, remembering, and demonstrating academic knowledge and skills (Deshler & Schumaker, 2006). Comprehension strategies (Berkeley, Scruggs, & Mastropieri, 2010; Block & Parris, 2008; Gajria, Jitendra, Sood, & Sacks, 2007; Swanson et al., 2012; Vaughn et al., 2011; Watson, Gable, Gear, & Hughes, 2012) and content-enhancement tools such as graphic organizers and visual displays (Bulgren et al., 2013; Dexter & Hughes, 2011; Kim, Vaughn, Wanzek, & Wei, 2004) are helpful for students with processing difficulties, and are associated with high effect sizes for content learning and comprehension in grades four through twelve (Scruggs et al., 2010; Solis et al., 2012). Mnemonic strategies (e.g., keyword, acronyms) (Jitendra et al., 2004; Scruggs & Mastropieri, 2000; Scruggs, Mastropieri, Berkeley, & Marshak, 2010) and note-taking (Boyle, 2010, 2012) assist students with memory and attention difficulties. Self-regulated strategy development has a solid research base supporting its effectiveness with students with SLD in writing (Gillespie & Graham, 2014; Graham & Harris, 2013), as do other self-regulation strategies such as goal-setting, self-instruction, and self-monitoring for academic and behavioral targets, including time management and organization (Guare et al., 2013; Lienemann & Reid, 2006; Reid et al., 2005).

Collaboration

The CCSS raise the bar for both students and educators (including SLPs). The standards emphasize teaching fewer topics in greater depth, more hands-on learning, and innovative assignments that require students to show greater understanding across disciplines. Students must use their knowledge and skills to solve problems, demonstrate their knowledge in writing and multimedia presentations, and complete real-world tasks. Collaboration among education professionals and with families is essential to accomplish the changes necessary for success in this new milieu (Bulgren et al., 2013; Friend & Cook, 2013; Phillips & Hughes, 2012). When focused on student work, collaboration builds capacity to address students' academic needs by designing and implementing common-core aligned lessons, tracking student progress, and adjusting instruction as needed. It also provides opportunities for educators to share what works and to build on each other's ideas.

Collaboration may take many forms in schools including grade-level teams, school leadership teams, lesson study teams, interdisciplinary teams that review progress of students, and co-teaching teams. Particularly relevant to students with SLD and CCSS are teams tasked with unpacking or unwrapping the standards to identify the component knowledge and skills necessary to master each standard (Morgan et al., 2013), and co-teaching teams of general and special educators and/or related service personnel (Friend & Cook, 2013).

Morgan et al. (2013) recommend that collaboration teams engage in a process of analyzing each grade-level CCSS, creating a task-analysis of the concepts and skills contained in each broad standard and developing assessment techniques to monitor progress and component skills. General educators and special educators must be familiar with the standards in order to have a clear idea of what is being expected of students at their respective grade levels as well as the foundational skills needed to meet those expectations. Teachers participating in the unwrapping process reported it was best completed in small groups of educators giving each other feedback about the order and sequencing of skills, potential resources, and ideas for effective lessons that teach to the standards and meet individual student's needs (Gareis & Grant, 2008; Morgan et al., 2013).

Co-Teaching

Co-teaching is a potentially powerful form of collaboration for implementing instruction to address the CCSS in general education classrooms, where the majority of students with SLD spend most of their school day (U.S. Department of Education, 2014). In this arrangement, "two or more professionals jointly deliver substantive instruction to a diverse, blended group of students, primarily in a single physical space" (Friend & Cook, 2013, p. 163). These credentialed professionals have different, but complementary, primary areas of expertise that they bring to classroom instruction. Variations of co-teaching include one teaching, one observing; station teaching (students rotate in small groups to various centers or stations addressing different skills); parallel teaching (each co-teacher teaches a similar lesson to half the class); alternative teaching (one partner teaches a small group while the other teacher instructs the rest of the class); teaming (both teachers interactively instruct the entire class); and one teaching, one assisting. Partners should vary the types of co-teaching used and, overall, have approximately the same level of responsibility and accountability for instruction, assessment, and supervision of students (Friend & Cook, 2013).

The most likely partners for educators serving students with SLD are general educators, special educators, and speech-language pathologists (SLPs), with occasional involvement of occupational therapists, physical therapists, behavior specialists, and others. Typically, the general educator has primary content expertise, while the specialists have more preparation in the language and learning characteristics of diverse students, strategy instruction, individualized instruction, accommodations, and behavior. Together, these professionals can develop effective plans to ensure appropriate instruction that adheres to students' IEPs, addresses CCSS expectations for the entire class, and capitalizes on team members' unique expertise to provide an integrated, coherent educational program for all students.

Co-Planning

In order to maximize the potential of co-teaching, partners must engage in effective and efficient co-planning. Friend and Cook (2013) recommend that the general educator outline the curricular content and related instructional activities prior to face-to-face meeting time with the specialist. Then both co-teachers review the curricular material and decide how to arrange teachers and students (i.e., which variations of co-teaching) in order to accomplish the learning objectives, then discuss the concepts and skills likely to prove challenging for students with special needs. After the joint meeting, the special educator or SLP takes primary responsibility for preparing any significantly changed or alternative materials needed by students. Planning may be further supported by technology through the use of collaborative software, learning management systems, and online group tools that allow teachers to post lessons for partners, suggest changes, and post alternate materials and assessments. Although e-mail, texting, tweeting, and the like should not be used as primary planning tools, they may assist communication between co-teachers when planning time is limited. Ideally, planning time for co-teaching teams is part of the master schedule, but Friend (2014a), Friend and Cook (2013), Murawski (2012), and Dieker (2001) offer creative suggestions for finding alternate or additional planning time.

Collaboration With Families

Family members (i.e., parents, guardians) are the experts on their children outside of school, and an integral part of students' with SLD IEP teams. As such, they deserve support in understanding what the CCSS are and what they mean for their children. IDEA requirements and state regulations closely govern parent participation in the special education process and IEP development and implementation. State departments of education and school districts typically provide information and guidance documents for families on legal requirements, rights, and responsibilities.

Although family participation related to the CCSS is not regulated as in the IEP process, a variety of resources for families have been provided by various states and organizations. For example, the official website for the CCSS initiative (http://www.corestandards.org) has a section devoted to "What Parents Should Know" on its website that allows families to find out what their states are doing to implement the standards, learn more about the CCSS, and get answers to frequently asked questions. New York provides materials, websites, and guides intended to help parents navigate the CCSS site (http://www.engageny.org). For educators, http://www.achievethecore.org provides resources that may be used to speak to parents and the community about the Common Core standards. The National Parent Teacher Association (http://www.pta.org/parents/content) also features documents addressing what parents need to know about the standards.

Although a wealth of information exists on websites and through various print materials, the most relevant collaboration with families regarding the CCSS occurs at the school level when parents meet with teachers about their children's progress in the CCSS-aligned curriculum and on their IEP goals designed to ensure access to, and success in, that curriculum. These face-to-face meetings as well as other communications with families provide opportunities for educators to share

family friendly information about the child's SLD, specially designed instruction, and progress on specific foundational and grade-level skills in the curriculum. They are also opportunities to gain parent perspectives on the child's perceptions of school, techniques that have worked in the past, and ideas to address current challenges in ways tailored to the child's characteristics. Suggestions for how family members can support student learning at home (e.g., ensuring nutrition and sleep, encouraging effective study habits and perseverance, practicing skills with materials at the student's level) may also be shared during school meetings.

IMPLEMENTING THE CCSS FOR STUDENTS WITH SLD

The following cases illustrate how educators might approach helping a variety of students with SLD achieve success in meeting various CCSS.

SLD in Reading

Henry is a fourth-grade student with a SLD in reading. Recent instructionally based reading assessments identified continued difficulties with the CCSS second-grade reading foundational skills in phonics and word recognition of knowing and applying grade-level phonics and word analysis skills in decoding words (CCSS.ELA-Literacy.RF.2.3) and in Grade 3 phonics and word recognition skills (CCSS.ELA-Literacy.RF.3.3). These decoding and word recognition difficulties affect Henry's reading fluency as well as his comprehension. His skills in reading expository or informational text fell below his performance when reading narrative texts where he benefits from context clues. Henry continues to need to learn to read while developing critical skills in reading to learn.

Henry's IEP targets improving his foundational reading skills, with the goal that he will use combined knowledge of all letter-sound correspondences, syllabication patterns, and morphology (e.g., roots and affixes) to read accurately unfamiliar multisyllabic words in context and out of context by the end of the school year (CCSS.ELA-Literacy.RF.4.3). His goals also address the fourth-grade reading foundational standard (CCSS.ELA-Literacy.RF.4.4.a), stating that Henry will read grade-level text with purpose and understanding by the end of the year.

Henry exhibits some attention problems that contribute to memory and detail difficulties while reading or listening. In social conversation, Henry is engaging and he has many friends. When attentive, he contributes to class discussions using developmentally appropriate language skills, although responses are sometimes lacking in specificity. Henry continues to exhibit some articulation and oral language (morphological awareness and syntax) difficulties for which he receives speech language services.

Henry's listening comprehension for details is much higher than his silent or oral reading comprehension, particularly when followed with discussion, simulations, and project-based learning. His IEP identifies a read-aloud accommodation for use in assessment and expository texts. Nonetheless, he has difficulty identifying the main idea and drawing conclusions from text.

Henry's general education and special education teachers are co-planning their fourth-grade social studies unit on colonial times in America. They will use a differentiated instructional planning approach (Murray et al., 2012; Tomlinson & McTighe, 2006) to provide Henry the intensive instruction he needs on foundational reading skills while developing more complex comprehension skills. Universal design for learning principles will guide how to assess Henry's progress in both areas (National Center on Universal Design for Learning, n.d.). In their unit, the teachers identified four Common Core English Language Arts Literacy Reading Informational Text Standards to target for instruction and assessment using social studies texts as the instructional medium. These standards include

- CCSS.ELA-Literacy.RI.4.1: Refer to details and examples in a text when explaining what the text says and when drawing inferences from the text.
- CCSS.ELA-Literacy.RI.4.2: Determine the main idea of a text and explain how it is supported by key details; summarize the text.
- CCSS.ELA-Literacy.RI.4.4: Determine the meaning of general academic and domain-specific words or phrases in a text relevant to a Grade 4 topic or subject area.
- CCSS.ELA-Literacy.RI.4.8: Explain how an author uses reasons and evidence to support particular points in a text. (NGA & CCSSO, 2010b)

Henry's teachers consulted with the SLP and invited him to participate in the co-planning since he has worked with Henry for several years with a focus on oral language, especially morphological awareness, and complex syntactic structures. Collaboratively, they reviewed the texts that would be available for use in the unit. Using a quantitative measure, they determined the reading grade level using standard readability measures; importantly, they discussed the qualitative dimensions of the text complexity examining the purpose, the language conventions used, background knowledge demands, and clarity. They also identified the domain-specific vocabulary as well as the academic vocabulary that would need to be taught or clarified, and agreed to assess only vocabulary and concepts that were essential to the standards with a focus on higher-level complexity of understanding. They discussed the scaffolding that all students would need, and the special educator noted where she anticipated Henry would require more supports. They agreed that all students needed to engage in close reading of text (NGA & CCSSO, 2010b), but that Henry (and other struggling readers) would need direct instruction in how to perform close reading.

The collaborators talked about how to use a close reading protocol based upon original source documents or period pieces from colonial times as a major weekly activity linked to developing the reading informational text standards for the unit. They agreed to differentiate for Henry by chunking the text rather than having him read it all at once for his first read, with the intention that he gets the flow of the text. If the text was too complex, they agreed that he could listen to the text using the same protocol. In close reading, the second read is devoted to capturing main ideas; the reader annotates and identifies what the reader knows such as the who, what, where, when, why, and how; identifies unknown or unfamiliar words or phrases (e.g., circle these); identifies the gist or main idea of each paragraph; and talks with a part-

ner to check meaning. The collaborators decided to share roles for the third read; in this phase of close reading a teacher reads aloud and demonstrates thinking aloud. The teacher asks text-dependent questions to develop text reading skills. The educators agreed that students will keep a journal summarizing what they learned from each close reading and accommodated Henry by allowing him to dictate his journal as specified in his IEP.

To offer opportunities for differentiation, the collaborators decided to use station teaching once a week during the 3-week unit after the whole group content instruction co-led by the general and special educator. During station teaching, the special educator would direct one station focused on teaching foundational decoding skills using both academic and domain-specific vocabulary words. The SLP would lead a station where students would discover the meaning of the academic vocabulary through context clues while mastering a paraphrasing and summarizing strategy. The general educator agreed to lead the station reviewing domain-specific vocabulary words and key subject matter content. A fourth computer station would provide for independent extension activities for students not requiring foundational skill work. The special educator would provide Henry with 15–30 minutes daily of intensive data-based instruction in decoding and fluency as specified in his IEP.

In addition to station teaching, the collaborators identified cooperative learning as a strategy that could capitalize on Henry's social skills and learning through discussion and engagement. They decided that each cooperative group would be given a problem encountered by people during colonial times and would develop a researched solution to the problem using only the tools available to people during that era. Groups must cite evidence and create a product (e.g., poster, video, model) illustrating the problem and the solution.

SLD in Mathematics

TJ is a seventh-grade student diagnosed with a SLD and ADHD. His oral language and vocabulary are appropriate for his age and grade, and he has well-developed social skills. His IEP notes poor short-term visual memory, poor visual-motor and perceptual skills, and difficulty with organization for both ideas as well as materials.

TJ's reading skills are several years below his current grade level; although he can apply the basic foundational skills for reading, he lacks fluency, which in turn affects his comprehension. Listening comprehension is above average for his age. For TJ, difficulty in mathematics may provide the greatest challenge to achieving his goal of going to college after high school. Standardized and informal assessments of his math skills as well as an error analysis of his written math products suggest that TJ has poorly developed number sense; he continues to use his fingers when solving computational problems (usually touching his chin as he counts), often miscounts, and does not self-correct his errors. TJ frequently uses a calculator for simple one-digit facts; he has poor handwriting and continues to occasionally reverse or transpose numerals. He makes errors because he has not aligned the numbers correctly or tries to solve computation problems from left to right, suggesting that he has not mastered essential numeracy skills from the CCSS

domains in the elementary mathematics standards across Grades 2 through 5 of Number and Operations in Base 10 or of Operations and Algebraic Thinking. For example, he is even inconsistent in fluently adding and subtracting within 20 using mental strategies (CCSS.Math. Content.2.0.B.2). Like many students with SLD, TJ has acquired many splinter skills in math, meaning that he typically understands the basic processes of number operations, yet has not acquired fluency when solving problems using these operations.

TJ usually rushes through his written work, failing to complete all problems; he seldom checks for accuracy. Lately, he has been giving up in frustration saying he is terrible at math and that the teacher is not being fair, though there are times when TJ is successful. For example, he demonstrated mastery of the skills in a recent geometry unit where the content was presented anchored to real-life problems.

TJ loves baseball and follows the batting averages of his favorite team players. He is fairly competitive and plays for his middle school team, but continued participation will be contingent on his academic achievement. He enjoys playing video games, especially related to sports. TJ received average grades in social studies and science using technology supports for reading fluency.

At TJ's middle school, students are assigned to grade-level teaching teams that include general education content teachers in the four core academic areas and a special educator. In addition, he has one period that switches each day for the arts and for physical education and one elective each semester. The daily schedule includes a 30-minute study period that is available for review, remediation, or extension. His teaching team meets weekly to collaborate and coordinate their units and lessons; the team monitors the progress of each student, reviewing IEP goals as appropriate to the student, and then using these data to create alternative groups as needed for differentiation. The math teacher identified the following CCSS goal (and subgoals not listed here) as the focus of her upcoming math unit:

■ CCSS.Math.Content.7.NS.A.1: Apply and extend previous understandings of operations with fractions to add, subtract, multiply, and divide rational numbers; represent addition and subtraction on a horizontal or vertical number line diagram.

For TJ, the team identified the following Math Practice Principles to address specifically during this unit:

■ CCSS.Math.Practice.MP1: Make sense of problems and persevere in solving them.
■ CCSS.Math.Practice.MP5: Use appropriate tools strategically.
■ CCSS.Math.Practice.MP6: Attend to precision. (NGA & CCSSO, 2010c)

TJ receives special education support through a co-taught math class; his special educator is highly qualified in mathematics as well as having special education methods expertise. His IEP named a calculator as an accommodation, but his overreliance on the calculator for simple arithmetic actually interferes with his fluency. The teachers decided to incorporate calculator instruction and practice, with the goal of TJ learning when using a calculator was more efficient.

During the co-taught class, the teachers decided to adopt an anchored instruction method (Jayanthi et al., 2008; Murray, Silver-Paicualla, & Helsel, 2007; Steedly, Dragoo, Arafeh, & Luke, 2008; Woodward et al., 2012) where each lesson will be tied to real-world problems, including lessons and assignments that incorporate baseball or other sports using resources from the Baseball Hall of Fame math curriculum as well as the National Council on Teaching Mathematics. Students will be directly taught a problem-solving heuristic such as the STAR strategy (Florida Department of Education, 2010; Mancini & Gagnon, n.d.). STAR is an acronym for the following four steps: search the word problem; translate the problem; answer the problem; and review the solution. To teach the strategy, the teachers will model the think-alouds that students will use for each step in the problem; instruction will proceed from the concrete to the semi-concrete (representational) to the abstract. A routine part of math classes will be small group discussions where students share the strategies they used to solve practice problems. Exit passes that require students to apply their numeracy skills will also be used as informal assessment tools. Students will be required to keep a math journal that will include goals and self-monitoring of their math progress in this unit; TJ will be allowed to dictate using an iPad (all students have iPads in TJ's school).

In addition, the team identified that TJ needs supplemental supports to intensify his instruction in math, including attempting to remediate his poorly developed number sense skills. TJ's special educator will lead a small group of students, including TJ, during the study block.

She will provide explicit instruction and modeling in Base 10 concepts, first using concrete physical manipulatives such as Base 10 blocks, and accessing technology supports such as the National Library of Virtual Manipulatives or the Khan Academy (Jayanthi et al., 2008; Murray et al., 2007; Steedly et al., 2008; Woodward et al., 2012). In this setting, TJ's progress monitoring will include evaluating how he develops in persevering through the assignments; he will chart his progress in both perseverance and in estimation accuracy using a teacher and student co-developed rubric (Steedly et al., 2008). TJ and his special educator will explore iPad applications that will reinforce his numeracy fluency and that he can use for independent practice. Once a week, high school students join the middle school team to offer academic tutoring or social support; TJ will be assigned a tutor to provide additional opportunities to develop numeracy fluency.

SLD in Writing

Selena, a ninth-grade student with a SLD in writing, was first eligible for special education in third grade. She is an avid soccer player and made the Junior Varsity team at her school. In addition, Selena is a promising watercolor impressionist artist using environmental issues as her primary subject; her painting of an oil spill and its impact on wildlife received first place in the local art show last year. She demonstrates excellent verbal skills using a wide vocabulary reflective of her experiences and, in particular, her deep social interest in protecting the environment. She tends to perseverate when debating her position which contributes to some social skill concerns, particularly when others do not agree with her argument on environmental issues; she has some difficulty viewing the issues from a lens different from her own.

CCSS.ELA.Literacy.SL 9-10.1.D standard specifies that students will be able to respond thoughtfully to diverse perspectives, summarize points of agreement and disagreement, and when warranted, qualify or justify their own views and understanding and make new connections in light of the evidence and reasoning presented; this Speaking and Listening standard was noted in Selena's IEP, and Selena receives speech-language services in a group setting to address these skills. Selena is an active member of the GREEN school club that conducts community education and projects supporting the environment. With accommodations, Selena demonstrated good conceptual understanding in her Earth Science class.

Although Selena's reading fluency skills are below grade level, her determination and tenacity help her read content material with the support of video and text read-aloud. She received Cs and Ds in her content classes, but these grades do not reflect her above-average abilities; her grades are impacted by her poor writing skills on essay tests and her reluctance to complete written assignments. She passed the state reading and math tests but has never passed the writing assessment. Error analysis of her test performance as well as observation show that Selena spends a lot of time researching ideas for her writing, but little time actually planning or organizing her writing assignments. In the end, she has less time to generate coherent ideas and does not proofread or revise writing assignments, resulting in multiple mechanical errors such as misspellings and grammatical mistakes. Her handwriting is poor; while using a word processer is helpful, she has not really mastered typing/keyboarding. Dictation or speech-to-text applications reflect the same organizational challenges and illustrate the frustration that Selena is experiencing meeting the writing standards. Her current practice is to avoid writing or to rush through written assignments, using the least amount of effort possible. Her writing performance and grades have the potential to jeopardize her participation in sports or other extracurricular activities and to take college preparatory classes.

Selena's IEP team included Selena and her parents, her special educator, SLP, school administrator, and school counselor, along with her soccer coach, art teacher, and science teacher (who is the advisor for the GREEN club). Selena identified postsecondary education and employment goals that involved attending a 4-year college and possibly a master's degree to prepare for a career as an environmental scientist. Her soccer coach expressed the potential for her to receive an athletic scholarship, and her art teacher shared some universities where it would be possible to double major in art and environmental science. The team discussed that these outcomes were highly dependent on Selena mastering the writing standards and developing her writing skills commensurate with college readiness. The first evidence-based practice that the team introduced at the IEP meeting was for Selena to agree to work with the special educator to identify specific measurable goals toward improving her written production and for which she would be responsible (Gillespie & Graham, 2014). The IEP team agreed that the following ninth grade Common Core Writing Standards would serve as the framework for the development of a rubric evaluating

Selena's ninth-grade written work in content areas. These ninth-grade standards reflect a culmination of developmental elementary and middle school writing standards:

- CCSS.ELA-Literacy.WHST.9-10.1: Write arguments focused on discipline-specific content.
- CCSS.ELA-Literacy.WHST.9-10.1: Introduce precise claim(s), distinguish the claim(s) from alternate or opposing claims, and create an organization that establishes clear relationships among the claim(s), counterclaims, reasons, and evidence.
- CCSS.ELA-Literacy.WHST.9-10.4: Produce clear and coherent writing in which the development, organization, and style are appropriate to task, purpose, and audience.
- CCSS.ELA-Literacy.WHST.9-10.5: Develop and strengthen writing as needed by planning, revising, editing, rewriting, or trying a new approach, focusing on addressing what is most significant for a specific purpose and audience.
- CCSS.ELA-Literacy.WHST.9-10.6: Use technology, including the Internet, to produce, publish, and update individual or shared writing products, taking advantage of technology's capacity to link to other information and to display information flexibly and dynamically. (NGA & CCSSO, 2010b)

With her agreement, Selena's science teacher, special educator, and SLP planned to collaborate to teach and integrate specific strategies to improve Selena's writing skills. Gillespie and Graham (2014) reported that explicit strategy instruction resulted in the greatest improvement in students' writing skills. In particular, they found that using the process of self-regulated strategy development (SRSD) was the most powerful intervention in teaching writing strategies. SRSD includes six stages. First the teacher(s) examine(s) the student's skill deficits and strengths. Then there is a direct discussion with the student enlisting his or her willingness to learn a new strategy. The teacher then models the strategy and has the student memorize the strategy steps. Once the student is fluent, the teacher supports the student in using the strategy, scaffolding as needed, and then offering support as the student uses the strategy independently (Santangelo, Harris, & Graham, 2008). Together, Selena's science and special educators and SLP conferenced with Selena, examining her writing performance and developing goals aligned with the CCSS; they created a rubric to monitor her progress and practice on each of the CCSS standards named above. Once Selena committed to working on improving her writing, the special educator identified a specific writing strategy known by the acronym POW-TREE (Harris, Graham, Mason, & Friedlander, 2008). This strategy follows these steps: P, pick an idea or argument; O, organize and generate notes; T, choose a topic sentence; R, list reasons to support the topic (at least three); E, explain your reasons; E, create an ending; and then, W (of POW), write more.

Continuing the SRSD process, the special educator and SLP began by modeling the POW-TREE strategy, applying it to a persuasive argument regarding the importance of writing and thinking aloud at each step of the strategy. Selena was given an opportunity to note what was easy and what was difficult for her. Together, they identified some ways Selena could stay motivated while writing. Selena memorized the strategy steps, and she and her teacher created a graphic organizer as a visual reminder of the steps. After memorizing the steps, Selena chose to write a newsletter article arguing for the school to add a green roof to the building. Over several days of instruction, as Selena worked on her article, her science teacher and special educator provided feedback and scaffolding to improve her writing and to support her use of the newly learned strategy. Selena practiced editing and revising her article to convince the school board of the merits of her argument. She asked a peer to review and provide feedback as well. Once the writing met the assignment rubric standards, Selena created the GREEN Club newsletter article as a Web-based article that included links to expand the information for those interested as well as pictures of her own artwork. Selena continued to apply the strategy to new writing assignments, including those assignments where she would dictate her narrative. Her art teacher required that she include a narrative essay to accompany her artwork and evaluated her writing using a rubric created by Selena and her team. As Selena became more fluent with using the writing strategy, her confidence increased; she was able to reframe her self-perception as a writer, recognizing that her written work may take longer than most, but that she could achieve the standard with assistance. With ongoing scaffolding and support, Selena began to use the strategy in all of her content courses with increasing success.

CONCLUDING THOUGHTS

The emphasis of the Common Core State Standards on preparation for all students, including students with SLD, to be college and career ready is both promising and daunting. The standards illuminate that educators have held too low expectations for students with learning disabilities which may explain the poor outcomes that many young adults with SLD experience. At the same time, the standards expose many of the difficulties these children and youth have because of their learning disabilities. Educators are called on to create instructional environments where students with SLD can master needed foundational skills and strategies, broaden their skills in critical thinking and strategy use, and discover the essential tools that grant them access to and success in the general curriculum that prepares them for college and careers.

REFERENCES

Barkley, R. (2006). *Attention-deficit hyperactivity disorder: A handbook for diagnosis and treatment* (3rd ed.). New York, NY: Guilford Press.

Berkeley, S., Scruggs, T. E., & Mastropieri, M. A. (2010). Reading comprehension instruction for students with learning disabilities, 1995–2006: A meta-analysis. *Remedial and Special Education, 31*(6) 423–436.

Block, C. C., & Parris, S. R. (Eds.). (2008). *Comprehension instruction: Research-based best practices.* New York, NY: Guilford Press.

Boyle, J. R. (2010). Strategic notetaking for middle-school students with learning disabilities in science classes. *Learning Disability Quarterly, 33*(2), 93–112.

Boyle, J. R. (2012). Note-taking and secondary students with learning disabilities: Challenges

and solutions. *Learning Disabilities Research & Practice, 27*(2), 90–101.

Brown, T. E. (2009). ADD/ADHD and impaired executive function in clinical practice. *Current Attention Disorder Reports, 1*, 37–41.

Bryant, D. P., Goodwin, M., Bryant, B. R., & Higgins, K. (2003). Vocabulary instruction for students with learning disabilities: A review of the research. *Learning Disability Quarterly, 26*(2), 117–128.

Bulgren, J. A., Graner, P. S., & Deshler, D. D. (2013). Literacy challenges and opportunities for students with learning disabilities in social studies and history. *Learning Disabilities Research & Practice, 28*, 17–27.

Calhoun, S. L., & Mayes, S. D. (2005). Processing speed in children with clinical disorders. *Psychology in the Schools, 42*(4), 333–343.

Center on Instruction. (n.d.). http://www.centeroninstruction.org/

Cortiella, C., & Horowitz, S. H. (2014). *The state of learning disabilities: Facts, trends, and emerging issues.* New York, NY: National Center for Learning Disabilities.

Deshler, D., & Schumaker, J. (Eds.). (2006). *Teaching adolescents with disabilities: Accessing the general education with curriculum.* Thousand Oaks, CA: Corwin.

Dexter, D. D., & Hughes, C. A. (2011). Graphic organizers and students with learning disabilities: A meta-analysis. *Learning Disability Quarterly, 34*(1), 51–72.

Dieker, L. A. (2001). What are the characteristics of "effective" middle and high school co-taught teams? *Preventing School Failure, 46*(1), 14–25.

Florida Department of Education. (2010). *Research based strategies for problem-solving in mathematics: K–12.* Tallahassee, FL: Division of Public Schools and Community Education, Bureau of Exceptional Education and Student Services.

Friend, M. (2014a, April). *Scheduling for co-teaching and other inclusive practices: Common problems, realistic solutions.* Paper presented at the Annual Convention of the Council, for Exceptional Children, Philadelphia, PA.

Friend, M. (2014b). *Special education: Contemporary perspectives for school professionals.* Columbus, OH: Pearson.

Friend, M., & Bursuck, W. D. (2011). *Including students with special needs: A practical guide for classroom teachers* (6th ed.). Columbus, OH: Pearson.

Friend, M., & Cook, L. (2013). *Interactions: Collaboration skills for school professionals* (7th ed.). Columbus, OH: Pearson.

Fuchs, L., Powell, S., & Zumeta, R. (2014, April). *Addressing the needs of student with persistent math difficulties through intensive intervention.* Paper presented at the Council for Exceptional Children Annual Convention, Philadelphia, PA.

Gajria, M., Jitendra, A. K., Sood, S., & Sacks, G. (2007). Improving comprehension of expository text in students with LD: A research synthesis. *Journal of Learning Disabilities, 40*(3), 210–225.

Gareis, C. R., & Grant, L. W. (2008). *Teacher-made assessments: How to connect curriculum, instruction, and student learning.* Larchmont, NY: Eye on Education.

Gersten, R., Chard, D. J., Jayanthi, M., Baker, S. K., Morphy, P., & Flojo, J. (2009). Mathematics instruction for students with learning disabilities: A meta-analysis of instructional components. *Review of Educational Research, 79*, 1202–1242.

Gillespie, A., & Graham, S. (2014). A meta-analysis of writing interventions for students with learning disabilities. *Exceptional Children, 80*(4), 454–464.

Graham, S., & Harris, K. R. (2013). Common Core State Standards, writing, and students with LD: Recommendations. *Learning Disabilities Research & Practice, 28*, 28–37.

Guare, R., Dawson, P., & Guare, C. (2013). *Smart but scattered teens: The "executive skills" program for helping teens reach their potential.* New York, NY: Guilford Press.

Haager, D., & Vaughn, S. (2013). The Common Core State Standards and reading: Interpretations and implications for elementary students with learning disabilities. *Learning Disabilities Research & Practice, 28*, 5–16.

Hallahan, D. P., Lloyd, J. W., Kauffman, J. M., Weiss, M. P., & Martinez, E. A. (2005). *Learning disabilities: Foundations, characteristics, and effective teaching* (3rd ed.). Columbus, OH: Pearson.

Harris, K. R., Graham, S., Mason, L., & Friedlander, B. (2008). *Powerful writing strategies for all students.* Baltimore, MD: Brookes.

Hunt, J. H., & Little, M. E. (2014). Intensifying interventions for students by identifying and remediating conceptual understandings in mathematics. *Teaching Exceptional Children, 46*(6), 187–196.

Individuals with Disabilities Education Improvement Act of 2004, Pub. L. No. 108-446, 20 U.S.C. § 1400et seq. (2004).

Jayanthi, M., Gersten, R., & Baker, S. (2008). *Mathematics instruction for students with learning disabilities or difficulty learning mathematics: A guide for teachers.* Portsmouth, NH: RMC Research Corporation, Center on Instruction.

Jitendra, A. K., Edwards, L. L., Sacks, G., & Jacobson, L. A. (2004). What research says about vocabulary instruction for students with learning disabilities. *Exceptional Children, 70*(3), 299–322.

Kim, A., Vaughn, S., Wanzek, J., & Wei, S. (2004). Graphic organizers and their effects on the reading comprehension of students with LD: A synthesis of research. *Journal of Learning Disabilities, 37*(2), 105–118.

Kilpatrick, J., Swafford, J., & Findell, B. (Eds.) (2001). *Adding it up: Helping children learn mathematics. Mathematics Learning Study Committee, National Research Council.* Washington DC: National Academy Press. Retrieved from http://www.nap.edu/openbook.php?record_id=9822

Leko, M. M., & Brownell, M. T. (2009). Crafting professional development for special educators: What every school leader should know. *Teaching Exceptional Children, 42*(4), 64–70.

Lerner, J., & Johns, B. (2009). *Learning disabilities and related mild disabilities: Characteristics, teaching strategies, and new directions.* Boston, MA: Houghton Mifflin.

Lienemann, T. O., & Reid, R. (2006). Self-regulated strategy development for students with learning disabilities. *Teacher Education and Special Education, 29*(1), 3–11.

Mancini, P., & Gagnon, J. (n.d.). *Mathematics instruction for middle school students with learning disabilities.* The Access Center. Retrieved July 1, 2014, from http://digilib.gmu.edu/jspui/bitstream/1920/284/1/MathSlforMiddleSchoolStudentswithLD.2.pdf

Martinussen, R., & Major, A. (2011). Working memory weaknesses in students with ADHD: Implications for instruction. *Theory Into Practice, 50*(1), 68–75.

Mayes, S. D., Calhoun, S. L., & Crowell, E. W. (2000). Learning disabilities and ADHD:

Overlapping spectrum disorders. *Journal of Learning Disabilities, 33*, 417–424.

Meltzer, L. (2010). *Promoting executive function in the classroom.* New York, NY: Guilford Press.

Meltzer, L., Katzir-Cohen, T., Miller, L., Reddy, R., & Roditi, B. (2004). Academic self-perceptions, effort, and strategy use in students with learning disabilities: Changes over time. *Learning Disabilities Research & Practice, 19*(2), 99–108.

Morgan, J. J., Brown, N. B., Hsiao, Y., Howerter, C., Juniel, P., Sedano, L., & Wendie, L. C. (2013). Unwrapping academic standards to increase the achievement of students with disabilities. *Intervention in School and Clinic, 49*(3), 131–141.

Murawski, W. W. (2012). Ten tips for using co-planning time more efficiently. *Teaching Exceptional Children, 44*, 8–15.

Murray, B., Silver-Paicualla, H., & Helsel, F. I. (2007, February). Improving basic mathematics instruction: Promising technology resources for students with special needs. *Technology in Action, 2*(5). Arlington, VA: Council for Exceptional Children Technology Media Division.

Murray, C. S., Coleman, M. A., Vaughn, S., Wanzek, J., & Roberts, G. (2012). *Designing and delivering intensive interventions: A teacher's toolkit.* Portsmouth, NH: RMC Research Corporation, Center on Instruction.

National Center on Intensive Intervention. (n.d.). http://www.intensiveintervention.org/

National Center on Universal Design for Learning. (n.d.). http://www.udlcenter.org/

National Governors Association Center for Best Practices & Council of Chief State School Officers. (2010a). *Common Core State Standards.* Washington, DC: Author. Retrieved from http://www.corestandards.org/read-the-standards/

National Governors Association Center for Best Practices & Council of Chief State School Officers. (2010b). *Common Core State Standards for English Language Arts and literacy in history/social studies, science, and technical subjects.* Washington, DC: Author. Retrieved from http://www.corestandards.org/ELA-Literacy/

National Governors Association Center for Best Practices & Council of Chief State School Officers. (2010c). *Common Core State Standards for mathematics.* Washington, DC: Author. Retrieved from http://www.corestandards.org/Math/

National Reading Panel. (2000). *Teaching children to read: An evidence-based assessment of the scientific research literature on reading and its implications for reading instruction.* Retrieved from http://www.nichd.nih.gov/publications/pubs/nrp/pages/smallbook.aspx

Newman, L., Wagner, M., Huang, T., Shaver, D., Knokey, A.-M., Yu, J., . . . Cameto, R. (2011). *Secondary school programs and performance of students with disabilities. A special topic report of findings from the National Longitudinal Transition Study-2 (NLTS2) (NCSER 2012-3000).* U.S. Department of Education. Washington, DC: National Center for Special Education Research.

Phillips, V., & Hughes, R. L. (2012, December 4). Teacher collaboration: The essential common-core ingredient. *Education Week.* Retrieved from http://www.edweek.org/ew/articles/2012/12/05/13hughes.h32.html

Powell, S. R., Fuchs, L. S., & Fuchs, D. (2013). Reaching the mountaintop: Addressing the common core standards in mathematics for students with mathematics difficulties. *Learning Disabilities Research & Practice, 28*(1), 38–48.

Reid, R., Trout, A. L., & Schartz, M. (2005). Self-regulation interventions for children with attention deficit/hyperactivity disorder. *Exceptional Children, 71*(4), 361–377.

Santangelo, T., Harris, K. R., & Graham, S. (2008). Using self-regulated strategy development to support students who have "Trubol giting thangs into werds." *Remedial and Special Education, 29*(2), 78–89.

Scruggs, T. E., & Mastropieri, M. A. (2000). The effectiveness of mnemonic instruction for students with learning disabilities and behavior problem: An update and research synthesis. *Journal of Behavioral Education, 10*(23), 163–173.

Scruggs, T. E., Mastropieri, M. A., Berkeley, S., & Graetz, J. E. (2010). Do special education interventions improve learning of secondary content? A meta-analysis. *Remedial and Special Education, 31*, 437–449.

Scruggs, T. E., Mastropieri, M. A., Berkeley, S. L., & Marshak, L. (2010). Mnemonic strategies: Evidence-based practice and practice-based evidence. *Intervention in School and Clinic, 46*(2), 79–86.

Sideridis, G. D. (2003). On the origins of helpless behavior of students with learning disabilities: Avoidance motivation? *International Journal of Educational Research, 39*, 497–517.

Solis, M. R., Ciullo, S., Vaughn, S., Pyle, N., Hassaram, B., & Leroux, A. (2012). Reading comprehension interventions for middle school students with learning disabilities: A synthesis of 30 years of research. *Journal of Learning Disabilities, 45*(4), 327–340.

Stecker, P. M., Fuchs, D., & Fuchs, L. S. (2008). Progress monitoring as essential practice within response to intervention. *Rural Special Education Quarterly, 27*(4), 10–17.

Steedly, K., Dragoo, K., Arafeh, S., & Luke, S. (2008). Effective mathematics instruction. *Evidence for Education (III, 1).* NICHY. Retrieved from http://nichcy.org/wp-content/uploads/docs/eemath.pdf

Stevenson, N. (2014, April). *Making time for everything: Creating time for intervention without sacrificing core instruction.* Paper presented at the Council for Exceptional Children Annual Convention, Philadelphia, PA.

Swanson, E., Hairrell, A., Kent, S., Ciullo, S., Wanzek, J. A., & Vaughn, S. (2012). A synthesis and meta-analysis of reading interventions using social studies content for students with learning disabilities. *Journal of Learning Disabilities, 20*(10), 1–18.

Swanson, H. L., & Deshler, D. (2003). Instructing adolescents with learning disabilities: Converting a meta-analysis to practice. *Journal of Learning Disabilities, 36*(2), 124–135.

Thompson, S. J., Morse, A. B., Sharpe, M., & Hall, S. (2005). *Accommodations manual: How to select, administer and evaluate use of accommodations and assessment for students with disabilities* (2nd ed.). Council for Chief State School Officers. Retrieved from http://www.ccsso.org/Documents/2005/Accommodations_Manual_How_2005.pdf

Tomlinson, C. A., & McTighe, J. (2006). *Integrating differentiated instruction and understanding by design: Connecting content and kids.* Alexandria, VA: ASCD.

U.S. Department of Education, Office of Special Education Programs. (2014). *35th Annual Report to Congress on the Implementation of the Individuals with Disabilities Education Act, 2013.* Retrieved from http://www.ed.gov/about/reports/annual/osep

Vaughn, S., Klingner, J. K., Swanson, E. A., Boardman, A. G., Roberts, G., Mohammed, S. S., & Stillman-Spisak, S. J. (2011). Efficacy of collaborative strategic reading with middle school students. *American Educational Research Journal, 48*, 938–964.

Vaughn, S., Wanzek, J., Murray, C. S., & Roberts, G. (2012). *Intensive interventions for students struggling in reading and mathematics: A practice guide.* Portsmouth, NH: RMC Research Corporation, Center on Instruction.

Watson, S. R., Gable, R. A., Gear, S. B., & Hughes, K. C. (2012). Evidence-based strategies for improving the reading comprehension of secondary students: Implications for students with learning disabilities. *Learning Disabilities Research & Practice, 27*(2), 79–89.

Wei, X., Blackorby, J., & Schiller, E. (2011). Growth in reading achievement of students with disabilities, ages 7–17. *Exceptional Children, 78*(1), 89–106.

Woodward, J., Beckmann, S., Driscoll, M., Franke, M., Herzig, P., Jitendra, A., . . . Ogbuehi, P. (2012). *Improving mathematical problem solving in grades 4 through 8: A practice guide* (NCEE 2012-4055). Washington, DC: National Center for Education Evaluation and Regional Assistance, Institute of Education Sciences, U.S. Department of Education. Retrieved from http://ies.ed.gov/ncee/wwc/publications_reviews.aspx#pubsearch/

CHAPTER 9

Students With Severe Disabilities at the Secondary Level

Perry Flynn

Students at the secondary level are often given decreasing attention by speech-language pathologists (SLPs) at this critical time in their development. Much attention in school-based speech-language pathology is focused on early intervention with preschool-aged children and students in the early elementary grades. The Common Core State Standards (CCSS) propose college and career readiness for all (NGA & CCSSO, 2010), thus necessitating services for high school students in addition to those in earlier grades. However, services to high school students tend to be meager for a variety of reasons (Ehren, 2002). According to the National Longitudinal Transition Studies (Wagner, Blackorby, Cameto, Hebbeler, & Newman, 1993; Wagner et al., 2005), this population is at risk for higher dropout rates, higher absenteeism, lower grade point averages, higher rates of course failure, increased recurrence of poor self-esteem, higher rates of inappropriate behaviors, and lower rates of pursuing postsecondary education. There is also a perception among some professionals that by adolescence little progress can be achieved by an SLP (Ehren, 2000, 2002).

The general information section of the CCSS states that the standards enable high school students to "graduate from high school prepared to succeed in college, career and life" (NGA & CCSSO, 2010). This chapter highlights how the CCSS can be used by SLPs to help secondary students, particularly those with intellectual or multiple disabilities, meet the high expectations of the standards by becoming college and career ready.

THE ROLE OF SPEECH–LANGUAGE PATHOLOGISTS

In order for SLPs to connect their services fully to the CCSS, they must engage in a variety of activities beyond simply providing direct services to students. An increasing number of school districts around the country are adopting a workload approach (ASHA, n.d., 2010) to better define all the duties school-based SLPs need to complete in the course of their work. ASHA defines the workload of an SLP as falling into four categories:

- direct services to students;
- indirect activities that support students in the least restrictive environment and general education curriculum;
- indirect services that support students' educational programs; and
- activities that support compliance with federal, state, and local mandates (ASHA, n.d., 2010).

An interprofessional approach to serving adolescent students with intellectual or multiple disabilities is particularly important due to the increasing number of collaborators involved in adapting the standards to meet the individualized and unique needs of this population.

Direct Services to Students

It is widely recognized within the school environment that SLPs provide direct services to students. Direct services that SLPs provide to help students master CCSS include

- evaluating students to know more about their learning for a variety of reasons including but not limited to determining eligibility;
- implementing Individual Education Programs (IEPS) and Individual Family Service Plans (IFSPs); and
- providing direct intervention to students using a continuum of service delivery options.

These direct services are an essential portion of the SLP's role within a school.

However, SLPs also provide a number of additional services that are discussed later in this chapter.

Evaluating Students

As with any population, the assessment of adolescent students should include a variety of assessment instruments. These instruments include observations, vocational assessments, classroom work samples, and written or oral language samples in addition to standardized tests. Especially for students with intellectual disabilities, these assessment instruments should include observations in a variety of environments and nonstandard measures (Larson & McKinley, 2003).

Although standard assessment tools may help the SLP determine the existence of a speech or language disability, they are not related to the CCSS or to what may be functional communication in the student's academic, social, or vocational environments. Additionally, because these instruments typically do not have students with intellectual disabilities in their norming group, the scores are neither reliable nor valid for this population. However, these scores may be used for informational purposes to describe the student's areas of relative strength and need. Although standard assessments may be used, it is important to not base eligibility decisions on the scores for this population because of their previously stated lack of validity. Nonstandard or curriculum-based assessments are much more likely to reveal strengths and areas of need as they relate to the standards (Lain & Kamhi, 2003).

The SLP should, to the extent possible, conduct environmental assessments (Larson & McKinley, 2003) across a variety of locations to establish a true picture of the student's communication skills. The SLP may want to observe and record data in such locations as the classroom, the cafeteria, or the vocational settings. By observing the student in multiple settings, the SLP will learn if and how the student's communication skills vary across environments. Strengths discovered by these assessments may be used to facilitate change in areas of weakness. For example, a student may be able to use the following standard in the cafeteria but not in the classroom: "Adapt speech to a variety of contexts and tasks, demonstrating command of formal English when indicated or appropriate" (CCSS.ELA-LITERACY. SL.9-10.6) (NGA & CCSSO, 2010).

Nonstandard or curriculum-based measures can be tailored to assess the communication concepts found in the CCSS. Results from these measures are often very informative for an SLP developing educationally relevant interventions within the school setting. Quality assessment information not only helps the SLP plan for intervention, but also informs the educational team of appropriate job or educational placements for the secondary student. Communication strengths and weaknesses may also suggest suitable (and unsuitable) vocational placements when considering jobs or post-high-school education opportunities. For example, a student may have difficulty with the standard "Engage effectively in a range of collaborative discussions (one-on-one, in groups, and teacher-led) with diverse partners on Grade 8 topics, texts, and issues, building on others' ideas and expressing their own clearly" (CCSS.ELA-LITERACY.SL.8.1) (NGA & CCSSO, 2010). If this is the case, the student might not be a good candidate for a greeter or receptionist at a doctor's office or retirement community. After the educational team settles on placements where the student is likely to be successful, it can begin to plan goals and intervention strategies for the student.

Implementation of IEPs

The Individualized Education Program (IEP) process documents all of the special education services a student will receive and those that are considered part of direct services in the workload model. A thoughtfully written IEP tied to the standards will help the educational team, parents, and student have a clear vision of the anticipated outcomes for that student (Rudebusch, 2012).

Collaboration With Members of the Educational Team

An important part of the IEP process is the creation of an educational team that can make thoughtful decisions about the student's course of study. As students become older, additional people may or should become members of their educational team. These members may include vocational rehabilitation counselors, job coaches, work supervisors, teachers, parents, child nutrition specialists, and, most importantly, the student. The inclusion of all these members ensures that students will be college or career ready and competitive in the global marketplace when they leave school. The standards provide the opportunity for all of the previously mentioned professionals to work together to exponentially improve outcomes for students. A thoughtfully assembled IEP team provides the foundation for collaboration that best serves adolescent students.

Frequently, students are left out of decisions made by the IEP team, even though such decisions have a significant impact on their lives. Including students in their educational teams is both helpful and enlightening. Students can inform the team what they prioritize as goals for themselves. Including the student fosters self-determination and may help the entire team focus on issues of highest priority. The student should top the list of collaborators on IEP teams and be included in all decisions that are made on his or her behalf. Student involvement in determining goals, planning intervention, and collecting data is proving invaluable in facilitating the student's mastery of special education goals and the standards (Flynn, 2010).

Supporting Students' Self-Determination

Self-determination is the ability of an individual to make choices and decisions based on their own preferences and interests, to monitor and regulate their own actions, and to be goal-oriented and self-directing (Wehmeyer, n.d.). Increasingly, these skills are being valued and taught to secondary-level students with an IEP. In many cases, SLPs are the ideal professionals for helping instruct students in the skills of self-determination. The CCSS have many goals that support independent thinking and sharing of personal perspectives, which include the language skills required for strong self-advocacy. For example, CCSS.ELA-LITERACY.SL.11-12.4 states, "Present information, findings, and supporting evidence, conveying a clear and distinct perspective, such that listeners can follow the line of reasoning, alternative or opposing perspectives are addressed, and the organization, development, substance, and style are appropriate

to purpose, audience, and a range of formal and informal tasks" (NGA & CCSSO, 2010). In accomplishing this standard as it relates to self-determination, students will be able to speak for themselves and inform the IEP team of their hopes for their future. At age 16, student input is mandated by the IDEA and should be valued by the educational team. Unfortunately, student participation in the IEP process is often minimal. By fully implementing the expectations of IDEA regarding student participation in IEP teams, the IEP process will become richer, as students can inform the team of their perceived areas of strengths and needs, specify preferences, prioritize services, and suggest goals.

SLPs help provide lifelong advocacy skills for students when their intervention includes the skills involved in self-determination that are represented in the CCSS. Several other standards also speak to the student's ability to share his or her own perspectives and influence conversations, including

- CCSS.ELA-LITERACY.SL.11-12.1.C: Propel conversations by posing and responding to questions that probe reasoning and evidence; ensure a hearing for a full range of positions on a topic or issue; clarify, verify, or challenge ideas and conclusions; and promote divergent and creative perspectives.
- CCSS.ELA-LITERACY.SL.11-12.1.D: Respond thoughtfully to diverse perspectives; synthesize comments, claims, and evidence made on all sides of an issue; resolve contradictions when possible; and determine what additional information or research is required to deepen the investigation or complete the task.

- CCSS.ELA-LITERACY.SL.11-12.2: Integrate multiple sources of information presented in diverse formats and media (e.g., visually, quantitatively, orally) in order to make informed decisions and solve problems, evaluating the credibility and accuracy of each source and noting any discrepancies among the data.
- CCSS.ELA-LITERACY.SL.11-12.3: Evaluate a speaker's point of view, reasoning, and use of evidence and rhetoric, assessing the stance, premises, links among ideas, word choice, points of emphasis, and tone used (NGA & CCSSO, 2010).

Present Level of Academic Achievement and Functional Performance (PLAAFP)

After completing an assessment that focuses on CCSS and the application of the standards across a variety of educational environments, the IEP team has the information necessary for writing the individualized Present Level of Academic Achievement and Functional Performance (PLAAFP) section of the IEP, which describes the student's areas of strength and need. This narrative should speak to how the student's areas of need affect his ability to master the standards. Areas of strength are often targeted in therapy to remediate deficits. The PLAAFP should include data and focus on academic achievement and functional communication performance. It should tie special education services to general education and the CCSS. A well-written PLAAFP will drive all the services documented in the IEP. Educationally relevant goals and service delivery result from a function-ally descriptive PLAAFP. After the IEP team has comprehensive knowledge of strengths and areas of need found in the PLAAFP, it can set educationally relevant goals to help the student master the standards of the CCSS.

Academic and Functional Goals Tied to the CCSS

IEP goals should address student needs as they relate to the standards from the "lens" of the SLP. For example, when addressing CCSS.ELA-LITERACY.SL.2.1.A ("Follow agreed-upon rules for discussions [e.g., gaining the floor in respectful way's, listening to others with care, speaking one at a time about the topics and texts under discussion]"), the SLP will see that turn taking, active listening, and topic maintenance are all requisite skills for mastery of this goal (NGA & CCSSO, 2010). IEP goals should be written for the speech and language underpinnings of the standard rather than simply be copied from the standard itself. For instance, to master the above standard, students will have to

- Use appropriate pragmatic skills to gain the attention of conversational partners.
- Use active listening skills.
- Comprehend the information provided by the conversational partner.
- Take conversational turns.
- Maintain a topic.
- Have or gain some knowledge of the topic.
- Use a polite tone of voice.

Although the majority of speech and language targets found in this goal appear to be pragmatic skills, other language domains (syntax, semantics, phonology, morphology) are present in more obscure ways. Students must understand the semantic meaning of vocabulary and content while having knowledge of syntactic rules of the language to formulate interrogative and declarative sentences with their conversational partner. They must have knowledge of English morphology to encode their words so their message is accurately perceived by the listener. Finally, they must have proficient phonological skills so that they can produce the speech sounds composing their message accurately. By reviewing each standard through the lens of an SLP, the underlying speech and language skills that contribute to the standard's mastery will be made evident.

Teachers, parents, and the student will help SLPs determine strengths and needs by providing information about performance on grade-level standards. Some students with mild intellectual disabilities will achieve mastery of the English Language Arts standards on the CCSS. However, others with more severe intellectual disabilities will achieve mastery of standards by accessing their most essential elements, also known as extended standards, through Dynamic Learning Maps (http://dynamiclearningmaps.org/) or through the National Center and State Collaborative (http://www.ncscpartners.org/resources). These standards extend the CCSS to its most essential and basic skills so that all students will have access and can become college and career ready. The set of extended standards used by the SLP will depend on the state in which the student resides. Currently, states have the option to adopt the set of extended standards they choose.

The CCSS speaks to inclusion of the principles of Universal Design for Learning (UDL), to make the standards acces-sible to all students, including those with more severe disabilities. UDL is a set of principles for curriculum development that emphasizes alternative approaches for assessment and instruction, giving all students equal opportunities to learn (Center for Applied Special Technology [CAST], n.d.). Teachers and SLPs use the principles of UDL to help all students succeed, differentiating instruction to tailor learning to the unique needs of students. The collaboration between teachers and SLPs exponentially improves outcomes for students.

This concept is picked up in the work of the Dynamic Learning Maps (DLM) and the National Center and State Collaborative (NCSC) in developing standards for students with more significant disabilities that are aligned with the CCSS (Kansas University, n.d.; NCSC, n.d.). For example, in the area of Reading and Language Arts, Key Ideas and Details, the CCSS includes this third-grade standard: "Ask and answer questions to demonstrate understanding of a text, referring explicitly to the text as the basis for the answers" (CCSS.ELA-LITERACY.RI.3.1) (NGA & CCSSO, 2010). The essential elements of that standard from the DLM include, "Answer who and what questions to demonstrate understanding of details in a text" (Kansas University, n.d.). The NCSC's Strand 4: Reading Informational Texts (RI) states: "Recognize and use knowledge of expository text structures (e.g., sequence, description, definition, compare-contrast, cause-effect) and genre-specific features to read and comprehend informational texts: Identify, compare, and draw inferences about concepts, central ideas, point of view, and supporting details" and addresses a similar point (NCSC, n.d.). NCSC is speaking to the importance of using reading to bring meaning at the textual level and understanding of the unique genre features, text structures, and purposes of print and non-print informational texts. The use of both the DLM essential elements and NCSC standards will assist SLPs and their teams in identifying appropriate standards for this population of students.

Students with intellectual disabilities access the standards by mastering the most basic essential elements. Both DLM and the NCSC have assessments to determine if students are meeting the extended standards in a standardized, systematic way. Acquisition of the extensions of the standards will prepare students with intellectual disabilities for career and technical education or employment past their high school years.

Accommodations and Modifications

IEP teams include accommodations and modifications to the educational environment as part of the IEP. The student's teachers and related services providers will implement these accommodations and modifications throughout the day. All members of the IEP team and other educators may need some training from the SLP on how to implement the accommodations and modifications to the content they teach. By providing training to these educators, the IEP is delivered with fidelity across content areas and educational settings. Some examples of accommodations and modifications may include use of voice-to-text devices to complete creative writing assignments, a dedicated teacher assistant, or instruction for all educational staff involved with the student on the use of a particular strategy that facilitates communication for the student. Any accommodation or modification that improves access to the general curriculum given the student's disability and areas of need is permissible, if the IEP team agrees on its necessity.

Service Delivery Providers

After the IEP team creates goals for the student, it should determine what service delivery providers are required to meet those goals. Unfortunately, the team typically predetermines the service delivery providers, and each person writes goals in his or her area of expertise with little collaboration. This method does not reflect the sequence intended by the IDEA. Instead, the team should work collaboratively, integrating goals whenever possible to avoid "siloing" services. Service delivery providers should integrate speech language services, occupational therapy, physical therapy, reading, and special education to the extent possible in all educational activities (Flynn, 2010).

The following is an illustrative IEP integrated goal where the SLP will provide direction and other team members (e.g., special education teacher, occupational therapist, physical therapist) will expect students to use those skills. All team members may share responsibility for data collection: "The student will independently initiate conversations using his augmentative communication device and express his wants and needs in three-word utterances to a variety of conversational partners across multiple academic settings (cafeteria, physical education class, drama club . . .) on at least four occasions during the school day." Integrated goals such as these help multiple service delivery providers work as a team to meet all the needs of the student. SLPs can help the team focus on functional communication skills required for work and daily living.

Standards-Based IEPs

Many states or districts require that the CCSS be cited in the IEP as they relate to goals, accommodations, and modifications. This practice ensures that special education professionals tie their services to the standards so that all students achieve mastery. These workload activities are required for districts to be compliant with the federal, state, and local mandates that govern the services SLPs provide. Rudebusch (2012) describes a procedure by which IEP teams use the standards and IEP process to problem solve and provide the best educational outcomes for students. Although general education teachers are experts in the standards, SLPs and special educators are experts in differentiated instruction. During the collaborative IEP process, SLPs help the team develop goals based on the standards that meet the communication and language needs of the student. The specially designed instruction documented by the IEP supports the student in mastery of the standards and allows the student to progress in the general education curriculum.

Transition Services

The IDEA provides for transition services for students with disabilities beginning at age 16. IDEA states that "transition services means a coordinated set of activities for a child with a disability that is designed to be within a results-oriented process, that is focused on improving the academic and functional achievement of the child with a disability to facilitate the child's movement from school post-school activities, including postsecondary education, vocational education, inte-grated employment (including supported employment), continuing and adult education, adult services, independent living, or community participation." (IDEA, 34 CFR §300.43(a)(1)). This requirement reflects the IEP team's consideration of anticipated living situations, hobbies, social life, work, and continued education for students with disabilities. In too many cases, the transition plan is not carefully considered and is simply one more piece of the IEP.

There are unique communication needs for a variety of jobs that the SLP will be able to identify in collaboration with a variety of professionals at school or in the community. Similarly, participation in hobbies or an array of living situations requires a wide range of communication abilities. For example, a person who plans to live independently will require the communication skills to complete such tasks as connecting utilities, reporting problems to a landlord, and reading and understanding lease agreements, while a person who lives in a sheltered living situation will not have these requirements. The involvement of vocational rehabilitation and other community-based agencies is important at this stage of the student's academic career. SLPs may also be employed by these agencies, as the agencies acknowledge the expertise they bring to encourage success for students as they transition to community-based settings.

SLPs and other related service providers (e.g., occupational therapists, physical therapists, and guidance counselors) can be important contributors to successful transitions for special education students. The CCSS states that all students should be college and career ready to be globally competitive citizens. Sadly, this is often not the case for many students with disabilities. The U.S. Bureau of Labor

Statistics (2015) reported in 2014 that approximately 82% of individuals with disabilities of working age were either unemployed or had never entered the workforce. There are likely many underlying reasons for this dismal statistic. It is often not economically advantageous for people who collect disability benefits to work, as in most cases, they will lose monetary support if they enter the workforce. Further, the jobs for which this population is qualified may not pay as much as disability support. In addition, few employers are willing to take the risks, modify the work environment, and/or provide the additional training required to employ a person with disabilities.

SLPs are essential to facilitating transition services for students, as they collaborate with other professionals and together they serve students directly and indirectly. These collaborators act as advocates for people with disabilities by seeking out and educating employers who may not likely consider employing this population. In collaboration with job coaches, teachers, and vocational rehabilitation specialists, SLPs can help cultivate internship or work sites for students with disabilities. They can support businesses in modifying the environment to facilitate the success of students and in creating a successful work environment for everyone regardless of disability.

Until relatively recently, related service providers were generally not directly involved in transition services. Increasingly, however, educational teams are valuing the input of related service providers and involving them directly in transition planning for students with disabilities. Services they provide may include helping engineer environments, supporting job coaches and employers, or providing direct services to students at job

settings. For example, if an SLP observes a student who is working at an elder care facility, the SLP may find opportunities for the student to use greeting behaviors, to ask residents questions, and to implement snack or mealtime rituals that encourage social interactions for both parties. SLPs may also find opportunities for students to be included in regular education activities at school. With support from an SLP, students with disabilities can participate in plays, manage high school sports teams, deliver messages, answer telephones, or work at a variety of other jobs on the high school campus.

Students with disabilities often learn skills situationally. However, they may require the direct instruction of the SLP in the natural environments, where communication occurs. For students with intellectual disabilities, skills learned in the speech room often do not transfer well to other environments (Vicker, 2009). In order for these students to be successful in a work setting, speech and language intervention must be provided in the environment where the skills will be used. School-based SLPs must be able and willing to provide intervention off-campus to help students generalize their success to the workplace. One manner in which SLPs may provide direct instruction at the work site includes working with the student on greeting patrons. The SLP may anticipate many of the questions asked of a greeter and script the student through answers. Similarly, the SLP may help the student know what questions to ask of a potential employer or script answers to frequently asked interview questions.

Many students will be placed in off-campus settings during their high school career to begin the transition process. The SLP needs to assess both the speech and language demands of the work setting and the student's ability to meet those demands. SLPs play a crucial role in all stages of this process. In supporting transition services, SLPs work with job coaches, vocational rehabilitation workers, and other educational team members to provide both diagnostic and therapeutic services to students in career technical or post-secondary settings after high school. For example, the SLP may observe a student who works for a landscaping company and collaborate with the job coach to encourage the student to ask for clarification in order to understand directions accurately. The SLP may work with the job team to write down instructions and break them into a task analysis sequence for each duty at the work site similar to this:

- Help unload the truck.
- Fill the mower with gas from the red can.
- Put your glasses and ear plugs on and begin to blow leaves.
- Ask the boss if you can do anything else after all the leaves are blown to the curb.
- Help load the equipment back onto the truck.

This task analysis would relate directly to standard CCSS.ELA-Literacy.RST.6-8.3: "Follow precisely a multistep procedure when carrying out experiments, taking measurements, or performing technical tasks" (NGA & CCSSO, 2010).

Although community-based services continue to be related to the CCSS, they may look very different than those previously provided on campus. This type of intervention often focuses on the vocabulary of the work setting and social interactions. Pragmatic skills may be of utmost

importance in supporting student success on job sites. Other communication skills that may be of particular importance include

- following directions;
- following a sequence;
- asking for clarification;
- engaging in collaborative conversations;
- providing clarification or help;
- giving directions of one or two steps;
- asking questions of another employee, boss, or vocational rehabilitation worker;
- comprehending information; and
- reading instructions and signs.

Many of the CCSS at the high school level related to these skills are reflected in CCSS.ELA-LITERACY.SL.9-10.4: "Present information, findings, and supporting evidence clearly, concisely, and logically such that listeners can follow the line of reasoning and the organization, development, substance, and style are appropriate to purpose, audience, and task" (NGA & CCSSO, 2010). It is also necessary to look at standards from earlier grade levels to find some of the skills needed in the workforce. Examples of such standards are listed below:

- CCSS.ELA-LITERACY.SL.3.1.C: Ask questions to check understanding of information presented, stay on topic, and link their comments to the remarks of others.
- CCSS.ELA-LITERACY.SL.3.1.D: Explain their own ideas and understanding in light of the discussion (NGA & CCSSO, 2010).

Least Restrictive Environment

One of the tenets of the IDEA is to serve all students in the least restrictive environment (LRE). This means that, as much as possible, SLPs and special educators should attempt to serve students in natural education environments. Although students who experience autism and intellectual disabilities often spend much of their day in self-contained special education classrooms, removed from typically developing peers, it is incumbent on the IEP team to strive to place these students with typically developing peers as much as possible. In addition to suggesting a place for special education, LRE also speaks to whether these services will be provided with nondisabled peers. The IEP team should look for opportunities for special education students to be intentionally and thoughtfully included with their age peers. Lunch and many enrichment classes, including drama and home economics, provide prime opportunities for special education students to interact with their typically developing peers. When services can be provided in these alternative locations, it affords the SLP and special educators the opportunity to enlist the help of the students' peers during therapeutic activities. Typically, developing peers have reported that they too benefit from being involved with special education students. The CCSS speak to the importance of exposure to many different kinds of people and cultures, so the inclusion of students with disabilities facilitates all students' experience with this standard.

A continuum of service delivery exists under the IDEA. Everything along this continuum, from consultative/collaborative services to a self-contained special education classroom, is available for every special education student. The IEP team should consider what constitutes LRE. Although LRE suggests a place because it includes the word "environment," the phrase also speaks to whether the student will be served with (or without) typically developing peers. The goal of every special education provider should be to serve students in classroom environments when the class is together and when it is a time that works well with the student. The LRE can include the classroom and a variety of other settings such as the playground, the cafeteria, or a field trip. There is certainly a place for the quiet, one-on-one or small group environment of the speech room; however, all special education providers should move students to the LRE as often as possible in accordance with the IDEA and the students' preparation for college and career readiness.

Many adolescents, especially those with intellectual disabilities, will require the services of an SLP during high school as they begin to transition to work or higher education. Therefore, as discussed earlier in this chapter, SLPs who serve this population may need to provide direct intervention in work environments or consultative services with job coaches or employers at vocational sites. Provision of services in these natural locations represents the LRE for these students. Figure 9–1 depicts the continuum of service delivery from the nonrestrictive environments used in consultative and collaborative services on the left side to the very restrictive environments found in separate schools where all students have disabilities on the right side. Services provided in classrooms or job sites serve students in natural educational settings, while those provided in speech rooms and resource classrooms have no

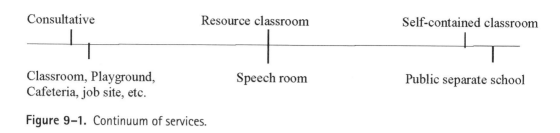

Figure 9–1. Continuum of services.

typically developing peers and are thus more restrictive. Services provided in self-contained classrooms or in public separate schools also have no typically developing peers included. SLPs and other related service providers (e.g., occupational therapists, physical therapists, or psychologists) may have the keys to vocational success for students with intellectual disabilities as they transition to higher education or work settings (Flynn, 2013). Therefore, wisdom dictates that we honor the LRE tenet of the IDEA by serving students in places where they will be using the communication skills we teach.

Increasingly, evidence suggests that communication skills taught to students with more severe disabilities in separate, unnatural environments do not carry over to locations where the skills are used naturally (Vicker, 2009). However, many parents, teachers, and SLPs continue to believe that providing one-on-one services in the quiet, separate environment of the speech room is the best approach. Although the evidence is mixed, there is a trend toward natural environments with typically developing peer interaction (Cirrin et al., 2010). The "tipping point" for the decision may be that the IDEA requires students to be served in the LRE. Many students do require some one-on-one practice initially to learn skills, but then SLPs should search for opportunities to support the use of the

student's new skills in natural settings. From a procedural compliance perspective, some states allow for flexibility of service delivery locations on the IEP, allowing two or more locations for service delivery to be documented on the IEP.

Least Restrictive Environment Case Study

The following case study provides examples of how a parent came to believe that her child's special education services were best provided with typical peers as much as possible. It also explains an outcome for those typical peers that she believes would not have occurred had she not advocated for services for her son to be integrated in regular education environments.

Dante is a student with Down syndrome who tests in the mild to moderate range of intellectual disability. Initially, his mother believed that more occupational therapy, physical therapy, and speech-language services in a pullout situation would provide the greatest benefit to her child. When Dante was in kindergarten, the SLP began to inform his mother about the emerging trend of providing related services in natural education settings with typically developing peers. The mother was skeptical but agreed to a trial period of classroom-based intervention. She came to observe services being delivered in the kindergarten classroom using curriculum-based materials and marveled at how motivated her son (who could be stubborn) was and how he seemed to be progressing while enjoying his time with the related service providers. As a result, she became an advocate for inclusive/integrated services and began to work for an organization that provided guidance to parents and professionals and conducted research on the topic of integrated/curriculum-based special education.

During high school, Dante spent part of every day in a self-contained special education classroom. He also spent a portion of each day in regular education environments and was provided many typical high school experiences. Per the IEP, the SLP remained involved with him throughout high school, on a consultative basis. The SLP helped athletic coaches, job coaches, and regular education teachers know what accommodations and modifications Dante needed to communicate successfully. She also helped facilitate communication opportunities with both adults and peers throughout the school day. During his junior year of high school, Dante became manager of the baseball team and was a valuable member of the team. A compelling picture of inclusive education is Dante's prom picture dressed in a tuxedo with all the members of the baseball team around him. Dante's mother asserts that this picture and many other anecdotes of Dante's typical high school experience would not have occurred if she had not strongly advocated for much of his special education to be provided with his typical peers and connected to the CCSS.

This case study not only illustrates the need to serve students in the LRE, but also how many of the standards were woven throughout Dante's participation in regular education activities, including his participation on the baseball team. These standards included

- CCSS.ELA-LITERACY.SL.3.1.C: Ask questions to check understanding of information presented, stay on topic, and link their comments to the remarks of others.
- CCSS.ELA-LITERACY.SL.3.3: Ask and answer questions about information from a speaker, offering appropriate elaboration and detail.
- CCSS.ELA-LITERACY.SL.3.6: Speak in complete sentences when appropriate to task and situation in order to provide requested detail or clarification. (See Grade 3 Language Standards 1 and 3 here for specific expectations.)
- CCSS.ELA-LITERACY.SL.11-12.2: Integrate multiple sources of information presented in diverse formats and media (e.g., visually, quantitatively, orally) in order to make informed decisions and solve problems, evaluating the credibility and accuracy of each source and noting any discrepancies among the data.
- CCSS.ELA-LITERACY.SL.11-12.6: Adapt speech to a variety of contexts and tasks, demonstrating a command of formal English when indicated or appropriate. (See Grades 11–12 Language Standards 1 and 3 here for specific expectations) (NGA & CCSSO, 2010).

One can see that through mastery of these standards and others, both at Dante's grade level and preceding levels, Dante became successful in a variety of settings including many regular education classes and extracurricular activities.

Direct Services to Students Case Study

When Jay, a 20-year-old student with autism spectrum disorder and mild intellectual disabilities, was preparing to graduate from high school, he began an internship as a bagger at a local grocery store. He showed good pragmatic skills and enjoyed greeting and carrying on appropriate brief conversations with nearly everyone whom he encountered at school. The educational team believed that the grocery store setting would be ideal for Jay. Unfortunately, they were wrong. Jay was accustomed to everyone in his environment sharing his appreciation for greetings and small talk. When customers at the grocery store did not exchange greeting or departing behaviors or engage in brief conversations, Jay would leave his duties to pursue the customer until the customer engaged in what he believed was an appropriate social interaction. Sometimes his conversations lasted many minutes and strayed from topics appropriate for grocery store "small talk." He was scaring and annoying customers and abandoning his duties.

The SLP was called in to help Jay with appropriate pragmatic interactions for the grocery store setting. The SLP and his team targeted these standards:

- CCSS.ELA-LITERACYSL.11-12.1: Initiate and participate effectively in a range of collaborative discussions (one-on-one, in groups, and teacher-led) with diverse partners on Grades 11–12 topics, texts, and issues, building on others' ideas and expressing their own clearly and persuasively.
- CCSS.ELA-LITERACY.SL.11-12.1.D: Respond thoughtfully to diverse perspectives; synthesize comments, claims, and evidence made on all sides of an issue; resolve contradictions when possible; and determine what additional information or research is required to deepen the investigation or complete the task.
- CCSS.ELA-LITERACY.SL.11-12.6: Adapt speech to a variety of contexts and tasks, demonstrating a command of formal English when indicated or appropriate. (See Grades 11–12 Language Standards 1 and 3 here for specific expectations) (NGA & CCSSO, 2010).

The SLP first counseled Jay about the communication expectations in diverse social interactions, specifically, that not everyone returns greetings or wants to engage in polite social conversation. At the school, they role-played how some of these people might act, including walking away from Jay with no response. Initially, Jay had a difficult time not pursuing the intended communication partner, but, with coaching, he was able to let go of the impulse to pursue the targeted partner. The same activity was repeated at the job site, first with a familiar partner (the SLP), and then with less familiar listeners like the manager and other employees. Jay quickly became comfortable with a wider variety of responses to his greetings and attempts at polite conversation and became very successful at his job.

One year later, Jay is a full-time employee of the same grocery store and was named employee of the month. By providing direct services and counseling to this student in the LRE of his work setting, the SLP was able to create a very successful pairing of employee and work setting. Appendix 9–A analyzes the standards and collaborations that occurred to make Jay successful at his job site in a systematic way.

Indirect Services: Consulting With Teachers

If SLPs operate as members of the school community rather than as therapists who merely provide direct services to students every half hour, they need the opportunity to consult with teachers on a variety of topics. These conversations should include why individuals or groups of students are not meeting the standards. This kind of consultation implies that SLPs have established collaborative, trusting relationships with the school community. After teachers inform the SLP about which standards the student is not successful at accomplishing, the SLP can assess the student formally or informally to learn why the student is not successful. SLPs can consult with teachers and a variety of other school personnel to help create communication-rich classrooms or other environments. For example, SLPs can support both teachers and other students in communicating with augmented communication users by discussing the time it takes to form a response using a high- or low-technology device. Using a workload model, consulting services provided by the SLP are highly valued by the entire school community.

Multitiered Systems of Support (MTSS) Teams

In an MTSS environment, problem-solving teams work together to solve any behavioral, emotional, and communication problem that students experience as they relate to what is educationally relevant (Metcalf, n.d.)—in other words, the standards. The use of MTSS teams is growing at the middle and high school levels. The problems adolescents experience may be very different from those encountered at the elementary level. SLPs have a unique perspective from our "lens" on the reasons students are not mastering the CCSS. For this reason, it is critical that SLPs be included on these teams. Providing speech and language screening is an important role for the SLP as a member of these problem-solving teams. Although there are many published screening tools, they are often not tied to the CCSS. Districts may want to create their own instrument that is tied to the standards and normed on students in the district. SLPs may also consider norming informal tools to fit the demographics of their district. In addition, schools should be sure standardized assessment norms match their local population. For example, one rural district identified that the instrument it was using had many false positives using the scores published by the company. The district then used informal instruments developed by the SLPs and special educators as evidence to support their decision making.

Some districts do not permit speech and language screening during the MTSS (or similar) process because they feel it is a special education function and violates the law to engage in this activity before the formal exceptional child referral process is initiated. If the district conducts screening for all students at a grade level or through a referral to the MTSS process and if informed consent is provided to parents, special education personnel, including SLPs, are able to engage in screening procedures with all students. However, one must follow local mandates and policies. SLPs may also observe students in a variety of educational environments to inform the school team and help brainstorm solutions to individual or group classroom or grade-level needs as they relate to timely mastery of the standards. In short, SLPs help teams implement prevention activities at every level.

High School Multitiered System of Support Case Study

Brad was a 16-year-old football player and wrestler who became captain of both teams his senior year. Even though he was not an outstanding student, he consistently received B grades with the occasional A or C. However, during the fall of his junior year, his grades inexplicably declined. His teacher referred him to the MTSS team where an SLP was a standing member. As part of the first tier of intervention, a hearing screening was conducted which Brad failed. His audiologist detected a bilateral degenerative hearing loss and fitted Brad with hearing aids. The team determined that he would receive some intervention from the SLP in general education to see if he would require a referral to special education once fitted with his hearing aids. Brad initially was reluctant to wear the aids, as he was concerned that would negatively affect his popularity. The SLP created a contract with his coach and teachers stating that Brad would get a check from each teacher signifying that he was wearing his aids and that they were turned on or he would not get to start during the game or match at the end of the week. The first week of the contract, Brad did not get all his checks, did not start on Friday night, and was furious at the SLP. However, every week after that he did get all his checks,

and, as a result, started for both teams. His grades steadily returned to their previous levels.

In this case study, the SLP played a critical role in supporting the student through screening and then appropriately referring him to an audiologist. The SLP also supported Brad by implementing the intervention of a contract with teachers and coaches. Brad did not require special education. The MTSS team was able to address all of his needs.

Implement Accommodations and Modifications With Teachers

Teachers and other educators may require some support from the SLP on how to implement accommodations and modifications documented on the IEP across content areas and daily activities. SLPs regularly consult with all school personnel on how to implement a wide variety of accommodations and modifications in order for students to succeed in all aspects of the CCSS. (See Chapter 3 for a listing of common accommodations and modifications SLPs may recommend.) SLPs may train teachers or teacher assistants in particular communication strategies or programs. They may help other students interact appropriately with students with multiple disabilities or those who use augmented communication devices. SLPs may help art and physical education teachers to incorporate visual cues in their areas to help support the communication needs of a wide variety of students.

The SLP may need to collaborate with teachers to show them how their classroom activities include speech and language targets. SLPs may also collaborate with teachers to help them create language-rich classrooms and opportunities for communicating in every setting throughout the school day. Consultative services may include programming augmented communication devices, helping teachers and other students interact appropriately, and providing "wait time" for the augmented communication user to process and formulate a response. Other activities may include training "lunch buddies" or other peer mentors who facilitate communication with targeted students or help teachers plan opportunities for all students to communicate throughout the day. The SLP's role in consultative/collaborative services is no less important than his or her role in direct instruction and may be the most appropriate model for an individual.

Support Teachers in Differentiating Instruction

As earlier noted, teachers are curriculum experts and SLPs are specialists in differentiated instruction (Power-deFur & Flynn, 2012). Through collaboration, teachers help SLPs know the demands of the CCSS, while SLPs provide some recommendations on differentiating instruction and supporting language and communication to help all students access the standards. An example of indirect activities at the secondary level that support students in the LRE and general education curriculum is seen through literacy instruction for students who have not mastered the standards. For example, in the area of Reading Literature, CCSS.ELA-LITERACY .RL.9-10.2 states, "Determine a theme or central idea of a text and analyze in detail its development over the course of the text, including how it emerges and is shaped and refined by specific details; provide an objective summary of the text"

(NGA & CCSSO, 2010). After the teacher has informed the SLP about the skills in which an individual student is not progressing on, the SLP may suggest breaking the larger goal into some smaller tasks. For example, the SLP may suggest analyzing a text through a story grammar framework (Wolf & Gerhart, 1994) to help the student fully comprehend a piece of narrative literature.

By the secondary level, formal instruction in reading has ended whether or not students have mastered the standards that make them competent readers and writers. If students have not mastered basic reading skills, they inevitably fall behind in both reading and the acquisition of content knowledge. Some SLPs at the high school level and beyond provide reading instruction in classrooms or individually depending on the needs of the student and the available resources to provide this type of intervention.

There are special education students at the high school level without intellectual disability who also require the expertise of the SLP to be successful in school and meet the expectations of the CCSS. Typically, these students exhibit a reading disorder. SLPs possess a unique understanding of the underpinnings of language that are required for students to become successful readers. This knowledge thus qualifies the SLP to collaborate with special and general educators and intervene with students at any level who have not yet mastered these underlying literacy skills.

Some SLPs co-teach "elective" courses with English Language Arts teachers, or special education teachers, for students who struggle. Some schools require this "elective" when students do not demonstrate proficiency in reading. The curriculum varies, but research-validated programs are essential for students to close the literacy gap and become proficient readers who are commensurate with their peers in this area of academics. Collaboration between professionals at this level often exponentially improves the outcomes for language-literacy impaired students.

Indirect Activities That Support Students in the LRE Case Study

Amy was a student who tested in the moderate range of intellectual disability on intelligence quotient testing, but functioned in the mild range on adaptive behaviors. During her junior and senior years, she received academic instruction at the school part of the day, and then had an internship at a variety of community-based locations. Although Amy had received speech-language therapy in elementary and middle school, the IEP determined she no longer required this related service during high school. She loved horses, and through a connection with the SLP who served the high school, Amy began a trial internship at a large boarding stable with about a hundred horses. She began work at the farm accompanied by her job coach. The first few days proved to be very successful; however, as the involvement of the coach faded, so did Amy's success on the job. The coach, the farm owner, and Amy became very frustrated.

Because the SLP had facilitated the pairing and knew all parties, he was called in to help. The farm owner reported that while Amy did quality work, she did not complete tasks and did not interact appropriately with people who boarded their horses at the facility. Amy had trouble completing tasks because she did not know when she was finished and had forgotten all the steps to her jobs. The SLP was able to visit the farm while Amy was

working and, after a period of observation, helped the job coach and the owner engineer the barn environment to facilitate Amy's success.

The SLP considered the CCSS and identified both the high school CCSS and those from earlier grades to target the following:

- CCSS.ELA-LITERACY.SL.2.2: Recount or describe key ideas or details from a text read aloud or information presented orally or through other media.
- CCSS.ELA-LITERACY.SL.3.1.c: Ask questions to check understanding of information presented, stay on topic, and link their comments to the remarks of others.
- CCSS.ELA-LITERACY.SL.9-10.1: Initiate and participate effectively in a range of collaborative discussions (one on one, in groups, and teacher led) with diverse partners on Grades 9–10 topics, texts, and issues, building on others' ideas and expressing their own clearly and persuasively (NGA & CCSSO, 2010).

The SLP created a simple task analysis of each job (i.e., raking the aisle, watering and haying stalls, and cleaning stalls and water buckets) by breaking each duty into its simplest components. The barn manager wrote a detailed sequence daily on a dry-erase board for Amy. Amy then worked through her tasks, checking the dry-erase board to be sure she completed each task accurately. Amy wanted very much to be successful, and in a very short period, she achieved that success with the accommodations and modifications the SLP was able to implement. As Amy felt comfortable with her duties and proud of her work, her usual socially appropriate interactions with boarders returned. Amy was not placed in speech as a related service for these consultative services, but rather the SLP contributed time in a workload model to make this a very successful internship for both the student and the farm owner.

In this case study, the SLP used the workload model in a nontraditional way to help the job coach, farm owner, and student implement accommodations and modifications to the work environment to make a successful internship that capitalized on the student's interests and strengths.

Dismissal

Wisdom in knowing when to dismiss students from speech-language services is as important as the services SLPs provide. For most students with more severe disabilities, speech-language services should not span their entire academic career. Many parents and teachers believe that once students receive speech services, those services remain for the length of their time in public schools; that is not the case. SLPs should determine eligibility, set goals, and when those goals are met, dismiss students. The definition of a related service, according to IDEA, is that the student requires the service to benefit from special education in the primary area of disability (IDEA, 34 CFR § 300.34). This helps the IEP team know that a related service is not typically in place for an entire academic career. When IEP teams have data that a student requires speech-language services to fully benefit from special education, in other words, to meet the current goals of the IEP, the student should receive that related service. However, if services do not meet the requirement, they should not remain on

the IEP. Many teachers in self-contained classrooms collaborate with SLPs to differentiate instruction and meet the communication needs of their students, thus not requiring the specially designed instruction that the SLP provides. If this is the case, then dismissal from speech as a related service will occur, and the teacher will address the communication needs of the student. Parents and teachers will be assured that if the need for the direct intervention of the SLP arises, the IEP can be amended to add speech-language services.

Indirect Services Case Study

Jason is a 19-year-old student who tests in the moderate range of intellectual disability. He spends the majority of his day in a self-contained classroom, but part of every day is spent in a vocational setting on or off campus. He is cooperative and motivated to communicate. During a spontaneous 5-min conversation, 72% of his connected speech was judged intelligible by a familiar listener. Nearly 100% of his single-word utterances were judged intelligible by the same familiar listener. Jason uses an iPad to repair unintelligible utterances. He is able to type and spell phrases and sentences with great accuracy. Even though he has picture symbols loaded on the device, he prefers to type words or phrases that are misunderstood by the listener. During a 30-min group activity, Jason did not initiate a conversation with the clinician or peers. If prompted to start a conversation, he can do so on a limited variety of topics. He is good at topic maintenance, frequently carrying on a conversation for four or more turns. If he does not know the answer to a question or problem, he gives up and does not pursue asking questions or looking in a variety of sources provided for him for the answer. Although Jason uses the iPad to repair misunderstood words or phrases and does so with great enthusiasm, he does not want to use it to write short paragraphs of more than one sentence or use it independently for academic work or research. If prompted by the clinician to continue to write and "tell more" about a topic, he is very capable; however, he does not independently complete writing assignments.

Jason is very sociable and motivated to interact with adults and peers. Increasing his intelligibility by slowing his rate, using an open-mouth posture, and increasing his volume improves his intelligibility dramatically. He requires verbal and/or visual prompts to use these strategies with consistency. He enjoys social interactions, so vocational jobs with a high amount of interaction, like greeting patrons at a retail store, are of interest to him. He has an excellent work ethic and wants to complete tasks accurately. He takes great pride in his work. He can be nearly 100% intelligible with phrases he uses frequently and wants to practice those phrases if he needs to be understood by unfamiliar listeners.

As Jason's teacher and SLP prepared for the IEP meeting, 2 years before his anticipated graduation, they identified many areas where the SLP could support Jason through indirect services. The team identified standards that would be necessary for his success on a job site, including these standards from earlier grades:

- CCSS.ELA-LITERACY.SL.3.1.B: Follow agreed-upon rules for discussions (e.g., gaining the floor in respectful ways, listening to others with care, speaking one at a time about the topics and texts under discussion).
- CCSS.ELA-LITERACY.SL.3.1.C: Ask questions to check understanding of information presented, stay on topic, and link their comments to the remarks of others.
- CCSS.ELA-LITERACY.SL.3.1.D: Explain their own ideas and understanding in light of the discussion.
- CCSS.ELA-LITERACY.SL.3.3: Ask and answer questions about information from a speaker, offering appropriate elaboration and detail.
- CCSS.ELA-LITERACY.SL.3.6: Speak in complete sentences when appropriate to task and situation in order to provide requested detail or clarification. (See Grade 3 Language Standards 1 and 3 here for specific expectations) (NGA & CCSSO, 2010).

While observing Jason in a variety of settings around campus, the SLP suggested that becoming a greeter or receptionist at a business would be an appropriate job for him. This job would capitalize on Jason's interests and strengths. The SLP helped the teacher build similar opportunities into the academic day to see if Jason could generalize the pragmatic skills required for being a greeter across a variety of environments. Jason became skilled at greeting and departing behaviors, providing directions, and answering or finding answers to questions. He was very motivated to perform to high expectations.

Through ongoing conversations with Jason's parents, the IEP team learned that his favorite restaurant was a small family owned Japanese restaurant close to his home. The team decided this might be an opportunity to explore as a place of employment for Jason. The restaurant owners were willing to give Jason a trial period as the host. Jason was thrilled at the chance to work at his favorite restaurant. The SLP provided some instruction for the owners on reasonable expectations and techniques to teach Jason new duties or refine already existing skills. The SLP visited the restaurant and helped the owner and Jason use good communication or the iPad when there were breakdowns. The SLP programmed some appropriate vocabulary onto the iPad and showed the owner and family members how to do the same. The SLP posted some visual cues for speaking slowly, opening your mouth, and increasing volume, as well as posted common phrases Jason would use most frequently at the host stand. Jason became a successful host at the restaurant and used his iPad to keep up with tables that were vacant and carried it with him to seat patrons in case communication breakdowns occurred.

Throughout the process of acclimating Jason to his position at the restaurant, the SLP provided a variety of indirect activities to support Jason, including

- analyzing educational and vocational environments that increase opportunities for communication;
- analyzing the demands of curriculum and effects on students;
- participating with teachers and other educational team members to solve problems and progress monitor for students;
- communicating with outside agencies;
- designing and implementing plans that provide services on behalf of students

- planning and preparing lessons with teachers or independently; and
- training teachers, parents, and others on the use of augmented communication systems or other techniques to facilitate communication.

With the SLP's support, Jason was successful and was able to graduate from high school and secure a job at the restaurant. The experience was positive for all parties, including the restaurant's patrons.

CONCLUDING THOUGHTS

Speech-language pathologists play a critical role in connecting the special education services they provide to not only the English Language Arts section of the CCSS, but all the areas of the standards. Language and communication underpin every area of the standards, and SLPs have knowledge in these areas like no other professional in the schools. This chapter detailed SLPs' many direct and indirect roles in helping students master the CCSS across the school day and educational environments. It should be clear that the standards provide the framework to provide educationally significant speech-language intervention in school settings. School-based SLPs' connection to the standards represents the differentiation between educationally relevant services provided in school settings and those delivered by community-based SLPs. The case studies illustrate real examples of how school-based SLPs have used the standards to help students become college and career ready.

REFERENCES

American Speech-Language-Hearing Association. (n.d.). *Caseload and workload.* Retrieved February 26, 2015, from http://www.asha.org/PRPSpecificTopic.aspx?folderid=8589934681&section=Resources

American Speech-Language-Hearing Association. (2010). *Roles and responsibilities of speech language guage pathologists in schools.* Retrieved February 18, 2015, from http://www.asha.org/policy

Center for Applied Special Technology. (n.d.). *What is Universal Design for Learning?* Retrieved February 18, 2015, from http://www.cast.org/udl/

Cirrin, F. M., Schooling, T. L., Nelson, N. W., Diehl, S. F., Flynn, P. F., Staskowski, M., . . . Adamczyk, D. F. (2010). Evidence-based systematic review: Effects of different service delivery models on communication outcomes for elementary school-age children. *Language, Speech, and Hearing Services in Schools, 41,* 233–264. doi:10.1044/0161-1461(2009/08-0128)

Ehren, B. (2000). Maintaining a therapeutic focus and sharing responsibility for student success: Keys to in-classroom speech-language services. *Language Speech and Hearing Services in Schools, 31,* 219–229.

Ehren, B. (2002). Speech-language pathologists contributing significantly to the academic success of high school students: A vision for professional growth. *Topics in Language Disorders, 22,* 60–80.

Flynn, P. (2010, August 31). New service delivery models: Connecting speech-language pathologists with teachers and curriculum. *The ASHA Leader, 15,* 22.

Flynn, P. (2013). Effective service delivery in middle and high schools. *Perspectives on School Based Issues, 14*(3), 68–71. doi:10.1044/sbi14.3.68

Individuals with Disabilities Education Improvement Act of 2004 (2004). Pub. L. No. 108-446~632,118 Stat. 2744 (2004).

Kansas University. (n.d.). *Dynamic learning maps —Essential elements for English language arts. Dynamic Learning Maps.* Retrieved September 29, 2014, from http://dynamiclearningmaps.org

Lain, S., & Kamhi, A. (2003). Alternative assessment of language and literacy in culturally and linguistically diverse populations.

Language, Speech, and Hearing Services in the Schools, 34, 44–55.

Larson, V., & McKinley, N. (2003). *Communication solutions for older students: Assessment and intervention strategies.* Eau Claire, WI: Thinking Publications.

Metcalf, T. (n.d.). *What's your plan? Accurate decision making within a multi-tier system of supports: Critical areas in Tier 1.* Retrieved from http://www.rtinetwork.org/essential/tieredinstruction/tier1/accurate-decision-making-within-a-multi-tier-system-of-supports-critical-areas-in-tier-1

National Center and State Collaborative. (n.d.). *National Center and State Collaborative General Supervision Enhancement Grant.* Retrieved February 17, 2014, from http://www.ncscpartners.org/resources

National Governors Association Center for Best Practices and Council of Chief State School Officers. (2010). *Common Core State Standards.* Washington, DC: Authors. Retrieved December 27, 2014, from http://www.corestandards.org/read-the-standards/

Power-deFur, L., & Flynn, P. (2012). Unpacking the standards for intervention. *Perspectives on School-Based Issues, 13*(1), 11–16. doi:10.1044/sbi13.1.11

Rudebusch, J. (2012). From Common Core State Standards to standards-based IEPs: A brief tutorial. *Perspectives on School-Based Issues, 13*(1), 17–24. doi:10.1044/sbi13.1.17

U.S. Bureau of Labor Statistics. (2015, February 6). *Table A-6: Employment status of the civilian population by sex, age, and disability status, not seasonally adjusted.* Retrieved February 18, 2015, from http://www.bls.gov/news.release/empsit.t06.htm

Vicker, B. (2009). The 21st century speech-language pathologist and integrated services in classrooms. *The Reporter, 14*(2), 1–5, 17. Retrieved February 18, 2015, from http://www.iidc.indiana.edu/?pageId=495#sthash.DSsLa3Nv.dpuf

Wagner, M., Blackorby, J., Cameto, R., Hebbeler, K., & Newman, L. (1993). *The transition experiences of young people with disabilities. A summary of findings from the National Longitudinal Transition Study of Special Education Students.* Menlo Park, CA: SRI International. Retrieved from ERIC website: http://eric.ed.gov/?id=ED365086

Wagner, M., Newman, L., Cameto, R., Garza, N., & Levine, P. (2005). *After high school: A first look at the postschool experiences of youth with disabilities. A report from the National Longitudinal Transition Study-2 (NLTS2).* Washington, DC: Institute of Educational Sciences.

Wehmeyer, M. (n.d.). *National gateway to self-determination: What is self-determination.* Retrieved February 18, 2014, from http://www.ngsd.org/everyone/what-self-determination

Wolf, S., & Gearhart, M. (1994). Writing what you read: Narrative assessment as a learning event. *Language Arts, 71,* 425–444.

Appendix 9–A. Analysis Worksheet: Direct Services Case Study

Analysis of Common Core State Standards for Students With Special Needs

Step 1: Review relevant standards to identify skills needed for success.

Step 2: Identify the language and communication skills needed for success (consider phonology, morphology, syntax, semantics, pragmatics, and metalinguistic skills).

Review current grade-level standards.		Review preceding grade-level standards for prerequisite skills.		Skill Area	Specific Skills Needed
Grade, Standard, Number	Key Concepts	Grade, Standard, Number	Key Concepts		
Literacy 11–12.1	Collaborative discussion with diverse partners	Literacy 3.3 Literacy 2.1	Follow rules of discussion (listening), build on other's conversation, ask and answer questions	Social language	Greeting, departing, choosing topics, "small talk," turn-taking without interruption

Step 3: Identify the student's current skills and needs (consider PLAAFP from IEP, standardized and curriculum-based assessments, observations, checklists).

Step 4: Review classroom materials and activities.

Step 5: Design and implement intervention.

Child's current skills and needs (consider PLAAFP from IEP, standardized and curriculum-based assessments, observations, checklists).	Child's instructional goals (consider IEP, 504 plan).	Job description and setting expectations:	Intervention
Need #1 difficulty concluding conversations	Use greetings and departure comments (with customers)	Greeting customers Asking if customers need help Carrying grocers to the car	Direct: SLP counseling regarding social interactions (topics for small talk, appropriate behaviors, length of conversational turns) Role-playing at school
Need #2 Difficulty with appropriate turn-taking	Carry on two- to three-turn conversation regarding "small talk"	Managing "small talk" Taking turn in conversations	Collaborative at work setting: SLP role-playing Expanded role-playing with job coach, and store manager

CHAPTER 10

Students Who Are English Language Learners

Judy Rudebusch and Elda M. Rojas

INTRODUCTION

Bilingual and multilingual students are the fastest-growing population in public schools in the United States, with estimates that up to 40% of school enrollment by 2030 will be English language learners (ELLs) (American Speech Language Hearing Association [ASHA], 2014). This population growth prediction has significant implications for school-based speech-language pathologists (SLPs) and the students with communication disorders whom they serve. The Common Core State Standards (CCSS), adopted by most states, the District of Columbia, and four territories (National Governors Association Center for Best Practices [NGA] & Council of Chief State School Officers [CCSSO], 2014), are intended to standardize student preparation for later success in college, careers, and the workforce. The CCSS promote shared responsibility for implementing the rigorous language and literacy standards across disciplines

(Murza, Malani, & Hahs-Vaughn, 2014). See Chapter 1 for further discussion of the CCSS.

English learners are challenged not only with adjusting to the mainstream American culture and learning English with the fluency needed to understand and produce academic language, but also with making progress in and mastering the CCSS while learning English. English Language Proficiency Development (ELPD) standards have been developed by states or consortia of states and aligned with the CCSS in order to more clearly outline the language practices that ELLs must acquire in order to successfully meet the standards (TESOL International Association [TESOL], 2013). With the current and future population trends of ELLs composing more than one third of public school enrollment, it is crucial that school-based SLPs participate with classroom teachers and special educators to examine the language-learning needs of their students and understand how to develop and implement Individualized

Education Programs (IEPs) that are aligned with both the CCSS and the ELPD standards.

BACKGROUND INFORMATION: ENGLISH LANGUAGE LEARNERS IN AMERICA'S SCHOOLS

Education for ELLs in this country has been controversial for many years and has been the subject of court cases, state legislation, and political statements. In short, education for ELLs is a topic about which passions run high. There are two prevailing views that drive the controversy. Many U.S. English speakers advocate an English-only position, with a "leave the home language and culture at home, enter the mainstream, and become fully American" view. The opposing view holds that language is about identity, culture, and history. Maintenance of the native or home language is a way to affirm identity and culture, as well as a way to push back against discrimination and lack of access to equal opportunities at school or in the workplace (Goldenberg & Coleman, 2010). Much of the debate has focused on the language of instruction for ELLs: should they be instructed in their home language for a period of time, fully immersed in English instruction, or somewhere in between? The history of court cases, federal and state legislation, and the movement for national achievement standards in the CCSS bring educators to the point of carefully considering the language of instruction for ELLs. This consideration includes focusing on promoting oral English proficiency; assessing mastery of the standards and the testing implications for ELLs; and understanding the cultural, sociolinguistic, economic, and emotional factors that influence achievement.

Population Trends

ELLs are a rapidly growing population in U.S. public schools, with an enrollment of close to five million (TESOL, 2013). In the decade between 1998 and 2009, the number of ELLs in public schools increased by 51%, while the general population of students increased by 7%. In 2014, almost one in ten students was an English learner, and by 2025, it is predicted that ELLs will make up 25% of the student population (National Education Association [NEA], 2008; U.S. Department of Education [USDE], 2014a). The U.S. Department of Education National Center for Education Statistics (2014b) shows eight states reporting that over 10% of their student enrollment was English learners in 2011–2012, with 14 states and Washington, DC, reporting that between 6% and 10% of enrollment are English learners. The heaviest concentrations of the nation's ELL population were in California, Arizona, Texas, New York, Florida, and Illinois. These six states contained 61% of the ELLs enrolled in public schools (Payán & Nettles, 2007; USDE, 2014b).

Although there were close to one million recent immigrant children and youth enrolled in public schools in the 2013–2014 school year (USDE, 2014a), native-born U.S. citizens predominate in the ELL student population with 76% of elementary and 56% of secondary ELL students born in this country. More than half of the ELLs in public secondary schools are second- or third-generation U.S. citizens (NEA, 2008).

As reported for 2013–2014, Spanish and Asian languages are the most common first/home languages among English learners enrolled in public schools: 79% of ELLs claimed Spanish as their home language with 2% Vietnamese, 1.6% Hmong, and 1% Chinese (Cantonese), 1% Korean, and 15.4% other languages (USDE, 2014a).

Laws, Regulations, Policies, and Practices

Three major types of federal laws interact to protect the rights of ELLs: civil rights, language learning education, and special education laws. In combination, these laws guarantee access to a meaningful public education (Serpa, 2011). Civil rights laws ensure that schools do not discriminate against students on the basis of their national origin or exclude them from meaningful participation in education because they cannot understand English. Language learning education laws require that ELLs be provided with instruction to help them learn English and achieve the same grade-level standards as students whose first language is English. Special education laws provide protections for students with disabilities, including ELLs who meet eligibility for special education services, ensuring that they have access to a free and appropriate public education (FAPE) in the least restrictive environment (LRE).

Civil Rights Laws

All children in the United States are entitled to equal access to a public elementary and secondary education, regardless of their or their parents' national origin, citizenship, or immigration status. The Civil Rights Act of 1964 prohibits discrimination on the basis of race, color, religion, sex, or national origin in public facilities, including any elementary or secondary school. Specifically, this law creates protections of the civil rights of ELLs by ensuring that schools do not exclude children from participation in school because they do not understand, read, or speak English. Further, the act requires that schools teach English to language minority children, provide alternative language programs to ensure that ELLs have access to the schools' programs, communicate with parents in a language they understand, and avoid any language-based placement that permanently puts ELLs in an ability group or "track." Finally, the act prohibits schools from placing children in special education because of language differences.

Other federal civil rights laws include Section 504 of the Vocational Rehabilitation Act of 1973, which prohibits the denial of services to individuals with disabilities and requires a school district to provide FAPE to each student with a disability regardless of the nature or severity of the disability. The Equal Educational Opportunities Act (EEOA) of 1974 requires school districts to take action to overcome students' language barriers that impede equal participation in educational programs. The Americans with Disabilities Act (ADA) of 1990 requires that students with disabilities receive benefits and services comparable to those given their nondisabled peers. These civil rights laws apply to all students including English language learners.

Language Learning Education Laws

Language learning education laws are an outcome of the civil rights laws. Two federal laws had strong implications for language instruction for ELLs prior to the enactment of No Child Left Behind (NCLB) in 2001. The Bilingual Education Act of 1964, also known as Title VII of the Elementary and Secondary Education Act (ESEA), was intended to assist local school districts in building capacity to establish, implement, and sustain specialized programs of instruction for ELLs that would allow for the same academic performance expected of all children. The Improving America's Schools Act (1994) was the fifth reauthorization of ESEA and the Bilingual Education Act. This law promoted bilingualism for ELLs, rather than sole reliance on rapid transition to English.

The dominant and prevailing national education policy for most children in the United States, including English learners, since 2002 is NCLB, the most recent reauthorization of ESEA. NCLB requires all states to identify English learners, measure their English proficiency, and include them in state testing programs that assess academic skills (Payán & Nettles, 2007). States are also required to establish statewide English proficiency standards and assess each English learner with a statewide English proficiency assessment that reflects the English proficiency standards. Each state must set Annual Measurable Achievement Objectives (AMAOs) for ELLs in the areas of English language proficiency and performance in academic content. These annual objectives must include annual increases in progress in learning English, annual increases in English language proficiency, and measurable progress of ELLs in the academic content areas (No Child Left Behind [NCLB] Act, 2002). Court decisions regarding equal access for ELLs to public education and subsequent federal education legislation

have resulted in accountability systems that hold districts and states responsible for the educational progress of their ELLs.

Provisions for English language learners are included under both Title I and Title III of NCLB. The purpose of Title I, Improving the Academic Achievement of the Disadvantaged, is to ensure that all children have a fair, equal, and significant opportunity to obtain a high-quality education and reach proficiency on challenging state academic achievement standards and state academic assessments, including limited English proficiency children (NCLB, 2002).

The purposes of Title III–English Language Acquisition, Language Enhancement, and Academic Achievement are to help ensure that children who are limited English proficient, including immigrant children and youth, attain English proficiency, develop high levels of academic attainment in English, and meet the same challenging academic content and student academic achievement standards as all children are expected to meet (NCLB, 2002). Title III funds are to be used to provide language instruction educational programs so that ELLs attain English proficiency, while meeting challenging state academic content standards. Title I and Title III require English proficiency tests annually in K–12, beginning during the first year of enrollment in U.S. schools. Districts must test oral language, reading, and writing in English each year under Title I; annual testing in English-language proficiency in speaking, listening, reading, and writing is required under Title III. States are required to have both English-language proficiency standards and academic standards, and the proficiency standards must be linked to the state academic standards (Center for Public Education, 2007). The CCSS represents the rigorous academic content standards in states that have adopted them. The Council of Chief State School Officers (2012) provided a framework for states to use in developing English language proficiency standards corresponding to the CCSS.

Special Education Laws

Special education laws at the federal and state levels are also based on civil rights laws. The Education for All Handicapped Children Act (1975), known as PL 94-142, mandated that school-age children with disabilities receive a FAPE in the LRE. The Individuals with Disabilities Education Act (IDEA) of 2004 is a reauthorization of the original PL 94-142. Among other requirements, IDEA (2004) requires that student evaluations be conducted in the child's native language or mode of communication; that parents be informed of the evaluations and their rights in a language that they can understand; that students cannot be found eligible or placed in special education if their performance is due to limited proficiency in English; and that the IEPs include the present levels of performance, measurable annual goals, and an explanation of the extent the student will not participate in general education with students without disabilities. The implication of these requirements for ELLs with disabilities is that IEPs should be consistent with research and implemented to help students utilize learning strengths to overcome learning challenges due to the disability.

ELLs with disabilities therefore have protections under IDEA, language learning laws, especially Title I and Title III of NCLB, and civil rights laws that mandate access to full, meaningful participation in public education. Civil rights laws, language learning education laws, and special education laws intersect to provide protections and access to equal educational opportunity for ELLs in America's public schools.

State and School District Requirements for Educating English Language Learners

The inclusion of ELLs in assessment and accountability systems as spelled out under the NCLB Act represents a substantive and important shift in U.S. federal education policy. With most states phasing in their implementation of the CCSS during the 2014–2015 school year, these participating states are using the CCSS to meet requirements of NCLB. The correlating ELPD standards developed by individual states or consortia of states outline the standards and instruction that school districts must provide to ELLs in order for them to have full opportunity to learn English and succeed academically. State education agencies complete a variety of tasks, including determining how to define and identify the ELL subgroup; develop an annual plan for increasing English proficiency of ELLs in the domains for speaking, listening, reading, and writing; inform the USDE how it will align advancing English proficiency with the challenging academic standards; and involve a variety of stakeholders in the development of the annual measurable objectives for ELLs (NCPIE, 2014).

School districts are responsible for identifying the student's English language proficiency levels in the domains of listening, speaking, reading, and writing within the descriptors used in the state to describe English-language proficiency (e.g., beginning, intermediate, and advanced). School districts are also responsible for providing the curriculum to implement the CCSS and for implementing the ELPD standards as an integral part of each subject in the required curriculum so that content-based instruction is linguistically accommodated to help students acquire English language proficiency. When students are at the beginning levels of English language proficiency, in many states, districts must provide intensive and ongoing foundational second-language acquisition instruction for ELLs in Grade 3 or higher (Education Service Center Region XIII, 2008). Districts must provide a system to track the progress of ELLs in learning English, demonstrating English language proficiency growth from year to year, and demonstrating mastery of the academic content standards in the CCSS (NCLB, 2002). The ripple effects of implementing these requirements are strengthening the support systems available for ELLs in public schools (NEA, 2008; TESOL, 2013). Tracking the progress of each ELL toward English language proficiency as well as high achievement in academic content areas as measured by the state's assessment program, presents a compelling challenge for educators to work together in professional learning communities to explore ways to meet the needs of each learner. Greater coordination and collaboration among teachers, English as a Second Language (ESL) specialists, reading intervention specialists, SLPs, and student support specialists using data-driven decision making will create the system of supports needed by ELLs to meet the compliance requirements of NCLB and the rigorous language and academic content standards found in the CCSS.

ENGLISH LANGUAGE PROFICIENCY DEVELOPMENT STANDARDS AND THE COMMON CORE

At the time of the initial publication in 2010, the CCSS did not include a correlating set of ELPD standards for students learning English. The developers acknowledged in an addendum document (NGA & CSSO, 2010) that the needs of ELLs should be taken into account in the CCSS implementation and that all students should be held to the same high expectations outlined in the standards, including ELLs. The standards acknowledge that ELLs are a heterogeneous group with differences in ethnic background, first language, socioeconomic status, quality of prior schooling, and levels of English language proficiency. Effective education in the CCSS for English learners requires individualized instructional diagnosis, adjusting instruction, and closely monitoring student progress. The developers of the CCSS asserted that teachers should recognize that it is possible to achieve the standards for reading and literature, writing and research, language development, speaking, and listening without manifesting native-like control of language conventions and vocabulary (NGA & CCSSO, 2010). Since publication of the CCSS, several initiatives that address the role of English language proficiency development relative to the CCSS have been started. For example, Stanford University launched a privately funded initiative in 2012 called the Understanding Language Project aimed at heightening educator awareness of the critical role that language plays in the CCSS (TESOL, 2013). However, the question of how to implement the CCSS for ELLs is in large part left to the states. Many of the states have taken the ELPD standards they developed in response to requirements for NCLB and aligned them with the more rigorous language expectations found in the CCSS. In addition, the Council of Chief State School Officers released an ELPD framework in 2012 to assist states in revising their ELPD standards to align with the CCSS. The goal of the framework is to provide guidance for state education leaders in outlining the language demands of the CCSS and provide a protocol for states to specify ELPD standards and the language practices that all ELLs must acquire in order to successfully meet the CCSS. The framework highlights how language instruction in the four language domains of listening, speaking, reading, and writing can be provided and illustrates the academic language that teachers need to use while implementing the CCSS and NGSS (TESOL, 2013). When aligning instruction and intervention for ELLs with the CCSS, teachers and SLPs use the state's ELPD standards alongside the academic content standards to embed linguistic accommodations and scaffolding for English-language acquisition into the content instruction.

English Language Proficiency Development Assessments Aligned to the CCSS

Under federal policy guidelines established in NCLB, states are required to include ELLs in the state testing program that assesses academic skills as well as assessing each English learner with a state-wide English proficiency assessment (Payán & Nettles, 2007). In addition, states are required to adopt assessment benchmarks to measure student achievement of college- and career-ready standards (USDE, 2010). The expected outcome

for students who master the CCSS is that they will be college and career ready upon graduation from high school. The two consortia, the Partnership for Assessment of Readiness for College and Careers (PARCC) and the Smarter Balanced Assessment Consortium (SBAC), have developed content assessments, which were first released during the 2014–2015 school year, assessments that accommodate both ELLs and students with disabilities.

There is also a national effort for states to collaborate more closely in order to address many of the ELL assessment and accommodation issues (NEA, 2008). More than 25 states belong to one of four collaborative programs, with 18 states participating in the World-Class Instructional Design and Assessment (WIDA) Consortium. WIDA (2014) has developed English language proficiency development standards and a matched English language proficiency test called ACCESS for ELLs, which stands for Assessing Comprehension and Communication in English State-to-State for English Language Learners. It is a large-scale test that addresses ELPD standards at four grade-level clusters and in five content areas. There are five ELPD content areas: social and instructional language, English language arts, math, science, and social studies (WIDA, 2014). The efforts of the WIDA Consortium provide a good example of the inherent challenges in standards-based assessment for ELLs: measuring growth in English language proficiency as well as mastery of the content specified in the CCSS.

Whether assessing growth in English language proficiency or mastery of the CCSS, assessment informs instruction and is critical to influence student achievement for English learners. Teachers use results of the English language proficiency assessment to determine English language proficiency levels for each ELL in the language skills of listening, speaking, reading, and writing and differentiate instruction specifically for students who might be at varying degrees of language proficiency within one classroom. There are different models for coding language proficiency, with most models having between three and six designations from beginning through advanced levels of proficiency. Teachers use a variety of measures to monitor progress toward language and content objectives in the CCSS, using the state's ELPD standards. The annual assessments of English language proficiency and mastery of the academic content required in NCLB and the assessments used throughout a lesson or unit of instruction help teachers determine if students are comprehending and applying the content concepts (Education Service Center Region XIII, 2008). Examples of ways to assess and evaluate student progress on language and content objectives include clear, specific feedback to students on language output with monitoring of students' responses to the feedback; students' self-evaluation and monitoring; checking for individual and group understanding; and formal or informal assessment of content and language objectives using teacher-made tests, student work products, performance tasks, and authentic assessments.

CHARACTERISTICS OF STUDENTS WHO ARE ENGLISH LANGUAGE LEARNERS

English language learners are a heterogeneous group with differences in ethnic background, first language, socioeconomic status, quality of prior schooling, and levels of English proficiency (NGA & CCSSO, 2010). These differences have implications for instruction, assessment, and program design. Some English learners who are recent immigrants had strong academic backgrounds before coming to the United States and are at or above grade level in certain subjects. They are literate in their native language and may have already studied a second language. These learners need English language development so they can transfer what they have already learned to the courses they are taking in the United States (Echevarria, Vogt, & Short, 2014). Other immigrant ELLs had very limited formal schooling and have little or no literacy in their native language. They have gaps in educational background, lack content knowledge in specific subjects, and need time to become accustomed to school routines and expectations. Most ELLs have grown up in the United States (NEA, 2008). Some students in this group are literate in their home language and will add English to their knowledge base when they start school. Other native-born ELLs who do not speak English at home have not mastered either their native language or English. Students who have not mastered English after 5 or more years in U.S. schools are referred to as long-term English learners (Menken & Kleyn, 2010).

Sociocultural, emotional, and economic factors influence educational achievement for all students and especially for ELLs (Dianda, 2008). Economically disadvantaged students are, in general, less academically successful. High mobility has been shown to increase the risk for dropping out of school (Glick & White, 2004). Refugee students who have experienced trauma may struggle adapting to school routines and expectations in the United States. In order to develop strong educational programs for ELLs, educators need to understand their diverse backgrounds. Systematic review of certain factors should be conducted for each student: English knowledge; first language knowledge; educational background; sociocultural, emotional, and economic factors; and eligibility for services through categorical programs (e.g., special education, migrant education, gifted and talented education, services for homeless students) in addition to English-language development programs (Echevarria et al., 2014). Effective instruction for ELLs requires assessment of English-language proficiency across the language domains of listening, speaking, reading, and writing; identification of student's instructional needs across academic content areas; continuous adjustments to meet student needs; and close monitoring of student progress (NGA & CCSSO, 2010). Table 10–1 provides a description of varying levels of proficiency in English.

Acquisition of English as a Second Language

Second language acquisition, also called sequential language acquisition, involves learning a second language after the first language is established. Students learning English as a second language go through many of the same stages of language acquisition as in learning their first language. There are six predictable stages of language acquisition: preproduction, early production, speech emergence, beginning fluency, intermediate fluency, and advanced fluency (Hill & Björk, 2008; Robertson & Ford, 2008). In the preproduction stage the ELL has minimal comprehension and does not verbalize. This stage is also known as the silent period when the child is focused on understanding and making sense of English. During the early production stage the ELL begins to speak in short words and sentences and emphasis continues to be on listening and absorbing the second language. The ELL speaks in words and short sentences during the speech emergence stage and relies on contextual clues and familiar topics. In the beginning fluent stage, the ELL is fairly fluent in social situations, but academic language is still considerably challenging. The ELL is fluent with few errors in social situations and is gaining academic language fluency during the intermediate fluency stage, and has near-native fluency during the advanced fluency stage (Table 10–2).

As children learn a second language (L2), there are several normal phenomena that may occur that should not be confused with a language learning disability (ASHA, 2014; Roninson, 2003). The ELL may demonstrate interference or transfer from the first language (L1) to English (L2). For example, the child may make an error when speaking or writing in English due to the direct influence of an L1 language structure. In Spanish, "esta casa es mas grande" means "this house is bigger." The literal translation is "this house is more big." If a child says or writes this, it is a manifestation of transfer or influence from Spanish to English. This is a normal phenomenon and a sign of a language difference, not a language disorder. Another normal phenomenon is a silent period when the child is first exposed to L2 and is focused on listening and comprehension. During this period that can last from a few weeks to several months, the child may be very quiet and rarely speak. Code switching (changing language within phrases or sentences) is also a normal phenomenon used by many fluent bilingual speakers. Language loss,

Table 10–1. Progression of English Language Proficiency Development

	Listening	Speaking	Reading	Writing
Beginner/Emerging	Little or no ability to understand spoken English in academic and social settings; struggle to identify and distinguish individual words and phrases; may not seek clarification	Little or no ability to speak English in academic and social settings; single words or phrases—highly familiar phrases to get needs met; lack English grammar conventions to connect ideas and speak in sentences	Little or no ability to use English to build foundational reading skills or to read and understand English used in academic and social contexts; limited sense of English language structures; highly dependent on visuals (e.g., environmental print)	Lack English vocabulary and language structures for writing tasks; may have ability to label, list, and copy; use present tense; short simple sentences using memorized or highly familiar material
Intermediate/Expanding	Understand simple, high-frequency spoken English used in classroom routines and social settings; understand simple directions, short conversations and discussions; identify key words; seek clarification	Speak English using simple vocabulary and syntax heard in routine academic and social settings; able to speak in short conversations and discussions using basic vocabulary and simple sentences; frequent pauses to think about how to say it	Read and understand simple, high-frequency English; read slowly and in short phrases; growing understanding of English syntax; literal meanings of common words; able to apply basic reading strategies to aid comprehension	Approach grade-level writing tasks in a limited way with simple vocabulary and syntax; academic writing has an oral tone; repetition of ideas due to lack of vocabulary and language structures; present tense used accurately
Advanced/Bridging	Ability to understand with some second language acquisition support; grade-appropriate spoken English in academic and social settings; understand longer, more elaborate conversations and discussions	Ability to speak in English with minimal second language acquisition support in academic and social settings; communicate effectively using abstract and content-based vocabulary; English grammar use nearly comparable to native English	Read and understand English used in social and academic contexts with minimal supports; read grade-level familiar text with appropriate rate, speed, intonation and expression; apply basic and higher-order thinking skills when reading	Use English vocabulary and language structures in grade-level writing tasks with minimal support; errors associated with second language acquisition are minor; errors rarely interfere with communication

Source: Education Service Center Region XIII, 2008; CCSSO, 2012; California Department of Education, 2012.

Table 10–2. Stages of Second Language (L2) Acquisition

Stage	Characteristics	Time	Teacher Strategies
Preproduction	Silent period; minimal comprehension; does not verbalize; nods yes/no; points	A few weeks–6 months	Read aloud; music; speak slowly; gesture; total physical response (TPR) Prompts: show me, circle the, where is, who has
Early production	Speaks L2 in words and short sentences; still working to absorb L2; key words to aid comprehension; familiar phrases; present tense	6 months–1 year	Group students in pairs or small groups; use sentence stems Prompts: yes/no questions, either/or, who, what, how many
Speech emergence	Good comprehension; simple sentences; pronunciation and grammar errors; relies on context clues and familiar topics; misunderstands jokes	1–2 years	Re-tell experiences; correct when errors affect meaning; fill-in-the-blank with vocabulary listed on page; model use of vocabulary in sentences; more academic vocabulary Prompts: how, short sentence answers
Beginning fluency	Fairly fluent in social situations; gaps in vocabulary knowledge; academic language still challenging	2–4 years	Think-pair-share; respond and explain; pre-identify errors that will be corrected in writing; visual supports; agree-disagree Prompts: why, inference and judgment, rephrase with correct syntax
Intermediate fluency	Excellent communication; few grammar errors; can offer opinion; good academic language	3–5 years	Graphic organizers with detail; brainstorming, prioritizing, categorizing, compare/contrast; summarize; introduce idioms; specific grammar correction
Advanced fluency	Near-native level of language proficiency	5–7 years (schooled); 7–10 years (unschooled)	Note taking; specific error correction

called subtractive bilingualism, is the loss of skills and fluency in L1 as the child learns L2. Ideally, the child can maintain his or her first language and culture while learning English. Other normal phenomena in second language acquisition are unusual prosody, speech sound production that is influenced by the phonemes in L1, grammar that is influenced by L1, word-finding difficulties, and limited vocabulary.

Other factors that can influence acquisition of English as a second language include motivation, age, family factors, access to English, personality, first language development, quality of instruction at school, and cognitive ability (Echevarria & Graves, 2011).

Social Language

Making a distinction between everyday conversational ability and the academic proficiency required for academic success was first presented by Jim Cummins (1981, 1989, 2003). The conversational language proficiency needed in everyday situations is termed *social language* or *basic interpersonal communicative skills* (BICS). The oral language used for conversations in interpersonal, social situations takes the ELL about 2 years to acquire with good comprehension and beginning to intermediate fluency of English, the second language. Conversational-social language is informal, context embedded, interpersonal, and supported with gestures, facial expression, intonation, and expression. The vocabulary used in conversations is familiar, and precise meanings are not as important as maintaining the conversational flow (Goldenberg & Coleman, 2010). Conversational-social language tends to use grammatical shortcuts, such as using pronouns whose referents are apparent in the context of the conversation. When the ELL sounds fluent in social-conversational language but continues to have significant academic difficulties, teachers may refer the student for testing because of this apparent English-

language proficiency in social situations (Roninson, 2003). The student planning team at the student's school should look carefully at the available data to determine whether interventions through general education are needed prior to referral to special education. The acquisition of academic language will take more time than the development of social language, and the student should be provided language acquisition interventions prior to referral for comprehensive special education evaluation.

Academic Language

The more cognitively demanding language necessary for school success is called *academic language* or *cognitive academic language proficiency* (CALP) (Cummins, 2003). Academic language is the language used in textbooks, lectures, and discussions about academic content. It takes between 5 and 7 years for a student who has schooling in the first language to acquire advanced fluency in academic language in English (Hill & Björk, 2008) and between 7 and 10 years for a student with interrupted or limited schooling in the first language (Collier & Thomas, 2009). Academic language is abstract, impersonal, deals with concepts rather than concrete topics, and tends to be more decontextualized and complex than conversational-social language. The reader or listener has to provide his or her own relevant background knowledge or context necessary for understanding. Emphasis, mood, and tone are communicated through words and content without the gestures, facial expressions, and intonation that are inherent with social-conversational communication. Vocabulary can be technical and abstract, with precise meanings that the reader/listener is expected to understand.

Writing and speech are more formalized and structured, and the syntax is denser with complex-compound sentences used to convey complicated ideas. Academic language expresses complexity through summarization, analysis, and connections between ideas, interpretation, evaluation, and reasoning for problem solving (Goldenberg & Coleman, 2010).

Language and Literacy Skills

One of the fundamental issues in facilitating mastery of the CCSS for English learners is the interplay of English oral language development and learning to read and write in English at the levels expected in the standards. The English Language Arts (ELA) standards of the CCSS specify "Anchor Standards" in reading, writing, speaking and listening, and language that follow students from kindergarten through 12th grade, and have language as their foundation (NGA & CCSSO, 2010). The developers of the CCSS identified three key advances that make the standards more rigorous: "1) regular practice with complex texts and their academic language; 2) reading, writing, and speaking grounded in evidence from texts; and 3) building knowledge through content-rich nonfiction" (NGA & CCSSO, 2014 "Key Shifts in English Language Arts," para. 2). The issue of text complexity is a key consideration for working with ELLs because it is largely the sophistication of the morphology and syntax in text that determines its complexity. English learners need to develop the knowledge, skills, and strategies in English that are loaded with sophisticated vocabulary and syntax.

The ability to speak and understand English is the foundation for reading and writing, the visual portals for language processing. Learning to read and write in English is intertwined with learning to understand and speak English. Effective reading and writing instruction for ELLs involves many of the same strategies as effective reading instruction for native speakers of English with emphases on vocabulary and constructing meaning through the printed word (Dunlap & Wiesman, 2006; Goldenberg & Coleman, 2010). Important considerations when developing a literacy plan for ELLs include the student's English proficiency level, background knowledge, and, first language literacy level. In addition, teachers must consider the need for both explicit skills instruction and interactive teaching where teachers challenge students cognitively and linguistically (Goldenberg & Coleman, 2010). Explicit instruction in morphological and syntactical awareness has proven effective for improving reading, vocabulary, and spelling knowledge and skills (Bowers, Kirby & Deacon, 2010; Ehren, 2009; Goodwin & Ahn, 2010; Scott, 2004; Wolter & Green, 2013). Providing models, patterns, structure, organization, scaffolds, and direct guidance are important for teaching ELLs to write well in English. Embedding oral language into the reading and writing processes with prewriting brainstorming, interactive word walls, personal dictionaries, and concrete experiences to aid background knowledge will make literacy activities meaningful.

English Language Learners With Disabilities

Special education services in the form of specially designed instruction, related services, and supplemental aids and services are available to students who have identified disabilities that lead to an adverse effect on educational performance. Of the 6.4 million students with disabilities who receive special education services, 37% have specific learning disabilities (LDs) as a primary disability, and another 22% have a communication disorder and are coded with a speech-language impairment (SLI) as the primary disability (USDE, 2013). Accurate identification of ELLs with learning disabilities and/or speech-language impairment is challenging and is best conducted by a multidisciplinary team of experts in the disability area and in the areas of language acquisition and English language proficiency in order to discriminate between language differences and language-based learning disabilities (Cortiella, 2011). When ELLs struggle in school, they should be referred to a site-based team that considers an array of information about the students and makes recommendations for interventions to be implemented in the general education program through response to intervention (RTI) (Ortiz, 2002). Interventions are most commonly provided in reading, math, and English acquisition. If the student does not make progress after intensive intervention and progress monitoring have been provided and documented, referral for comprehensive special education evaluation is warranted.

It is beyond the scope of this chapter to discuss formal and informal assessment tools for the evaluation of ELLs who may have learning disabilities or speech-language-communication disorders. However, there are general principles regarding nonbiased assessment to follow: conduct the assessment in both English and the first language whenever possible; establish the student's level of English proficiency and the amount of English instruction the student has received and is receiving in academic settings; use valid and reliable instruments with culturally and linguistically appropriate sample procedures; examine changes in language proficiency and language use over time and in comparison to ELL peers; obtain culturally and linguistically sensitive assessment of intelligence and achievement; rule out all factors that may appear to be causing the learning difficulties; review responsiveness to intervention data; assess the student's need for individual assistance in the classroom in comparison to ELL peers; and consider the possibility that norm-referenced and standardized test scores are not an accurate reflection of language skills (Hamayan, Marler, Sanchez-Lopez, & Damico, 2007; Moore & Montgomery, 2008; Ortiz, 2002; Roninson, 2003). Adherence to these principles will facilitate completion of a nonbiased assessment of the ELL student.

One of the most important roles of the school-based SLP in working with ELLs is determining whether a real communication disorder exists or whether there is the perception of a disorder that is based on a language difference. Laing and Kamhi (2003) documented both the overdiagnosis and underdiagnosis of language and literacy problems in ELLs. A language disorder exists in an ELL when the child's language skills deviate significantly from the norms and expectations of the child's home community and are considered defective by the child's cultural community (Taylor, 1992; Wilson, Wilson, & Coleman, 2000). In order to be identified with a speech-language impairment for IEP services under IDEA, the language/communication disorder must be present in the child's native/home language.

Signs of a possible language disorder in an ELL include difficulty communicating in the home and parents' or family concerns about communication issues; a history of developmental delay; problems in both L1 and English (L2); low mean length of utterance (MLU) in both languages; slower rate of English (L2) acquisition than other ELLs of the same age; social-communication problems after 1–2 years in U.S. schools; speech production difficulties in both languages; and higher scores on vocabulary tests than on reasoning tests (Roninson, 2003).

Special Education Services

Once it has been determined that an ELL student qualifies for special education services, the IEP is developed and will include instructional strategies and modifications that are tailored to meet the educational needs arising from the identified disabilities. The student's IEP must also include the intensive English-language instruction the student needs in order to demonstrate progress in learning English and demonstrating mastery of the CCSS. Special education services must be provided in the LRE. For students with disabilities who are also ELLs, implementation of IEP goals and objectives as well as intensive English language instruction is often effectively provided in the classroom working collaboratively with the

classroom teacher, often in one of the language instructional models identified in the box below.

> **CHALLENGES FOR ENGLISH LANGUAGE LEARNERS IN THE COMMON CORE**

The College- and Career-Readiness Standards found in the CCSS contain rigorous communication expectations that may be especially challenging for ELLs across the language domains of listening, speaking, reading, and writing. The students who meet the standards set out in the CCSS demonstrate independence and confidence during interaction and are able to request clarification, ask relevant questions, construct effective arguments, and convey intricate information. They are self-directed learners and build strong content knowledge across a range of subject matter, listen attentively, and have a variety of strategies to use context to make sense of text. Students respond to varying demands of the audience, task, and purpose, and are able to set and adjust the purpose for reading, writing, speaking, listening, and language use as warranted

---

Language Instruction Models for English Language Learners

There are several instructional models available for ELLs, depending on state laws regarding bilingual education and language of instruction, differences in instructional delivery at elementary and secondary levels of education, and the number or proportion of ELLs relative to overall student enrollment at the school or in the school district.

Dual-language immersion programs provide the opportunity for both native English speakers and ELLs to learn another language. In these two-way bilingual programs, half the students in the class are native English speakers, and the other half of the class speaks the second language used in the program. Instruction is provided in both languages at a predetermined ratio of time (e.g., 50% English and 50% Spanish) without repeating the content. Therefore, the teacher moves forward with instructional content delivery and changes the language of instruction based on the predetermined schedule (Goldenberg & Coleman, 2010).

One-way dual-language enrichment programs refer to one language group being schooled through two languages. For example, Spanish speakers receive the mainstream academic curriculum through both English and Spanish in the same way it is provided in two-way dual-language programs. If a school has very few native English speakers, one-way dual-language enrichment programs can get students starting in the program in kindergarten, to grade-level English in the CCSS by around eighth grade (Collier & Thomas, 2009).

Transitional bilingual education programs are designed to help children with the same native/home language acquire the English skills needed to be successful in an English-only mainstream classroom. Bilingual education programs provide some initial instruction in the students' first language, primarily in reading and language arts, and later instruction for support to clarify concepts in the other core subject areas. Bilingual education programs are most common in elementary grades. *Early-exit transitional bilingual programs* usually phase out the first language after 2 or 3 years of bilingual instruction in the native language and support for reading in the native/home language. For students starting in kindergarten, early exit transitional bilingual programs will phase out first language

instruction at the end of first or second grade. *Late-exit transitional bilingual programs* continue for a longer period, and students may continue to receive 40% or more of their instruction in their first language, even when they have been reclassified as fluent-English-proficient (Rennie, 1993).

English as a Second Language (ESL) programs provide language support and a strong English language development component for students, but all instruction is in English. Self-contained ESL classrooms have only ELLs assigned to them for instruction in the core subjects, and then ELLs have the opportunity to interact with other students in music, art, physical education, library, and lunch. Integrated ESL classrooms have approximately half ELLs and half native-English speakers. Emphasis is on cooperative learning and use of English-speaking role models, hands-on activities, visuals, demonstrations, and modeling.

Sheltered content ESL instruction is an integrated content language approach that is most commonly used at the secondary level to support ELLs in developing English language skills in content classes. This model helps ELLs learn both English and academic content as quickly as possible.

ESL pullout programs provide instruction in English as a second language in a pullout model. English learners spend part of the school day in a mainstream classroom with English instruction and part of the day in an ESL pullout program (Rennie, 1993). ESL pullout programs are commonly used at the secondary level or in schools with very few ELL.

by the task or situation. In addition, students who are college- and career-ready understand other perspectives and cultures, can communicate effectively with people of varied backgrounds, and read classic and contemporary works of literature representing a variety of cultures and world views (NGA & CCSSO, 2010). The standards that may prove most challenging for ELLs are the Speaking and Listening and Language Standards related to the use of sophisticated vocabulary and complexity in syntax and morphology, as well as the skills needed to present increasingly complex information, ideas, and evidence in classroom academic discussions.

Speaking and Listening

The key points in the Speaking and Listening Standards that may pose challenges for ELLs are those skills needed to present increasingly complex information, ideas, and evidence in classroom academic discussions and formal presentations in one-on-one, small group, and large group/ whole class situations. The following anchor standards across grade levels may require both direct, explicit instruction and interactive practice activities:

- Engage effectively in a range of collaborative discussions (one-on-one, in groups, and teacher-led) with diverse partners on grade-level topics and texts, building on others' ideas and expressing their own clearly (CCSS.ELA-Literacy. CCRA.SL.1).
- Present claims and findings, sequencing ideas logically and using pertinent descriptions, facts, and details to accentuate main ideas or themes, use appropriate eye

contact, adequate volume, and clear pronunciation (CCSS.ELA-Literacy. CCRA.SL.4).
- Adapt speech to a variety of contexts and tasks, using formal English when appropriate to task and situation (CCSS.ELA-Literacy. CCRA.SL.6) (NGA & CCSSO, 2010).

Language

The Language Standards that may be most challenging for ELLs relate to sophisticated vocabulary and complexity in syntax and morphology, as seen in the anchor standards that cross grade levels:

- Demonstrate command of the conventions of Standard English grammar and usage when writing or speaking (CCSS.ELA-Literacy. CCRA.L.1).
- Use knowledge of language and its conventions when writing, speaking, reading, or writing (CCSS.ELA-Literacy.CCRA.L.3).
- Determine or clarify the meaning of unknown and multiple-meaning words and phrases based on grade-level reading and content choosing flexibly from a range of strategies (CCSS.ELA-Literacy.CCRA.L.4).
- Demonstrate understanding of figurative language, word relationships, and nuances in word meanings (CCSS.ELA-Literacy. CCRA.L.5).
- Acquire and use accurately grade-appropriate conversational, general academic, and domain-specific words and phrases, sufficient for reading, writing, speaking, and listening at the college- and career-readiness level; demonstrate

independence in gathering vocabulary knowledge when encountering an unknown term important to comprehension or expression (CCSS.ELA-Literacy. CCRA.L.6).

CASE STUDIES

Four case studies are provided to demonstrate planning and instructional support for English learners to perform well and make progress in the CCSS. In each case, a Language Action Plan was developed

for the student when needed (Table 10–3), and the Linguistic Accommodations to Support ELL's Proficiency Levels in listening, speaking, reading, and writing were used to clarify the student's English proficiency level and the linguistic accommodations that can be used in the classroom (Tables 10–4 through 10–7).

Case Study #1: Alan

Alan is an 8-year, 1-month-old boy in the second grade. He has been enrolled in a two-way dual-language program since kindergarten. His home language is

Table 10–3. Language Action Plan

Complete for students in Grades 3–12 who are at a beginning or intermediate English proficiency or who have not met yearly expectations.						
Student:		D.O.B.:		ID#:		
Teacher:		Campus:		Grade:		
No. of Years in U.S. Schools:			Country of Origin:			
Program	Entry Date		Oral Language Proficiency Assessment— English			
			Date:			
			CALP Score:			
			Stand. Score:			

Table 10–3. *continued*

State Assessment Data									
	Grade		Grade		Grade		Grade		
	Score Met	Admin Date	Score Met	Admin Date	Score Met	Admin Date	Score Met	Admin Date
ELA/Reading									
Writing									
Mathematics									
Science									
Social Studies									

Factors to Consider		
X	High Mobility	Comments:
	Gaps in Education	
	Low Attendance	
	IEP Services in Place	
	504 Services in Place	
	Needs Language Action Plan	
	Conference with Parent	
	Other	

Date:	Date:	Date:
Instructional Plan:	MOY Follow-Up:	EOY Follow-Up

Planning Team:	
_____ Name/Title	_____ Name/Title

Table 10–4. Linguistic Accommodations to Support ELL's Proficiency Levels: Listening

Proficiency Level	English–Language Proficiency Level Descriptors: Listening *The student understands . . .*	Linguistic Accommodations *Teachers . . .*
Beginning/ emerging	• Few simple conversations with linguistic support • Modified conversation • Few words, does not seek clarification, watches others for cues	• Allow use of same language peer and native language support • Expect student to struggle to understand simple conversations • Use gestures and movement and other linguistic support to communicate language and expectations
Intermediate/ expanding	• Unfamiliar language with linguistic supports and adaptations • Unmodified conversations with keywords and phrases • Need to seek clarification by requiring/requesting the speaker to repeat, slow down, or rephrase speech	• Provide visuals, slower speech, verbal cues, simplified language • Preteach vocabulary before discussion and lectures • Teach phrases for student to request that speakers slow down, repeat, or rephrase speech
Advanced/ bridging	• Unfamiliar conversations with some processing time, and visuals, verbal cues, and gestures • Most unmodified interaction • Occasional or rare requests for the speaker to repeat, slow down, rephrase, and clarify meaning	• Allow some processing time, visuals, verbal cues, and gestures for unfamiliar conversation and new academic content, especially when material is complex and unfamiliar • Provide opportunities for student to request clarification, repetition, and rephrasing

Note. Adapted from Education Service Center Region XIII, 2008.

Spanish. His teacher expressed concerns about his low achievement in reading, writing, math, and science. Alan struggles to express his thoughts, has a limited vocabulary, and does not easily understand second-grade concepts across all subject areas. Alan does not have strong language dominance. His language proficiency scores for both English and Spanish are at the beginning fluency level. Alan was tested (in English and Spanish) for language, cognition, and overall development at age 2 years, 10 months. He was not found eligible for any special education services. He was tested again at age 5 years, 3 months in English and Spanish, and found eligible for services with a speech-language impairment (expressive language disorder). Alan has been receiving speech-language therapy services since kindergarten. Current testing, again in both English and Spanish showed similar strengths and weakness in both languages. Strengths were noted in

Table 10–5. Linguistic Accommodations to Support ELL's Proficiency Levels: Speaking

Proficiency Level	English-Language Proficiency Level Descriptors: Speaking *The student speaks . . .*	Linguistic Accommodations *Teachers . . .*
Beginning/ emerging	• Using single words and short phrases with practiced material • Using limited bank of key vocabulary words • With recently practiced familiar material • With frequent errors that hinder communication • With pronunciation that inhibits communication	• Provide short sentence stems and single words for practice before conversations • Allow some nonparticipation in simple conversations • Provide word bank of key vocabulary • Model pronunciation of social and academic language
Intermediate/ expanding	• With simple messages and hesitation to think about meaning • Using basic vocabulary • With simple sentence structure and present tense • With errors that may inhibit unfamiliar communication • With pronunciation generally understood by those familiar with ELLs	• Allow extra processing time • Provide sentence stems with simple sentence structure and tenses • Model and provide practice in pronunciation of academic terms
Advanced/ bridging	• In conversations with some pauses to restate, repeat, and clarify meaning • Using content-based and abstract terms on familiar topics • With past, present, and future tenses • Using complex sentences and grammar with some to very few errors • With pronunciation usually understood by most	• Allow extra time after pauses • Provide sentence stems with past, present, and future tenses, and complex grammar and vocabulary with content-based and abstract terms • Provide opportunities for extended discussions on academic and complex topics

Note. Adapted from Education Service Center Region XIII, 2008.

following classroom instructions, understanding basic concepts, answering yes/no questions, and using plurals, tenses, and conjunctions. Deficits were noted in grammar, recalling and formulating sentences, understanding and using vocabulary, sentence structure, and semantic relationships.

Table 10–6. Linguistic Accommodations to Support ELL's Proficiency Levels: Reading

Proficiency Level	English–Language Proficiency Level Descriptors: Reading *The student reads . . .*	Linguistic Accommodations *Teachers . . .*
Beginning/ emerging	• Little except recently practiced terms, environmental print, high-frequency words, concrete words represented by pictures • Slowly, word by word • With very limited sense of English structure • With comprehension of practiced, familiar text • With need for visuals and prior knowledge	• Organize reading in chunks • Practice high-frequency, concrete terms • Use visual and linguistic supports • Explain classroom environmental print • Use adapted text
Intermediate/ expanding	• Wider range of topics including everyday and academic language • Slowly with re-reading • Simple sentences with visual cues, pretaught vocabulary and interaction • Grade-level text with difficulty • At higher levels when linguistic accommodations provided	• Allow wide range of reading • Allow grade-level comprehension and analysis of task including drawing and use of native language and peer collaboration • Provide high level of visual and linguistic supports with adapted text and pretaught vocabulary
Advanced/ bridging	• Abstract grade-level text • Longer phrases and familiar sentences appropriately • While developing the ability to construct meaning from text • At high comprehension level with some to minimal linguistic support for unfamiliar topics and to clarify meaning	• Allow abstract grade-level reading comprehension and analysis with peer support • Provide some to minimal visual and linguistic supports including adapted text for unfamiliar topics • Allow peer collaboration

Note. Adapted from Education Service Center Region XIII, 2008.

The SLP collaborated with the classroom teacher to identify the second-grade standards Alan is struggling with due to his expressive language disorder and overall low language levels in both English and Spanish. Together, they agreed which standards should be targeted, as the SLP addressed semantics, syntax, and oral narrative skills on the IEP. They also discussed the relevant English Language

Table 10–7. Linguistic Accommodations to Support ELL's Proficiency Levels: Writing

Proficiency Level	English–Language Proficiency Level Descriptors: Writing *The student writes . . .*	Linguistic Accommodations *Teachers . . .*
Beginning/ emerging	• With little ability to use English • Without focus and coherence, conventions, organization, voice • Labels, lists, and copies of printed text and high-frequency words/ phrases, short and simple, practiced sentences • Primarily in present tense • With frequent errors that hinder or prevent understanding	• Allow drawing and use of native language to express concepts • Allow student to use high-frequency, recently memorized, and short, simple sentences • Provide short, simple sentence stems with present tense and high-frequency vocabulary
Intermediate/ expanding	• With limited ability to use English in content area writing • Best on topics that are highly familiar with simple English • With simple oral tone in messages, high-frequency vocabulary, loosely connected text, and repetition of ideas • Mostly in present tense, with frequent errors and little detail	• Allow drawing and use of native language to express academic concepts • Allow writing on familiar, concrete topics • Avoid assessment of language errors in content area writing • Provide simple sentence stems and scaffolded writing assignments
Advanced/ bridging	• Grade-appropriate ideas with second language support • With a grasp of basic English usage and some to good understanding of complex usage with grade-appropriate vocabulary and a more academic tone • More like native speakers with clarity and precision and only occasional difficulties with naturalness of language	• Provide complex grade-level appropriate writing tasks • Allow abstract and technical writing with linguistic support including teacher modeling and student interaction • Provide complex sentence stems for scaffolded writing assignments • Use genre analysis to identify and use features of advanced English writing

Note. Adapted from Education Service Center Region XIII, 2008.

Proficiency Development standards for Alan and ways to integrate IEP targets with accelerated English instruction targets in Alan's Language Action Plan developed for each ELL with beginner or intermediate English proficiency.

Case Study #2: Carmen

Carmen is a very sweet and cheerful 16-year-old young lady placed in the tenth grade when she arrived in October of the school year from El Salvador. She has gaps in her formal education, having missed 2 years of school during her elementary years. Carmen's native language is Spanish. She is able to speak English using a few high-frequency words and short phrases she learned from a relative she lives with in her new city. Her English proficiency is at the beginning fluency level. Although Carmen is very eager to learn English, she lacks the knowledge of the grammar necessary to connect ideas. She has a difficult time conveying information beyond the memorized and practiced material. Her reading is highly dependent on visuals, and she reads very slowly, on a word-by-word basis. When writing, she used present tense and primary language features such as spelling patterns, word order, and words from her native tongue.

The student planning team, Carmen's English teacher, Sheltered English teacher, World History teacher, ELL-Specialist at the school, and SLP met to develop a Language Action Plan for Carmen. They developed an instructional plan and gave all of Carmen's teachers ideas for providing linguistic accommodations to support English acquisition. The team agreed to meet biweekly to coordinate key vocabulary words, sentence stems, and visual support systems for Carmen, and to discuss her response to the supports put in place to accelerate English acquisition. The SLP assumes the role of language consultant and attends these biweekly meetings as invited to provide technical assistance and reflection on the trajectory of Carmen's English language acquisition.

Case Study #3: Maria

Maria is a 10-year-old girl in a fourth-grade bilingual class. She has been enrolled in bilingual education programs in the school district since pre-kindergarten. Her home language is Spanish. Current concerns expressed by the teacher include low achievement in reading, writing, math, and science. Maria has beginning to intermediate language proficiency in both English and Spanish, and her teacher is concerned about slow progress in English language acquisition. She has trouble expressing herself in writing in both Spanish and English, and she appears to have less-developed academic language in Spanish than in English. Following reading and language interventions through the campus RTI services, Maria was referred for comprehensive special education evaluation. Maria was tested in English and in Spanish by a multidisciplinary bilingual evaluation team. Results of the evaluation identified a specific learning disability in oral expression and a speech-language impairment with a language disorder in Spanish. Maria's difficulty with language has an adverse effect on educational performance in reading comprehension, written expression, and verbal skills for participating well in groups or formulating complete answers in class.

The SLP and special education inclusion teacher worked with Maria's teacher to identify fourth-grade standards Maria is struggling with due to her expressive language disorder and specific learning disability. They also identified the linguistic accommodations in listening, speaking, reading, and writing the classroom teacher, special education inclusion teacher, and speech-language pathologist would use in implementing the IEP goals and objectives to help Maria close the gap in both language proficiency and academic language. Together they agreed on fourth-grade standards (and standards from prior grades) that they would target. They shared these at the new IEP meeting, in the development of the standards-based IEP. Following development of the IEP, the SLP and teachers developed a coordinated Language Action Plan to scaffold language skills and to accelerate English language acquisition.

Case Study #4: Araceli

Araceli is a 15-year-old from Mexico who is in the ninth grade. Her first language is Spanish. In algebra class, she listens to the teacher intently because she studied algebra before coming to the United States and wants her teacher to know that she understands the lessons. When the teacher asks a question, Araceli wants to answer, but by the time she has thought about the English words to use, the teacher has called on another student or given the answer himself. When speaking, Araceli exhibits an emerging awareness of English grammar and can speak using mostly simple or past tense. Her academic writing often has an oral tone to it and consists of mostly high-frequency vocabulary. Araceli's English proficiency is at the intermediate level.

The student planning team met to review Araceli's level of English proficiency and her progress toward meeting the CCSS. The student planning team consisted of the sheltered content teachers, algebra teacher, English teacher, science teacher, ELL specialist, and school counselor. The team developed a Language Action Plan for Araceli and carefully considered the linguistic accommodations needed for Araceli in each of the

CCSS content area classes. The counselor agreed to work on identifying extracurricular activities that Araceli might enjoy to accelerate acquisition of social language in a safe, fun environment with a peer mentor for learning English for interpersonal interaction. The team agreed to meet once a month to coordinate key vocabulary words, sentence stems, and visual support systems for Araceli, and to discuss her response to the supports put in place to accelerate English acquisition.

CONCLUDING THOUGHTS

English language learners are, and will continue to be, the fastest-growing population in U.S. public schools. This trend has significant implications for school-based speech-language pathologists who will also experience an increase in ELLs on their caseloads. The demands on ELLs are extremely challenging to acculturate to U.S. schools and master the challenging content of the CCSS, while learning English and increasing academic English-language proficiency to a native-English speaker level. School-based SLPs will be successful collaborating with ESL teachers to align their intervention approaches to both the CCSS and to the ELPD standards. This will enable the SLPs to support ELLS on their caseloads with the linguistic complexity in the areas of semantics, syntax, morphology, pragmatics, and metalinguistics that is woven throughout the standards.

REFERENCES

American Speech-Language-Hearing Association. (2014). *Acquiring English as a second language: What's normal and what's not.* Rockville,

MD: Author. Retrieved December 30, 2014, from http://www.asha.org/public/speech/development/easl.htm

Bowers, P. N., Kirby, J. R., & Deacon, H. S. (2010). The effects of morphological instruction on literacy skills: A systematic review of the literature. *Review of Educational Research, 80,* 144–179.

California Department of Education. (2012). *Overview of the California English Language Development Standards and Proficiency Level Descriptors.* Retrieved December 30, 2014, from http://www.cde.ca.gov/sp/el/er/documents/overviewpld.pdf

Center for Public Education. (2007). *What NCLB says about ELL students.* Retrieved December 28, 2014, from http://www.centerforpubliceducation.org

Collier, V. P., & Thomas, W. P. (2009). *Educating English learners for a transformed world.* Albuquerque, NM: Fuente Press.

Cortiella, C. (2011). *The state of learning disabilities.* New York, NY: National.

Council of Chief State School Officers. (2012). *Framework for English Language Proficiency Development Standards corresponding to the Common Core State Standards and the Next Generation Science Standards.* Washington, DC: CCSSO.

Cummins, J. (1981). *Schooling and language minority students: A theoretical framework.* Los Angeles, CA: California State University, National Evaluation, Dissemination and Assessment Center.

Cummins, J. (1989). A theoretical framework for bilingual special education. *Exceptional Children, 56,* 111–128.

Cummins, J. (1994). *Schooling and language minority students: A theoretical framework* (2nd ed.). Los Angeles, CA: California State University, National Evaluation, Dissemination and Assessment Center.

Cummins, J. (2003). Reading and the bilingual student: Fact and fiction. In G. Garcia (Ed.), *English learners: Reaching the highest level of English literacy* (pp. 2–33). Newark, DE: International Reading Association.

Dianda, M. (2008). *Preventing future high school dropouts: An advocacy and action guide for NEA state and local affiliates.* Washington, DC: National Education Association.

Dunlap, C. Z., & Wiesman, E. M. (2006). *Helping English language learners succeed.* Huntington Beach, CA: Shell Education.

Echevarria, J., & Graves, A. (2011). *Sheltered content instruction: Teaching students with diverse needs* (4th ed.). Boston, MA: Allyn & Bacon.

Echevarria, J., Vogt, M. E., & Short, D. J. (2014). *Making content comprehensible for secondary English learners: The SIOP® Model.* Boston, MA: Pearson.

Education Service Center Region XIII. (2008). *English Language Proficiency Standards Toolkit.* Austin, TX: Author.

Ehren, B. J. (2009). Reading comprehension and expository text structure: Direction for intervention with adolescents. In M. Nippold & C. Scott (Eds.), *Expository discourse in children, adolescents, and adults: Development and disorders* (pp. 217–242). London, UK: Psychology Press.

Elementary and Secondary Education Act, as reauthorized by the No Child Left Behind Act of 2001, Public Law 107-110, 115 statutes, 1425, January, 2002.

Glick, J. E., & White, M. J. (2004). Post-secondary school participation of immigrant and native youth: The role of familial resources and educational expectations. *Social Science Research, 33,* 272–299.

Goldenberg, C., & Coleman, R. (2010). *Promoting academic achievement among English learners: A guide to research.* Thousand Oaks, CA: Corwin.

Goodwin, A. P., & Ahn, S. (2010). A meta-analysis of morphological interventions: Effects on literacy achievement of children with literacy difficulties. *Annals of Dyslexia, 60,* 183–208.

Hakuta, K. (2008). English-language-learners in historical and contemporary perspectives: Challenges and opportunities. *Education Testing Service Policy Evaluation and Research Center, 16*(2), 3–4. Retrieved December 27, 2014, from https://www.ets.org/Media/Conferences_and_Events/pdf/ELLsympsium/Hakuta_Kenji.pdf

Hamayan, E., Marler, B., Sanchez-Lopez, C., & Damico, J. (2007). Reasons for the misidentification of special needs among ELLs. *Special Education Considerations for English Language Learners: Delivering a Continuum of Services* (pp. 2–7). Philadelphia, PA: Caslon Publishing. Retrieved December 29, 2014, from http://www.colorincolorado.org/article/40715/?theme=print

Hill, J. D., & Björk, C. L. (2008). *Classroom instruction that works with English language learners: Facilitators' guide.* Alexandria, VA: ASCD.

Individuals with Disabilities Education Improvement Act of 2004 (IDEA), 20 U.S.C. § 1400 *et seq.* (2004).

Laing, S., & Kamhi, A. (2003). Alternative assessment of language and literacy in culturally and linguistically diverse populations. *Language, Speech, and Hearing Services in Schools, 34,* 44–55.

Lau v. Nichols, 414 U.S. 563 (1974).

Menken, K., & Kleyn, T. (2010). The long-term impact of subtractive schooling in the experiences of secondary English language learners. *International Journal of Bilingual Education and Bilingualism, 13*(4), 399–417.

Moore, B. J., & Montgomery, J. K. (2008). *Making a difference for America's children* (2nd ed.). Greenville, SC: Thinking Publications.

Murza, K. A., Malani, M. D., & Hahs-Vaughn, D. L. (2014). Using the Common Core State Standards to guide therapy in the schools: Confidently accepting the challenge. *SIG 16 Perspectives.* Retrieved December 30, 2014, from http://sig16perspectives.pubs.asha.org/

National Coalition for Parental Involvement in Education (NCPIE). (2014). *Title III Programs of English language learners. NCLB Action Briefs.* Retrieved June 15, 2015, from http://www.publiceducation.issuelab.org/resource/title_iii_programs_of_english_language_learners_action_guide_for_parents_and_communities

National Education Association. (2008). *English language learners face unique challenges. NEA Policy Brief.* Washington, DC: Author. Retrieved December 27, 2014 from http://www.nea.org

National Governors Association Center for Best Practices & Council of Chief State School Officers. (2010). *Common Core State Standards.* Washington, DC: Author. Retrieved December 27, 2014, from http://www.corestandards.org/read-the-standards/

National Governors Association Center for Best Practices and Council of Chief State School Officers. (2014). *Key shifts in English language arts.* Retrieved December 29, 2014 from http://www.corestandards.org/other-resources/key-shifts-in-english-language-arts

No Child Left Behind Act of 2001, 20 U.S.C., § 6311 *et seq.* (2002).

Ortiz, A. (2002). Prevention of school failure and early intervention. In A. Artiles & A. Ortiz (Eds.), *English language learners with special education needs* (pp. 31–63). Washington, DC: Center for Applied Linguistics.

Payán, R. M., & Nettles, M. T. (2007). *Current state of English-language learners in the U.S. K-12 population. Education Testing Service ELL Fact Sheet.* Retrieved December 27, 2014, from https://www.ets.org/Media/Conferences_and_Events/pdf/ELLsympium/ELL_factsheet.pdf

Rennie, J. (1993). ESL and bilingual program models. *Streamlined Seminar, National Association of Elementary Principals, 12*(1).

Robertson, K., & Ford, K. (2008). *Language acquisition: An overview.* Retrieved December 30, 2014, from http://www.colorincolorado.org/article/26751

Roninson, O. Z. (2003). "But they don't speak English!: Bilingual students and speech-language services in public schools. *SIG 16 Perspectives in School-Based Issues.* Retrieved December 30, 2014, from http://sig16perspectives.pubs.asha.org/

Scott, C. M. (2004). Morphological processes. In C. A. Stone, E. R. Silliman, B. J. Ehren, & K. Apel (Eds.), *Handbook of language and literacy: Development and disorders* (pp. 340–362). New York, NY: Guilford Press.

Serpa, M. de L. B. (2011). An imperative for change: Bridging special and language learning education to ensure a free and appropriate education in the least restrictive environment for ELLs with disabilities in Massachusetts. *Gastón Institute Publications.* Paper 152. Retrieved December 29, 2014, from http://scholarworks.umb.edu/gaston_pubs/152

Taylor, J. (1992). *Speech-language pathology services in the schools* (2nd ed.). Needham Heights, MA: Allyn & Bacon.

TESOL International Association. (2013, March). Overview of the Common Core State Standards initiatives for ELLs. *A TESOL Issue Brief.* Alexandria, VA: Author.

U.S. Department of Education. (2010). Meeting the needs of English learners and other diverse learners. *Blueprint for Reform.* Retrieved December 27, 2014, from http://www2.ed.gov/policy/elsec/leg/blueprint/english-learners-diverse-learners.pdf

U.S. Department of Education. (2013). Digest of education statistics, 2012 (NCES 2014-15), Table 48. *National Center for Education Statistics.* Retrieved December 29, 2014, from http://www.nces.ed.gov/fastfacts/display.asp?id=64.

U.S. Department of Education. (2014a). *Fact sheet: Educational services for immigrant children and* those recently arrived to the United States. Retrieved December 27, 2014, from http://www2.ed.gov/print/policy/rights/guid/unaccompanied-children.html

U.S. Department of Education. (2014b). *The condition of education 2014 (NCES 2014-083), English Language Learners. National Center for Education Statistics.* Retrieved December 27, 2014 from http://www.nces.ed.gov/programs/coe/indicator_cgf.asp

Wilson, W., Wilson, J., & Coleman, T. (2000). Culturally appropriate assessment: Issues and strategies. In T. Coleman (Ed.), *Clinical management of communication disorders in culturally diverse children* (pp. 101–127). Boston, MA: Allyn & Bacon.

Wolter, J. A., & Green, L. (2013). Morphological awareness intervention and school-age language and literacy deficits: A case study. *Topics in Language Disorders, 33*(1), 27–41.

World Class Instructional Design and Assessment. (2014). *ACCESS for ELLs®.* Retrieved December 28, 2014, from https://www.wida.us/assessment/ACCESS/

Index

Note: Page numbers in **bold** reference non-text material.